This b

# IDENTIFICATION OF SYSTEMS

**Daniel Graupe**
Colorado State University
Fort Collins

ROBERT E. KRIEGER PUBLISHING COMPANY
HUNTINGTON, NEW YORK
1976

to my parents, my wife, and my children

Original Edition 1972
Second Revised Edition 1976

Printed and Published by
ROBERT E. KRIEGER PUBLISHING CO., INC.
645 NEW YORK AVENUE
HUNTINGTON, NEW YORK 11743



Printed in the United States of America

**Library of Congress Cataloging in Publication Data**

Graupe, Daniel.
Identification of systems.

Includes bibliographical references.
1. Systems engineering. I. Title.
[TA168.G68 1975] 620'.7 75-31781
ISBN 0-88275-359-2

# PREFACE

# TO SECOND EDITION

The second edition contains several new results relating to the identification of unstable stochastic and deterministic processes (in chapter 7), to identifying closed loop stochastic systems (in section 12.6), to Kalman filter parameter and covariance identification (in section 12.8) and to sensitivity analysis (in chapter 13). It also incorporates errata to the first edition. I am greatly indebted to my students and colleagues at Colorado State University and to readers throughout the world for pointing out to me many of these errors and for suggesting several addenda. Finally, I wish to apologize to the readers for any errors that may have remained in this edition.

DANIEL GRAUPE

*June, 1975*

# PREFACE

The engineer who is concerned with the controlling of a system will find many textbooks on designing the controller. However, he will discover that this design depends on the parameters of the system, such as its transfer functions, transition matrices, etc., all of which require direct or indirect identification, and are usually not otherwise available. Therefore, the very first problem that must be dealt with in practice is the identification of the system parameters.

Hundreds of papers on identification have been published in recent years in professional journals. The subject of identification also appears in most textbooks on control. However, in the latter it is often only briefly treated or limited to one or two approaches and is not given the rigorous treatment that problems of designing the controller itself are given. The purpose of the present text is, therefore, to provide the systems or control engineer in industry or the student at a university with a text devoted specifically to identification. It is hoped that this text will at least partially relieve the reader from the need to scan the vast literature on the subject. The present text thus attempts to guide the reader to the appropriate identification approach for his specific problem and explain the various approaches and their relative merits in sufficient depth, so that he can apply them to his problems. It further attempts to point out theoretical, computational, and realization problems that may arise in the various techniques and which often prevent successful identification if they are not properly dealt with. Consequently, the overcoming of these problems by appropriate design (of identification algorithms, their initialization, etc.) is discussed, and illustrative examples, problems, and solutions are given.

By no means are all identification problems presently soluble, nor does this text claim to cover all present-day know-how in identification. However, it attempts to bring together the main approaches, going from the simpler to the more sophisticated and advanced, explaining them and discussing their realization and merits.

This text is based on a one-term course of graduate lectures given at the Technion, Israel Institute of Technology, Haifa, in 1968–1970, and on lectures delivered at Liverpool University and at Colorado State University.

It is assumed that the reader is familiar with the mathematics and the concepts of a basic course in control theory (classical linear feedback theory), and with the terminology of characteristic equations and roots, with introductory matrix alegbra and with stability analysis of ordinary linear differential equations. It is therefore directed to systems, control, and process engineers in industry and to graduate students in university departments who are concerned with systems engineering. The text is not restricted to identification of electrical or mechanical or chemical processes. Though each of these types of processes brings its own specific instrumentation problems, the practice of identification is basically the same for all. Identification approaches thus differ according to the computational facilities that are available, or the mathematical features of the variables concerned, and not according to the branch of physics to which parameters belong.

The need for identification from input/output information arises in almost any discipline, such as engineering, physics, chemistry, biology, economics, information theory, data processing, etc., and is not restricted to systems or control engineering. Hence, the identification techniques that are discussed, and which present only a branch of a wider Estimation Theory, may also be of use in other disciplines where dynamic modeling from input/output information is required. Similar considerations, regarding the wide range of applicability, hold for the predictor identification methods that are discussed and which are based on output history only.

It is my pleasure to acknowledge the constant encouragement and the helpful comments of Dr. Russell J. Churchill, Head of the Electrical Engineering Department, Colorado State University. I gratefully acknowledge the help and advice of many colleagues at Colorado State University. I am specifically indebted to Mr. Daniel J. Krause for his important comments, and for computing several of the solutions to the examples of the text, and to Dr. Lee M. Maxwell and Dr. Daniel L. Alspach for their many helpful discussions. Finally, I wish to thank Mrs. Janice Utsler for her patience and care in typing the manuscript.

DANIEL GRAUPE

*February, 1972*

# CONTENTS

# 1

# INTRODUCTION

## 1.1 BASIC DEFINITIONS AND CLASSIFICATIONS

The problem of identifying the characteristics of a system may be considered as dual to that of controlling the system. One cannot control a system unless it has been identified, either a priori or while control is applied. We cannot control a car on the road unless we are familiar with the responses of its steering wheel, accelerator, and brakes to the driver's actions, i.e., unless we have learned something about the car. This process of learning to drive a car, namely, of "getting used" to it, is an identification process. We identify the responses of the car even if we do not require its sets of differential or other equations. Again, if we wish to move a system from point $A$ to point $B$, we can either rely on sheer luck, or learn the response of the system to one or to several control-actions. If we know that input $u_j$ brings the system closer to $B$, we may apply this input. Without that prior knowledge regarding $u_j$, we may apply and measure the responses (in terms of distances from $B$) with respect to a few input-actions, thus, in fact, performing identification. Some identification knowledge is, however, essential before control can be accomplished.

It has been mentioned that the knowledge of the differential equations of a process is one possible identification, though not the only one. We may alternatively tabulate the possible controls and their respective responses at a given future time (lead time) at which we are interested. From this table we may then select the best control for our purpose. Similarly, several other process formulations may yield identification models.

In the following chapters we deal with various methods of identification, which employ a number of different concepts concerning the form of identification model (say differential equations, difference equations, transfer functions, gradient expression, etc.).

None of the different identification techniques that are discussed can be employed to identify systems of all kinds. Each of the techniques presented has its own range or ranges of applicability. This does not imply that, at the present state of the art, identification must be considered as a set of recipes for different types of systems. It is possible to consider a theory of identification, which deals with the estimation of parameters from input and output data, i.e., from a history of measurements, and in which identification is improved with an increase in the number of measurements. Subsequently, errors in identification lead to errors in control or in the estimated system output and these errors are employed to improve further identification. Hence, identification theory is similar, or in fact dual, to control theory, where errors in control (assuming that the system has been identified) are employed to improve the next control. Again, as in control theory, there are several approaches in the framework of the theory, each of which is applicable to a number of situations and cases.

Identification theory, as discussed in the present text, is extended to estimating parameters of predictors and filters. This extension results from the close relation between prediction and identification, which is explained by the fact that the purpose of identification is to facilitate a prediction of the future behavior of the identified system. The prediction problem, however, differs from the identification problem in that the latter considers input/output relations for predicting future behavior, given the system parameters *and* its inputs. The prediction of a time series is based on a measured past history of the time series, whereas its input is often *not* measurable and not known at all. Hence, the identification of predictor parameters is based only on past measurements of the message that is to be predicted (which is considered as an output of a system whose input is not measurable) and cannot employ input/output data.

Broadly speaking, one distinguishes between different identification situations that call for different treatments as follows: *First*, one distinguishes between *linear* and *nonlinear* systems, the linear one being more easily identified because of the linearity properties of superposition. *Second*, one distinguishes between *stationary* and *nonstationary* systems, the latter being systems whose parameters vary with time. Systems may be considered stationary if their parameters vary slowly in comparison with the time required for adequate identification. *Third*, a classification of *discrete* and *continuous* systems is often considered, though a transformation from a continuous to a discrete formulation is usually straightforward. A *fourth* classification of identification techniques is that of distinguishing between *single-input* and *multi-input* techniques. This classification results from the fact that identification techniques are considerably simplified if the state of the system is affected by only one input, as compared with a state that is affected by a combination of several *simultaneous* disturbances or inputs. A *fifth* classification is that of identifying *deterministic* and *stochastic* processes. In the latter processes one has only, or mainly, a probabilistic knowledge of the exact state of the system. In practice all measurements are contaminated by noise, and filtering or smoothing is required to some extent for adequate identification. In deterministic identification approaches it is assumed that the above filtering has already been performed. A *sixth*, and perhaps the most important but least definable, classification of identification methods is classification according to the *degree of a priori knowledge* available regarding the system. Classification of a system as linear implies prior knowledge, as does classification of a system as stationary. These classifications (linearity, stationarity) may, of course, be learned from analyzing measured data, if they are not a priori given. A knowledge of the dimension of the state-vector is of great importance in any identification approach, as is knowledge of the nature of interactions or of nonlinearities.

The above classifications are, in a sense, classifications of the degree of difficulty in identification. Obviously, the identification of a deterministic linear, stationary, single-input process of a known order is easier than that of a stochastic process of which we have no knowledge of order and which may be nonlinear and nonstationary. We discuss in later chapters identification techniques which cover all the categories mentioned, with some of these techniques being restricted to only one category or to a few categories, while other techniques are applicable to more categories. Of necessity, identification techniques that assume less a priori knowledge are less accurate (if a priori knowledge is lacking) and are more complex in terms of mathematical difficulty, of convergence-rate, and of computation time, than those with more prior knowledge. Again, techniques applicable to nonlinear or nonstationary processes are more complex and often less accurate than those restricted to linear stationary processes. The approaches assuming very little a priori knowledge are certainly the more general ones. However, their application to single-input linear processes is often analogous to shooting a house fly with a gun, i.e., it is expensive in terms of the hardware and software required, and complex beyond justification. Consequently, we are justified in discussing not only the complex techniques that assume little prior knowledge, but also the simpler ones that are restricted to, say, linear stationary processes. Hierarchical procedures combining several techniques at different hierarchies are also possible.

Scanning the techniques discussed in the later chapters of this text, we may summarize them as follows.

Chapter 2 deals with basic dual concepts of controllability and observability, full observability being a prerequisite to complete identification of the state model of a system. Chapter 2 further discusses the derivation of state-space models from transfer-functions and vice versa, to facilitate the extension of results that are derived in terms of one of the latter formulations to the other.

Chapter 3 describes identification through employing specific types of input signals (steps, impulses, and sine-waves) that are applied to the system for identification purposes only. These methods may serve for off-line identification of linear, stationary, single-input processes (or for identifying responses of multi-input processes to one input at a time). The order of the process need not be given. However, noise must be filtered, especially in the step and impulse response cases. Since the Fourier transform provides the theoretical background to the techniques of this chapter and of Chapter 4, its relations to identification are discussed for any convergent input time-function.

Chapter 4 is again mainly concerned with cases where special identification signals are employed (white, grey, or pseudo-random noise). However, these techniques may be employed on-line if the noise amplitude is sufficiently low. The techniques described in Chapter 4 are restricted to linear or linearizable processes that may be identified with respect to one input at a time. On-line identification, when possible, is restricted to single-input systems.

Chapter 5 discusses identification techniques based on least-squares regression, which yield least-squares parameters estimates. The techniques of this chapter are valid for slow parameter nonstationarities (slow, compared with the regression). They are applicable to linear systems, yielding identification of discrete or continuous state-space or transfer-function models. Furthermore, they may serve to form part of an input-output-noise model and to estimate unknown parameters of given nonlinear functions or of polynomial approximations to unknown nonlinear functions. Regression methods allow identification with respect to several inputs simultaneously and may be formulated in sequential form as is discussed in Chapter 6. Regression identification algorithms are incorporated in further identification procedures as in chapters 10 and 12 below. Knowledge of the dimension of the state vectors is helpful but not essential. Prior knowledge of the noise covariances is shown to be employed to obtain minimum-variance estimates of maximum likelihood for Gaussian noise. Hence, the relation between least-squares regression estimates and maximum likelihood estimates is discussed.

Chapter 6 presents a sequential formulation of the least-squares regression techniques of Chapter 5, thus avoiding the need for matrix inversion and overcoming the resultant computational difficulties. It is therefore particularly important for on-line identification purposes. Convergence to the estimates of Chapter 5 is rapidly accomplished, because of the equivalence of the approaches of the two chapters.

Chapter 7 deals, in similarity to Chapter 6, with sequential identification methods. These methods are again applicable to linear processes and to estimating unknown parameters of given nonlinear functions (that describe or approximate nonlinear processes) but may take somewhat longer to converge than sequential regression. The first part of Chapter 7 describes the stochastic approximations identification approach. The latter approach possesses most attractive convergence features, since its convergence is guaranteed if only very weak conditions are satisfied. The approach provides computationally simple parameter estimates that converge to the true mean value along the gradient of a squared estimation error, in contrast to the regression approach where each estimate has least-squares properties when it is made. The second part of Chapter 7 is based on the learning method of Nagumo and Noda.[1] It provides sequential identification, differing from the stochastic approximation mainly in the derivation of its convergence features and in its applicability to a system with slow nonstationarities. The approach possesses attractive computational features. Its nonstationary formulation requires special nondisturbing noise inputs as in Chapter 4, but is far faster to compute.

Chapter 8 considers an identification approach that is of iterative nature, requiring a fixed and not a sequentially growing number of measurements. It is applicable to both linear and nonlinear processes. Measurements of only some of the states at various times may be sufficient for identification purposes. However, a knowledge of the dimension of the parameter vector is assumed, as is some prior knowledge of the range of possible values of the parameters that require identification. In cases where parameters of nonlinear systems are being identified, the nonlinear function must be given, or a specific polynomial approximation must be assumed, since only parameters of specific functions can be identified by any method.

Chapter 9 describes a sequential identification technique applicable to linear and nonlinear systems, which is based on a time solution of differential equations whose forcing functions are the measurements-vs.-time records. The approach of Chapter 9 is very lengthy in cases of systems with many parameters. However, it does not require filtering of measurement noise, and may yield estimates (in an optimal sense) of both states and parameters. A knowledge of the dimension of the state vector and of the parameter vector must be assumed. A vague knowledge of the range of possible values of the parameters that are identified is essential to guarantee an adequate convergence rate (though it is less critical than in the case of Chapter 8). Furthermore, some prior knowledge of weighting coefficients and of order of magnitude of the initial conditions to the co-differential equations arising in identification is shown to be most important in order to ascertain convergence.

Chapter 10 describes predictive identification techniques that are valid for linear and nonlinear systems. The first technique of this chapter is basically applicable to single and multi-input linear systems that may be slowly time-variant. The predictive gradient approach of the second part of Chapter 10 yields identification of a function relation between the control performance and the control vector, which is a meaningful relation if adequate control is required. The latter approach does not, however, identify the relations between the state-variables and the control. It is applicable also to nonlinear processes that are linearizable for small perturbations, and facilitates adequate control of these systems. The techniques of Chapter 10 assume smoothing of measurement noise.

Chapter 11 discusses a number of heuristic identification techniques, all of which are based on certain evaluations of scalar performance functions that describe the error between the behavior of the actual system and the respective behavior as estimated when identified parameters are employed. The identified parameters above are subsequently modified and the identification-performance is re-evaluated until the error converges satisfactorily. The techniques are not restricted to linearity, stationarity, or the number of inputs. However, they are very lengthy and slow in many-input processes (unless combined with techniques such as in Chapter 10).

Chapter 12 deals with aspects of prediction, and with the identification of the parameters of predictors or of time series, if they are not a priori given. These identification techniques are extended to facilitate joint parameter and state estimation of linear input/output processes. The prediction techniques of Chapter 12 are applicable to the prediction problems of Chapter 10, but may serve to identify parameters of predictors generally, in cases of a priori unknown messages. The identification of predictor parameters is based on message or output history only, since in this case no input (that is assumed to produce the message as its corresponding output) is available. Consequently, the parameters of a state-equation model are derived for cases where prediction of the state vector of the message is required as in the Kalman filter. Alternatively, a mixed autoregressive-moving-average model[2] is obtained, when prediction via input reconstruction is performed, and extension of this model to non-stationary sequences and input/output systems is discussed. The latter model may be transformed to yield a state space model for further optimal state prediction of Gaussian sequences via the Kalman filtering method described earlier in Chapter 12. It is extendable certain to non-Gaussian cases and may also be incorporated in an input-output-noise identification scheme discussed in Section 5.4.

Chapter 13 deals with effects of errors in the identification of linear systems on the control performance. It serves to point out those parameters where identification errors would result in large deviations of the true control-performance from the expected one, if control is computed on the basis of the identification. It therefore indicates where and if extra effort in identification is required and where vague identification is sufficient as far as the resulting control performance is concerned.

We note that identification of dynamic parameters on the basis of measurement is only possible if the measurements are taken when the system is in a transient state, since dynamic parameters cannot be identified by any approach when the system is in steady state. We re-emphasize that when parameters of nonlinear systems are identified, they must belong to a prespecified nonlinear formulation, since a certain parameter that best describes a system by one nonlinear formulation is inapplicable to other formulations of that system.

## 1.2 THE MATHEMATICAL BACKGROUND

The analysis in chapters 2 to 14 assumes a certain mathematical background which is more or less the standard background reached at Junior University level in electrical, mechanical, chemical, or aeronautical engineering departments and in mathematics or physics departments. This background, if forgotten or not adequately learned, may be obtained from almost any text in systems engineering or in control theory, such as in refs. 3, 4 or 5.

To be more specific, we assume that the reader is familiar with the basic definitions and operations of matrix algebra, such as addition, subtraction, and multiplication of matrices, with matrix inversion operations ($\mathbf{A}^{-1}$), with matrix transposition ($\mathbf{A}^T$), with deriving determinants of matrices, and with concepts of minors and of ranks of matrices. These are discussed in refs. 3 to 5 above and in the opening chapters of any introductory college text on matrices.[6]

We further assume that the reader is conversant with basic statistical terminology,[7] with concepts of transfer functions in Laplace transformed form, with the algebra of block diagrams, with fundamental concepts of characteristic equations and their roots, and with stability properties determined by the real parts of these roots, as discussed in the opening chapters of refs. 3 to 5 above or in any text on control theory or systems analysis.

With this background knowledge, that is essential to any engineer or applied mathematician in any area of work, we can proceed to analyze the identification problems of the present text in the coming chapters.

## 1.3 INTRODUCTORY BIBLIOGRAPHICAL COMMENTS

Since identification is essential to any control, the literature on identification is probably as old as that on control, as is indicated by the first major papers on the frequency response, of Nyquist[8] and of Bode,[9] which describe, in fact, methods of identification. These works show how one obtains the frequency response from input/output measurement, and how this response relates to the system's characteristic equations and roots. Again, the fundamental works in process control by Ziegler and Nichols[10] consider a step-response identification technique. The literature on identification has been considerably enriched with the progress in adaptive and optimal control theory during the 1950's and 1960's. Important survey papers have appeared, such as those by Hsieh in 1965,[11] by Eykhoff et al. in the IFAC (International Federation of Automatic Control) Congress in 1965,[12] by Eykhoff,[13] and by Cuenod and Sage[14] in the IFAC Symposium on Identification held in 1967.

Among the books dealing with identification we shall mention those by R. C. K. Lee[15] covering important topics in control and in sequential state and parameter estimation, by Mishkin and Braun[16] on adaptive control, and by Sage,[17] which devotes important chapters to identification and parameter estimation techniques. The important texts by Deutsch[18] and by Van Trees[19] are mainly devoted to state estimation. However, many of the techniques discussed in refs. 18 and 19 are applicable to sequential parameter identification and are of great value to the worker in this field. So are the texts by Mendel and Fu,[20] where two chapters are devoted to stochastic approximation and to gradient identification; by Box and Jenkins,[2] which is mainly concerned with the identification of mixed autoregressive-moving-average models; and by Lee, Adams, and Gaines,[21] where nonsequential regression techniques are discussed in depth.†

We note that the present paragraph is not concerned with reviewing, listing, or grading the extensive literature in this field. It merely refers to a few important works in this field, since most books on systems or control theory devote chapters or sections to identification and every journal or conference on control contains papers on this subject.

## REFERENCES

1. Nagumo, J., and Noda, A. "A Learning Method for System Identification," *IEEE Tral.*, Vol. AC-12, pp. 282–287, 1967.
2. Box, G. E. P., and Jenkins, G. M. *Time Series Analysis, Forecasting, and Control*, Holden Day, San Francisco, 1970.

† After completion of this text, a book entitled "Systems Identification" by A. P. Sage and J. L. Melsa, has appeared (Academic Press, N.Y. 1971).

3. Elgerd, O. I. *Control Systems Theory*, McGraw-Hill, New York, 1967.
4. Ogata, K. *State Space Analysis of Control Systems*, Prentice Hall, Englewood Cliffs, N.J., 1967.
5. Perkins, W. R., and Cruz, J. B. *Engineering of Dynamic Systems*, Wiley, New York, 1969.
6. Ayres, F. *Matrices*, Schaum, New York, 1962.
7. Sokolnikoff, I. S., and Redheffer, R. M. *Mathematics of Physics and Modern Engineering*, McGraw-Hill, New York, 1966.
8. Nyquist, H. "Regeneration Theory," *Bell Sys. Jour.*, Vol. 11, pp. 126–147, 1932.
9. Bode, H. W. *Network Analysis and Feedback Amplifier Design*, Van Nostrand Reinhold, New York, 1945.
10. Ziegler, J. G., and Nichols, N. B. "Process Lags in Automatic Control Circuits," *Trans. ASME*, Vol. 64, p. 759, 1942.
11. Hsieh, H. C. "Synthesis of Adaptive Control Systems by Function Space Methods," in *Advances in Control Systems*, Vol. 2 (edited by C. T. Leondes), Academic Press, New York, 1965.
12. Eykhoff, P., Van der Grinten, P. M. E. M., Kwakernaak, H., and Veltman, B. P. T. "Systems Modelling and Identification," Survey Paper, *Proc. of 3rd IFAC Congress*, London, 1966.
13. Eykhoff, P. "Process Parameter and State Estimation," Survey Paper .2, *Proc. of IFAC Symposium on Identification*, Prague, 1967.
14. Cuenod, M., and Sage, A. P. "Comparison of Some Methods Used for Identification," Survey Paper .1, *Proc. of IFAC Symposium on Identification*, Prague, 1967.
15. Lee, R. C. K. *Optimal Estimation, Identification and Control*, M.I.T. Press, Cambridge, Mass., 1964.
16. Mishkin, E., and Braun, L. *Adaptive Control Systems*, McGraw-Hill, New York, 1961.
17. Sage, A. P. *Optimum Systems Control*, Prentice-Hall, Englewood Cliffs, N.J., 1968.
18. Deutsch, R. *Estimation Theory*, Prentice-Hall, Englewood Cliffs, N.J., 1965.
19. Van Trees, H. L. *Detection, Estimation and Modulation Theory*, Wiley, New York, 1968.
20. Mendel, J. M., and Fu, K. S. (editors). *Adaptive, Learning and Pattern Recognition Systems*, Academic Press, New York, 1970.
21. Lee, T. H., Adams, G. E., and Gaines, W. M. *Computer Process Control Modeling and Optimization*, Wiley, New York, 1968.

# 2

# THE STATE SPACE, CONTROLLABILITY AND OBSERVABILITY

## 2.1 CONCEPTS OF THE STATE SPACE

Dynamic systems may be described by sets of ordinary or partial differential or difference equations that are of deterministic or probabilistic nature. The dynamic feature appears in these equations in terms of the time derivatives or their respective difference expressions. Systems that are described by partial differential equations may be approximated by sets of ordinary differential equations, containing only time derivatives, if the partial derivatives with respect to other independent variables are replaced by finite difference terms.

Any ordinary differential equation of $r$'th order may be transformed into a set of first-order differential equations. A set of $n$ first-order differential equations is fully described if its coefficients are given and if $n$ initial conditions are known for the $n$ differential equations. A minimum number of $n$ initial conditions is sufficient to solve the above set of differential equations. It therefore forms an $n$-dimensional vector that fully specifies the state of the system that is represented by these equations at an initial time $t_0$ and thereafter (assuming that all inputs or forcing functions are known from $t_0$ onwards). The latter vector is termed as the *state vector* of the system at time $t_0$, and its elements, whose values are given at $t_0$, are called *state variables*. The resulting vector-differential equation is the state equation of the above system. Since the above $n$ state variables are required to form a *minimum* set of initial conditions, it follows that none of them is a linear combination of any of the others.

## 2.2 LINEAR TRANSFORMATIONS

Many combinations of $n$ variables may form a state vector, as defined in Section 2.1 above. These may be derived by transformations as described below.

Consider a linear system given by the following vector-state-equation:

$$\dot{\mathbf{x}} = \mathbf{A}\mathbf{x} + \mathbf{B}\mathbf{u} \tag{2.1}$$

where

$\mathbf{x} = n \times 1 \equiv$ state vector

$\mathbf{u} = m \times 1 \equiv$ vector of forcing functions, or input-vector whose elements may be arbitrary time-functions

$\mathbf{A}, \mathbf{B} \equiv$ coefficient matrices

We may apply linear transformations to the system of Equation (2.1) to form an infinite number of state vectors, these transformed state vectors being linear combinations of the $n$ components of $\mathbf{x}$ as follows:

$$\mathbf{x}^* = \psi^{-1}\mathbf{x}; \qquad (\mathbf{x}^* = \text{transformed state vector}, \; \psi = \text{transformation matrix}) \tag{2.2}$$

Equation (2.2) yields a new state equation:

$$\dot{\mathbf{x}}^* = \mathbf{A}^*\mathbf{x}^* + \mathbf{B}^*\mathbf{u} \tag{2.3}$$

which is satisfied if:

$$\mathbf{A}^* = \psi^{-1}\mathbf{A}\psi \tag{2.4-a}$$

$$\mathbf{B}^* = \psi^{-1}\mathbf{B} \tag{2.4-b}$$

The above transformation is only possible if a finite $\psi^{-1}$ exists. Consequently, no variable may be considered as a state variable if it is a linear combination of one or several other state variables.

At this point it is interesting to note that the eigenvalues of the original system of Equation (2.1) and those of the transformed system of Equation (2.2) are identical, as arises from a derivation based on the following eigenvalue relation[1]:

$$\det(\mathbf{A} - \lambda_i \mathbf{I}) = 0 \qquad (i = 1, 2, \ldots, n) \tag{2.5}$$

$\lambda_i$ being the $i$'th eigenvalue of **A**. Subsequently, and noting that $\det(\mathbf{G}\cdot\mathbf{H}) = \det(\mathbf{G})\cdot\det(\mathbf{H})$, we derive for the transformed system of Equation (2.2):

$$\begin{aligned}\det(\mathbf{A}^* - \lambda_i^*\mathbf{I}) &= \det(\psi^{-1}\mathbf{A}\psi - \lambda_i^*\mathbf{I}) = \det(\psi^{-1}\mathbf{A}\psi - \lambda_i^*\psi^{-1}\mathbf{I}\psi)\\ &= \det(\psi^{-1})\cdot\det(\mathbf{A} - \lambda_i^*\mathbf{I})\cdot\det(\psi) = 0 \qquad (2.6)\end{aligned}$$

Furthermore, since $\det\psi \neq 0$ if $\psi^{-1}$ is finite, Equation (2.5) yields:

$$\det(\mathbf{A} - \lambda_i^*\mathbf{I}) = 0 \qquad (2.7)$$

We thus observe that the matrix **A** satisfies both Equation (2.5) and Equation (2.7), such that when suitably arranging the subscript $i$ of $\lambda_i$, we obtain:

$$\lambda_i^* = \lambda_i \qquad (2.8)$$

Example 2.1

The eigenvalues of the system:

$$\dot{\mathbf{x}} = \mathbf{A}\mathbf{x}; \qquad \mathbf{A} = \begin{bmatrix} 3 & 2 \\ 1 & 4 \end{bmatrix}$$

are given by:

$$\begin{aligned}\det(\mathbf{A} - \lambda_i\mathbf{I}) = 0 = \det\begin{bmatrix} 3-\lambda_i & 2 \\ 1 & 4-\lambda_i \end{bmatrix}\\ = (3-\lambda_i)(4-\lambda_i) - 2 = \lambda_i^2 - 7\lambda_i + 10\end{aligned}$$

yielding

$$\lambda_i = \frac{7 \pm \sqrt{49-40}}{2} = \frac{7 \pm 3}{2}$$

namely:

$$\lambda_1 = 5; \qquad \lambda_2 = 2$$

When the system of this example is transformed via a transformation matrix $\psi = \begin{bmatrix} 1 & 0 \\ 0 & 2 \end{bmatrix}$, we obtain:

$$\dot{\mathbf{x}}^* = \mathbf{A}^*\mathbf{x}^*$$

where, according to Equation (2.4):

$$\mathbf{A}^* = \psi^{-1}\mathbf{A}\psi = \begin{bmatrix} 1 & 0 \\ 0 & 0.5 \end{bmatrix}\begin{bmatrix} 3 & 2 \\ 1 & 4 \end{bmatrix}\begin{bmatrix} 1 & 0 \\ 0 & 2 \end{bmatrix} = \begin{bmatrix} 3 & 4 \\ 0.5 & 4 \end{bmatrix}$$

The eigenvalues of $A^*$ are given by:

$$\det(\mathbf{A}^* - \lambda_i^*\mathbf{I}) = 0 = \det\begin{bmatrix} 3-\lambda_i^* & 4 \\ 0.5 & 4-\lambda_i^* \end{bmatrix} = (3-\lambda_i^*)(4-\lambda_i^*) - 2$$

thus being identical to the eigenvalues of **A** above.

### 2.2.1 The Canonical Transformation

Among the various possible linear transformations of Equation (2.1), one transformation is of special importance as will be shown later in this text. This is the canonical transformation, where the transformation matrix is the eigen-vector-matrix **V**. The latter matrix results from the solution of the homogeneous form of the following linear state equation:

$$\dot{x} = \mathbf{A}\mathbf{x}; \qquad \mathbf{x}(0) = \mathbf{x}_0 \tag{2.9}$$

this solution being:

$$\begin{aligned} x_1(t) &= v_{11}\exp(\lambda_1 t) + \cdots v_{1n}\exp(\lambda_n t) \\ &\vdots \\ x_n(t) &= v_{n1}\exp(\lambda_1 t) + \cdots v_{nn}\exp(\lambda_n t) \end{aligned} \tag{2.10-a}$$

or, in vector form:

$$\mathbf{x}(t) = \mathbf{V}\cdot\exp(\boldsymbol{\lambda}t) = \mathbf{v}_1\exp(\lambda_1 t) + \cdots \mathbf{v}_n\exp(\lambda_n t) \tag{2.10-b}$$

where:

$$\exp(\boldsymbol{\lambda}t) \triangleq \begin{bmatrix} e^{\lambda_1 t} \\ \cdot \\ \cdot \\ \cdot \\ \cdot \\ \cdot \\ e^{\lambda_n t} \end{bmatrix} \tag{2.11}$$

and:

$$\mathbf{V} \triangleq \begin{bmatrix} v_{11} & \cdots & v_{1n} \\ \cdot & & \\ \cdot & & \\ \cdot & & \\ \cdot & & \\ \cdot & & \\ v_{n1} & \cdots & v_{nn} \end{bmatrix} = [\mathbf{v}_1 \cdots \mathbf{v}_n] \tag{2.12}$$

such that the derivation of $\mathbf{V}$ depends on that of the eigenvectors $\mathbf{v}_i$.

**2.2.1-a Direct derivation of eigenvectors** Differentiating Equation (2.10) with respect to $t$ yields:

$$\dot{\mathbf{x}} = \lambda_1 \mathbf{v}_1 \exp(\lambda_1 t) + \cdots \lambda_n \mathbf{v}_n \exp(\lambda_n t) \tag{2.13}$$

whereas, substituting for $\mathbf{x}$ from Equation (2.10) into (2.9), we obtain:

$$\dot{\mathbf{x}} = \mathbf{AV} \exp(\boldsymbol{\lambda} t) = \mathbf{A}[\mathbf{v}_1 \exp(\lambda_1 t) + \cdots \mathbf{v}_n \exp(\lambda_n t)] \tag{2.14}$$

Comparing equations (2.13) and (2.14), the eigenvectors $\mathbf{v}_i$ satisfy (for the case where all $\lambda_i$ are distinct):

$$\lambda_i \mathbf{v}_i \exp(\lambda_i t) = \mathbf{A}\mathbf{v}_i \exp(\lambda_i t) \tag{2.15}$$

and dividing both sides of Equation (2.15) by $\exp(\lambda_i t)$, yields:

$$\lambda_i \mathbf{v}_i = \mathbf{A}\mathbf{v}_i \tag{2.16-a}$$

or:

$$(\mathbf{A} - \lambda_i \mathbf{I})\mathbf{v}_i = 0 \tag{2.16-b}$$

Consequently, $\mathbf{v}_i$ may be derived from Equation (2.16). For obtaining unique vectors $\mathbf{v}_i$, we are required to allocate a specific value to one element of $\mathbf{v}_i$, say the first which may be set as 1. Hence, the bottom row of Equation (2.16-b) is redundant and is to be ignored in the algorithm for computing $\mathbf{v}_i$, as is illustrated by the following example.

EXAMPLE 2.2

Consider a matrix $\mathbf{A} = \begin{bmatrix} 1 & 2 \\ 4 & 3 \end{bmatrix}$. The eigenvectors $\mathbf{v}_i$ of $\mathbf{A}$ are determined through first computing the eigenvalues of $\mathbf{A}$ as follows:

$$\det(\mathbf{A} - \lambda_i \mathbf{I}) = \det \begin{bmatrix} 1 - \lambda & 2 \\ 4 & 3 - \lambda \end{bmatrix} = \lambda_i^2 - 4\lambda_i - 5 = 0$$

such that $\lambda_1 = -1$; $\lambda_2 = 5$. Subsequently, according to Equation (2.16);

$$-\mathbf{v}_1 = \begin{bmatrix} -v_{11} \\ -v_{12} \end{bmatrix} = \begin{bmatrix} 1 & 2 \\ 4 & 3 \end{bmatrix} \begin{bmatrix} v_{11} \\ v_{12} \end{bmatrix} = \begin{bmatrix} v_{11} + 2v_{12} \\ 4v_{11} + 3v_{12} \end{bmatrix}$$

yielding:

$$-2v_{11} = 2v_{12}$$
$$-4v_{11} = 4v_{12}$$

or:

$$v_{11} = -v_{12}$$

Setting $v_{11} = 1$, we obtain that:

$$\mathbf{v}_1 = \begin{bmatrix} 1 \\ -1 \end{bmatrix}$$

Similarly, according to Equation (2.16),

$$5\mathbf{v}_2 = \begin{bmatrix} 5 \cdot v_{21} \\ 5 \cdot v_{22} \end{bmatrix} = \begin{bmatrix} 1 & 2 \\ 4 & 3 \end{bmatrix} \begin{bmatrix} v_{21} \\ v_{22} \end{bmatrix} = \begin{bmatrix} v_{21} + 2v_{22} \\ 4v_{21} + 3v_{22} \end{bmatrix}$$

yielding

$$4v_{21} = 2v_{22}$$
$$2v_{22} = 4v_{21}$$

or:

$$2v_{21} = v_{22}$$

Setting $v_{21} = 1$, we thus obtain that:

$$\mathbf{v}_2 = \begin{bmatrix} 1 \\ 2 \end{bmatrix}$$

and:

$$\mathbf{V} = [\mathbf{v}_1, \mathbf{v}_2] = \begin{bmatrix} 1 & 1 \\ -1 & 2 \end{bmatrix}$$

**2.2.1-b Alternative algorithms for deriving eigenvectors** A faster sequential procedure to derive the eigenvectors of an $n \times n$ matrix $\mathbf{A}$ is that based on Krylov's method.[2] This method again assumes that the eigenvalues $\lambda_1 \ldots \lambda_n$ of $\mathbf{A}$ have been derived and that the characteristic equation

$\det(\mathbf{A} - \lambda_i \mathbf{I}) = 0$ is available. The method is applicable to matrices with distinct and nondistinct eigenvalues, as follows,

Defining coefficients $c_i$ such that:

$$\det(\mathbf{A} - \lambda \mathbf{I}) = (-1)^n(\lambda^n - c_{n-1}\lambda^{n-1} - \cdots - c_0) \tag{2.17}$$

and arbitrarily choosing an initial $n$-dimensional vector $\mathbf{d}_1$, say for $n = 2$:

$$\mathbf{d}_1 = [1, 0]^T \tag{2.18-a}$$

we construct:

$$\mathbf{d}_2 = \mathbf{A}\mathbf{d}_1;\ \mathbf{d}_3 = \mathbf{A}\mathbf{d}_2;\ \ldots\ \mathbf{d}_n = \mathbf{A}\mathbf{d}_{n-1} \tag{2.18-b}$$

Subsequently, we derive the elements of the $i$'th eigenvector $\mathbf{v}_i$, as follows:

$$\mathbf{v}_i = \sum_{k=1}^{n} p_{ik}\mathbf{d}_{n-k+1} \tag{2.19}$$

where:

$$p_{i1} = 1 \tag{2.20-a}$$

$$p_{i,j} = \lambda_i p_{i,j-1} - c_{n-j+1}; \qquad j = 2, \ldots, n \tag{2.20-b}$$

$$0 = \lambda_i p_{in} - c_0 \tag{2.20-c}$$

Equation (2.20-c) serving only to check the computation.

In cases where $\mathbf{A}$ is of the *companion form* of

$$\left[\begin{array}{c|c} 0 & \\ \vdots & \mathbf{I} \\ 0 & \\ \hline \alpha_1 & \cdots\ \alpha_n \end{array}\right]$$

a very fast algorithm may be derived for computing the eigenvector matrix $\mathbf{V}$, in terms of the Vandermonde matrix, as follows:

$$\mathbf{V} = \begin{bmatrix} 1 & 1 & \cdots & 1 \\ \lambda_1 & \lambda_2 & \cdots & \lambda_n \\ \lambda_1^2 & \lambda_2^2 & \cdots & \lambda_n^2 \\ \vdots & \vdots & & \vdots \\ \lambda_1^{n-1} & \lambda_2^{n-1} & \cdots & \lambda_n^{n-1} \end{bmatrix} \tag{2.21}$$

We note that $\mathbf{V}^{-1}$ exists only if all $\lambda_i$ are distinct.

EXAMPLE 2.3

Applying Krylov's method to Example 2.2, where:

$$\mathbf{A} = \begin{bmatrix} 1 & 2 \\ 4 & 3 \end{bmatrix} \qquad \lambda_1 = -1;\ \lambda_2 = 5;\ n = 2$$

we derive the eigenvectors of $\mathbf{A}$ as follows: We arbitrarily select:

$$\mathbf{d}_1 = \begin{bmatrix} 1 \\ 0 \end{bmatrix}$$

to yield:

$$\mathbf{d}_2 = \mathbf{A}\mathbf{d}_1 = \begin{bmatrix} 1 & 2 \\ 4 & 3 \end{bmatrix} \begin{bmatrix} 1 \\ 0 \end{bmatrix} = \begin{bmatrix} 1 \\ 4 \end{bmatrix}$$

and, noting Equation (2.17), $c_i$ become:

$$\lambda_i^2 - 4\lambda_i - 5 = \lambda^n - c_1\lambda - c_0$$

We obtain:

$$c_1 = 4; \qquad c_0 = 5$$

Equation (2.20) further yields:

$$p_{11} = 1; \qquad p_{12} = -1 \cdot p_{11} - c_1 = -1 - 4 = -5$$
$$p_{21} = 1; \qquad p_{22} = 5 \cdot p_{21} - c_1 = 5 - 4 = 1$$

The eigenvectors $\mathbf{v}_1$, $\mathbf{v}_2$ thus become:

$$\mathbf{v}_1 = p_{11}\mathbf{d}_2 + p_{12}\mathbf{d}_1 = \begin{bmatrix} 1 \\ 4 \end{bmatrix} - \begin{bmatrix} 5 \\ 0 \end{bmatrix} = \begin{bmatrix} -4 \\ 4 \end{bmatrix}$$
$$\mathbf{v}_2 = p_{21}\mathbf{d}_2 + p_{22}\mathbf{d}_1 = \begin{bmatrix} 1 \\ 4 \end{bmatrix} + \begin{bmatrix} 1 \\ 0 \end{bmatrix} = \begin{bmatrix} 2 \\ 4 \end{bmatrix}$$

Finally, normalizing $\mathbf{v}_i$ such that the first element is 1, we obtain:

$$\mathbf{v}_1 = \begin{bmatrix} 1 \\ -1 \end{bmatrix}; \qquad \mathbf{v}_2 = \begin{bmatrix} 1 \\ 2 \end{bmatrix}$$

as in Example 2.2.

**2.2.1-c The diagonalization procedure** Following the derivation of **V**, we now define a diagonal matrix $\mathbf{\Lambda}$ as follows:

$$\mathbf{\Lambda} \triangleq \text{diag}(\lambda_1 \ldots \lambda_n) \tag{2.22}$$

Hence, we obtain that:

$$\mathbf{V\Lambda} = [\lambda_1 \mathbf{v}_1; \ldots; \lambda_n \mathbf{v}_n] \tag{2.23}$$

Noting Equation (2.16), we subsequently derive:

$$\mathbf{V\Lambda} = \mathbf{A} \cdot (\mathbf{v}_1; \ldots; \mathbf{v}_n) = \mathbf{AV} \tag{2.24-a}$$

or:

$$\mathbf{\Lambda} = \mathbf{V}^{-1}\mathbf{AV} \tag{2.24-b}$$

Hence, the diagonalization of **A** is accomplished if its eigenvalues are distinct. Applying the canonical transformation to Equation (2.1), i.e. employing **V** as the transformation matrix, and noting Equation (2.4), we now derive the following canonical state equation:

$$\dot{\mathbf{x}}^* = \mathbf{\Lambda x}^* + \mathbf{B}^*\mathbf{u}; \ \mathbf{B}^* = \mathbf{V}^{-1} \cdot \mathbf{B} \tag{2.25-a}$$

or, in scalar form:

$$\begin{aligned}
\dot{x}_1^* &= \lambda_1 x_1^* + b_{11}^* u_1 + \cdots b_{1m}^* u_m \\
\dot{x}_2^* &= \lambda_2 x_2^* + b_{21}^* u_1 + \cdots b_{2m}^* u_m \\
&\vdots \\
\dot{x}_n^* &= \lambda_n x_n^* + b_{n1}^* + \cdots b_{nm}^* u_m
\end{aligned} \tag{2.25–b}$$

Consequently, the canonical transformation yields a set of state equations where *each derivative of a* (*canonical*) *state variable depends only on the corresponding* (*canonical*) *state variable* and on the inputs.

EXAMPLE 2.4

Consider the diagonalization of $\dot{\mathbf{x}} = \mathbf{Ax} + \mathbf{Bu}$ where $\mathbf{A} = \begin{bmatrix} 1 & 2 \\ 4 & 3 \end{bmatrix}$ as in Example 2.2, and $\mathbf{B} = \begin{bmatrix} 1 \\ -1 \end{bmatrix}$. The canonical transformation of **A** is performed according to Equation (2.24) as follows:

$$\mathbf{\Lambda} = \mathbf{V}^{-1}\mathbf{AV}$$

In Example 2.2 we obtained that $\mathbf{V} = \begin{bmatrix} 1 & 1 \\ -1 & 2 \end{bmatrix}$. Consequently,

$$\mathbf{V}^{-1} = \begin{bmatrix} \frac{2}{3} & -\frac{1}{3} \\ \frac{1}{3} & \frac{1}{3} \end{bmatrix}$$

and:

$$\Lambda = \begin{bmatrix} \frac{2}{3} & -\frac{1}{3} \\ \frac{1}{3} & \frac{1}{3} \end{bmatrix} \begin{bmatrix} 1 & 2 \\ 4 & 3 \end{bmatrix} \begin{bmatrix} 1 & 1 \\ -1 & 2 \end{bmatrix}$$

$$= \begin{bmatrix} -\frac{2}{3} & \frac{1}{3} \\ \frac{5}{3} & \frac{5}{3} \end{bmatrix} \begin{bmatrix} 1 & 1 \\ -1 & 2 \end{bmatrix} = \begin{bmatrix} -1 & 0 \\ 0 & 5 \end{bmatrix}$$

Noting, from Example 2.2 that $\lambda_1 = -1$; $\lambda_2 = 5$, the diagonal matrix $\Lambda$ is equal to $\begin{bmatrix} \lambda_1 & 0 \\ 0 & \lambda_2 \end{bmatrix}$ as required.

## 2.3 CONTROLLABILITY

The concept of controllability and its dual concept of observability were first introduced by R. E. Kalman[3] in 1960. Although in a discussion of identification techniques, the concept of observability is more important than that of controllability, both concepts are examined below since their duality makes the understanding of one concept related to the understanding of the other.

A system is said to be controllable if it can be moved from any state $\mathbf{x}(t_0)$ at $t = t_0$ to any other desired state $\mathbf{x}(t_1)$ in a finite time interval $\tau$, $(\tau = t_1 - t_0)$ by applying a piecewise continuous input-vector $\mathbf{u}(t)$; $t \in (t_0, t_1)$.

The concept of controllability may be illustrated by Figure 2.1. Hence, we observe that a system is uncontrollable if *not* every state variable is affected by the control inputs.

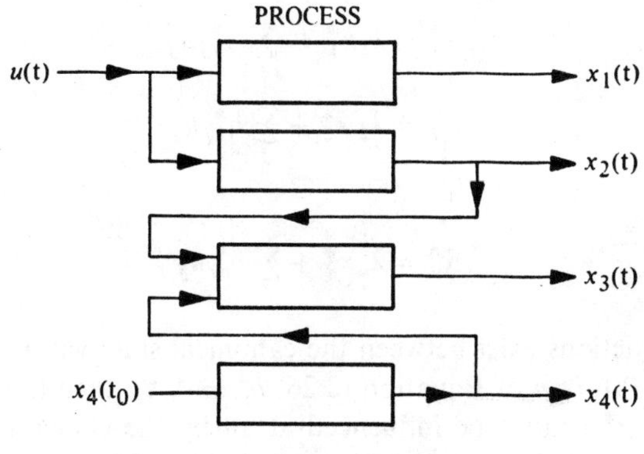


*Figure 2.1* An uncontrollable system.

A further feature of controllability is that a controllable linear system can assume any arbitrarily desired closed-loop eigenvalues, regardless of its open-loop eigenvalues. This feature is discussed in detail by Wonham in Ref. 4.

Several criteria are described in the literature for examining the controllability (and the dual concept of observability) of a system. These are (broadly) based on examining the canonical state equation[5], and on a polynomial expansion of $e^{\mathbf{A}t}$ due to Kalman[3]. (See also refs. 6 through 9.)

### 2.3.1 Controllability Criterion for Canonical Systems

We first describe a criterion due to Gilbert[5] (see also Ref. 10, pp. 87–117) for examining the controllability of a linear system, which is based on the canonical form of that system. This method implies that the systems be first transformed to their canonical form of equations (2.25). This form is convenient since no interactions exist between the canonical state variables. According to Gilbert's criterion, *a system given in canonical form as*:

$$\dot{\mathbf{x}}^* = \mathbf{\Lambda} x^* + \mathbf{B}^* \mathbf{u} \tag{2.26}$$

*is controllable if no row in* $\mathbf{B}^*$ *is zero* (i.e., in each row there must be at least one nonzero element of $\mathbf{B}$ for controllability). *Furthermore, if at least one row of* $\mathbf{B}$ *is zero, the system is uncontrollable.* We have shown in Section 2.2 that the canonical form of Equation (2.25) is valid only for cases where the $n \cdot n$ matrix $\mathbf{A}$ of the original system has $n$ *distinct* eigenvalues. However, we shall discuss later in this Section a Jordan-canonical transformation[6] to partly overcome this restriction.

The proof of the above controllability theorem is as follows. First, we consider the statement that if one or more rows of $\mathbf{B}^*$ are zero, the system is uncontrollable. We therefore rewrite Equation (2.25) in scalar form as:

$$\begin{aligned}
\dot{x}_1^* &= \lambda_1 x_1^* + \sum_{j=1}^{m} b_{1j}^* u_j \\
\dot{x}_2^* &= \lambda_2 x_2^* + \sum_{j} b_{2j}^* u_j \\
&\vdots \\
\dot{x}_n^* &= \lambda_n x_n^* + \sum_{j} b_{nj}^* u_j
\end{aligned} \tag{2.27}$$

Since no interactions exist between the canonical state variables, we observe that if in any $i$'th row of Equation (2.26) $b_{ij}^* = 0$, $\forall j$, then the corresponding state variable $x_i^*$ cannot be influenced at all by the choice of the controls. Hence, this state of the system is uncontrollable. However, if no row of $\mathbf{B}^*$

is zero, we prove that every $x_i^*(t_0)$ can be brought to any $x_i^*(t_1)$, by observing the solution to Equation (2.26), given by:

$$x_i^*(t_1) = e^{\lambda_i(t_1-t_0)}x_i^*(t_0) + \sum_{j=1}^{m} \int_{t_0}^{t_1} e^{\lambda_i(t_1-\tau)} b_{ij}^* u_j(\tau)\, d\tau \qquad \forall i = 1, \ldots n \qquad (2.28)$$

We may always define $x_i^*(t_0) \triangleq 0$, $t_0 \triangleq 0$, to yield:

$$x_i^*(t_1) = \sum_j e^{\lambda_i t_1} \int_0^{t_1} e^{-\lambda_i \tau} b_{ij}^* u_j(\tau)\, d\tau \qquad \forall i = 1, \ldots n \qquad (2.29)$$

Consider the case where $n$ inputs $u_1 \cdots u_n$ exist ($n$ being the number of states). Consequently, Equation (2.28) indicates that if all rows of $\mathbf{B}^*$ are linearly independent, we could require that $u_j$ ($\forall j = 1 \cdots n$) be constant valued inside the integration interval, and solve $n$ equations with $n$ unknown $u_j$ to satisfy $n$ arbitrary different $x_i^*(t_1)$. The situation appears to be more difficult if only one input exists. In that case, Equation (2.28) becomes:

$$x_i^*(t_1) = e^{\lambda_i t_1} \int_0^{t_1} e^{-\lambda_i \tau} b_i^* u(\tau)\, d\tau \qquad \forall i \qquad (2.30)$$

However, any finite interval $t_1 - t_0$ can be divided into $n$ subintervals $(t_{11} - t_0)$; $(t_{21} - t_{11}) \cdots (t_{n1} - t_{n+1})$ where $t_{n1} = t_1$. Consequently, the integral of Equation (2.29) becomes a sum of $n$ integrals over the above $n$ subintervals. Obviously $u(\tau)$ may take $n$ different values in these subintervals, which may be constant inside each subinterval. Hence, we derive $n$ simultaneous equations in $n$ unknowns (the $u$ values in each subinterval) to satisfy the $n$ arbitrary values for $x_i^*(t_1)$, $\forall i = 1 \cdots n$. The latter single input controllability criterion is also valid for multi-input systems, since, if a system has several inputs while no row of $\mathbf{B}^*$ is empty, we could force all inputs to be equal or interrelated such that our system becomes a single-input system.

EXAMPLE 2.5

Consider the system $\dot{\mathbf{x}} = \mathbf{Ax} + \mathbf{Bu}$ where $\mathbf{A} = \begin{bmatrix} 1 & 2 \\ 4 & 3 \end{bmatrix}$ as in Example 2.2, and $\mathbf{B} = \begin{bmatrix} 1 \\ 2 \end{bmatrix}$. According to Example 2.2, the transformation matrix for diagonalizing $\mathbf{A}$ is given by $\mathbf{V} = \begin{bmatrix} 1 & 1 \\ -1 & 2 \end{bmatrix}$, such that:

$$\mathbf{V}^{-1} = \begin{bmatrix} \frac{2}{3} & -\frac{1}{3} \\ \frac{1}{3} & \frac{1}{3} \end{bmatrix}$$

and

$$\mathbf{\Lambda} = \mathbf{V}^{-1}\mathbf{AV} = \begin{bmatrix} -1 & 0 \\ 0 & 5 \end{bmatrix}$$

According to Equation (2.25):

$$\mathbf{B}^* = \mathbf{V}^{-1}\mathbf{B} = \begin{bmatrix} \frac{2}{3} & -\frac{1}{3} \\ \frac{1}{3} & \frac{1}{3} \end{bmatrix} \begin{bmatrix} 1 \\ 2 \end{bmatrix} = \begin{bmatrix} 0 \\ 1 \end{bmatrix}$$

yielding a diagonalized (canonical) system given by:

$$\dot{x}_1^* = -x_1^*$$
$$\dot{x}_2^* = 5x_2^* + u$$

Since state $x_1^*$ cannot be affected by the control input, the system is obviously uncontrollable.

**2.3.1-a Cases of non-distinct eigenvalues** When not all eigenvalues of **A** are distinct, the canonical diagonalization of **A** cannot be performed. However, if **A** is nonderogative, it may be transformed into a *Jordan-canonical form*[11] **J**, as in the following equation:

$$\mathbf{J} = \left[\begin{array}{ccc|ccccc} \lambda_1 & 1 & 0 & 0 & \cdot & \cdot & \cdot & 0 \\ 0 & \lambda_1 & 1 & 0 & \cdot & \cdot & \cdot & 0 \\ 0 & 0 & \lambda_1 & 0 & \cdot & \cdot & \cdot & 0 \\ \hline 0 & 0 & 0 & \lambda_2 & 0 & \cdot & \cdot & 0 \\ \cdot & & \cdot & 0 & \lambda_3 & 0 & \cdot & 0 \\ \cdot & & \cdot & & & \cdot & & \\ \cdot & & \cdot & & & & \cdot & \\ 0 & 0 & 0 & 0 & \cdot & \cdot & 0 & \lambda_n \end{array}\right] \tag{2.31}$$

(for three identical eigenvalues $\lambda_1$)

**A** being nonderogative if its minimum polynomial and characteristic equation are identical. (The minimum polynomial of **A** is the polynomial equation of minimum order that satisfies:

$$\mathbf{A}^q + \alpha_{q-1}\mathbf{A}^{q-1} + \cdots \alpha_1\mathbf{A} + \alpha_0\mathbf{I} = 0$$

whereas the characteristic equation of **A** is given by:

$$\lambda^n + \alpha_{n-1}\lambda^{n-1} + \cdots \alpha_1\lambda + \alpha_0 = 0$$

$\lambda$ being an eigenvalue of **A**.) The upper diagonal matrix of (2.31) is known as a *Jordan-block*. Several Jordan-blocks may appear along the diagonal of **J** if more than one group of identical $\lambda_i$ exist, each being of the dimension of the multiplicity in the corresponding $\lambda_i$. For controllability, we require that at least one element of **B** in the row corresponding to the bottom row of each Jordan-block and at least one element of **B** in each other row are nonzero.[6]

We observe that the controllability criteria based on canonization requires the derivation of the eigenvalues and eigenvectors and subsequent transformation of the state equation. The computational effort that is involved may therefore be very considerable.

### 2.3.2 Controllability Criterion Based on Expanding exp(A$t$)

The controllability criterion, based on a polynomial expansion of the state transition matrix $e^{At}$, is due to Kalman.[3] This criterion is not restricted to systems with distinct eigenvalues of **A** and requires no canonization of the system, thus avoiding the derivation of its eigenvectors. However, the present criterion is less clearly related to the physics of the system than is the criterion of Section 2.3.1.

For checking controllability, Kalman investigates the solution of state equation (2.1), which is given by:

$$\mathbf{x}(t_1) = e^{\mathbf{A}(t_1 - t_0)}\mathbf{x}(t_0) + \int_{t_0}^{t_1} e^{\mathbf{A}(t-\tau)}\mathbf{B}\mathbf{u}(\tau)\, d\tau \tag{2.32-a}$$

or, when changing the definitions of the integration limits:

$$\mathbf{x}(t_0) = e^{\mathbf{A}(t_0 - t_1)}\mathbf{x}(t_1) + \int_{t_1}^{t_0} e^{\mathbf{A}(t_0-\tau)}\mathbf{B}\mathbf{u}(\tau)\, d\tau \tag{2.32-b}$$

**x**, **u** being $n$- and $m$-dimensional vectors, respectively.

Since one may always define $\mathbf{x}(t_1) \triangleq \mathbf{0}$, Equation (2.32) yields:

$$\mathbf{x}(t_0) = -\int_{t_0}^{t_1} e^{\mathbf{A}(t_0-\tau)}\mathbf{B}\mathbf{u}(\tau)\, d\tau \tag{2.33}$$

We note that, according to the Cayley-Hamilton theorem,[12] any $n \times n$ matrix **A** satisfies its own polynomial equation of order $n$, such that:

$$\mathbf{A}^n = \sum_{i=0}^{n-1} \beta_i \mathbf{A}^i \tag{2.34}$$

Hence, we may express any polynomial matrix equation of order $(n + r) > n$ by a polynomial equation of order $(n + r - 1) \geq (n - 1)$, as follows:

$$\mathbf{A}^{n+r} = \mathbf{A}^r\mathbf{A}^n = \mathbf{A}^r \sum_{i=0}^{n-1} \beta_i \mathbf{A}^i = \mathbf{P}_{n+r-1}(\mathbf{A}) \tag{2.35}$$

$\mathbf{P}_{n+r-1}(\mathbf{A})$ being a polynomial of order $n + r - 1$. According to the Sylvester theorem (see Ref. 12, p. 78), this result is shown to hold for infinite power series of **A**. Consequently, and noting that:

$$e^{\mathbf{A}t} = \mathbf{I} + \mathbf{A}t + \mathbf{A}^2t^2/2! + \cdots + \mathbf{A}^k t^k/k! + \cdots \tag{2.36}$$

we obtain:

$$e^{\mathbf{A}t} = \sum_{i=0}^{n-1} \gamma_i(t)\mathbf{A}^i \tag{2.37}$$

where, for a finite value of $t$, the scalar coefficients $\gamma_i(t)$ are finite for any matrix **A**. Substituting for $e^{\mathbf{A}t}$ from Equation (2.37) into (2.35) yields:

$$\begin{aligned} \mathbf{x}(t_0) &= -\int_{t_0}^{t_1} \sum_{i=0}^{n-1} \gamma_i(t_0 - \tau)\mathbf{A}^i\mathbf{B}\mathbf{u}(\tau)\, d\tau \\ &= -\sum_{i=0}^{n-1} \mathbf{A}^i\mathbf{B} \int_{t_0}^{t_1} \gamma_i(t_0 - \tau)\mathbf{u}(\tau)\, d\tau \end{aligned} \tag{2.38}$$

We subsequently define:

$$\mathbf{M} \triangleq [\mathbf{B}; \mathbf{AB}; \mathbf{A}^2\mathbf{B}; \ldots; \mathbf{A}^{n-1}\mathbf{B}] \tag{2.39}$$

$$\mathbf{W}_i \triangleq -\int_{t_0}^{t_1} \gamma_i(t_0 - \tau)\mathbf{u}(\tau)\, d\tau; \qquad \forall i \in (0, n-1) \tag{2.40}$$

and:

$$\mathbf{W} \triangleq \begin{bmatrix} \mathbf{W}_0 \\ \mathbf{W}_1 \\ \cdot \\ \cdot \\ \cdot \\ \mathbf{W}_{n-1} \end{bmatrix} \tag{2.41}$$

**M** being an $(n \times (n \times m))$ matrix and $\mathbf{W}_i$, **W** being an $m$ and an $(n \times m)$ dimensional vector, respectively, such that Equation (2.33) becomes:

$$\mathbf{x}(t_0) = \mathbf{M} \cdot \mathbf{W} \tag{2.42}$$

The system of Equation (2.1) is therefore controllable if $n$ independent scalar equations satisfy the matrix equation (2.42). Hence, the system is controllable if **M** is of rank $n$. In cases of single-input processes, where **B** is a column vector, the above condition implies that $\mathbf{M}^{-1}$ must exist for controllability. For arriving at $\mathbf{x}(t_0)$ in the general case where the dimension of **u** is smaller than that of **x**, the elements of **u** should assume several different piecewise continuous sets of values during the interval $(t_0 - t_1)$, if $\mathbf{x}(t_0)$ is to be reached, as has been mentioned in Section 2.3.1. We note that the controllability criteria are independent of any stability considerations. A system may therefore be controllable even though it may be unstable if uncontrolled, since controllability is concerned with the possible controlled features of a system. A controllable system is thus stabilizable regardless of its uncontrolled stability or instability.

EXAMPLE 2.6

In the present example we check the controllability of the system of Example 2.5 by the criterion based on expanding exp($\mathbf{A}t$). Noting that $\mathbf{A} = \begin{bmatrix} 1 & 2 \\ 4 & 3 \end{bmatrix}$, $\mathbf{B} = \begin{bmatrix} 1 \\ 2 \end{bmatrix}$ and $\mathbf{AB} = \begin{bmatrix} 1 & 2 \\ 4 & 3 \end{bmatrix}\begin{bmatrix} 1 \\ 2 \end{bmatrix} = \begin{bmatrix} 5 \\ 10 \end{bmatrix}$, we obtain that:

$$\mathbf{M} = \begin{bmatrix} 1 & 5 \\ 2 & 10 \end{bmatrix}$$

Since both columns (rows) of $\mathbf{M}$ are linearly dependent (det $\mathbf{M} = 0$), the system is uncontrollable, as has already been shown in Example 2.5 by canonical transformation.

### 2.3.3 Output Controllability

The previous sections (2.3.1; 2.3.2) were concerned with state controllability, i.e., with the possibility of moving the system from any state $\mathbf{x}(t_0)$ to any state $\mathbf{x}(t_1)$. The concept of *output controllability* is concerned with the possibility of moving the system's output $\mathbf{y}$ from $\mathbf{y}(t_0)$ to $\mathbf{y}(t_1)$, when the output $\mathbf{y}$ is given by:

$$\mathbf{y} = \mathbf{Cx} \tag{2.43}$$

$\mathbf{x}$, $\mathbf{y}$ being $(n \times 1)$ and $(q \times 1)$ vectors, respectively; $q \leq n$.

A system defined by equation (2.1), and (2.43) is output controllable if $\mathbf{y}(t_0)$ can be moved to any $\mathbf{y}(t_1)$ in a finite time-interval $\tau$, $(\tau = t_1 - t_0)$, by applying a piecewise continuous input-vector $\mathbf{u}(t)$; $t \in (t_0, t_1)$. This definition of output controllability is identical to that for state controllability if $\mathbf{y}(t_0)$ and $\mathbf{y}(t_1)$ replace $\mathbf{x}(t_0)$ and $\mathbf{x}(t_1)$, respectively. The criteria for output controllability are, therefore, also very similar, though obviously less restrictive. Hence, noting that $\mathbf{y}$ of Equation (2.43) is a $(q \times 1)$ vector, the criterion of Section 2.3.2 (based on polynomial expansion) requires that $\mathbf{M}'$ be of rank $q$, where:

$$\mathbf{M}' = [\mathbf{CB}; \mathbf{CAB}; \mathbf{CA}^2\mathbf{B}; \ldots ; \mathbf{CA}^{n-1}\mathbf{B}] \tag{2.44}$$

The proof for this condition is similar to the proof in Section 2.3.2 above.

## 2.4 OBSERVABILITY

It has been stated above that the concept of observability is a dual of the controllability concept. Whereas controllability requires every state of a system to be affected by the input, observability requires that every state of the system affect the measured output.

A system is observable if all its states are derivable from the output-vector of the system, directly or indirectly. Hence, when a certain state (or changes in that state) cannot affect the output-vector, the system is unobservable (see Figure 2.2), just as when a certain state cannot be affected by the input-vector, the system is uncontrollable (as in Figure 2.1). Furthermore, an unobservable system *cannot be identified*, in terms of its complete state space model, the identification of parameters belonging to unobservable states being obviously not possible.

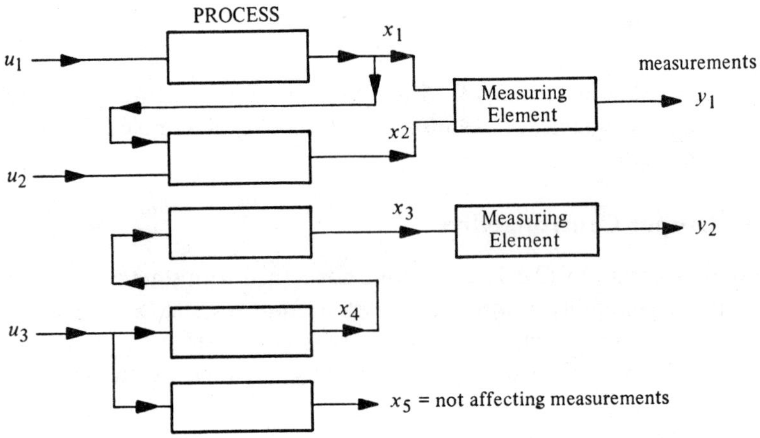


*Figure* 2.2 An unobservable system.

### 2.4.1 Observability Criterion of Canonical Systems

We next describe the observability criterion due to Gilbert[10] where linear systems are considered, and which first requires their diagonalization. This approach is analogous to that of the controllability criterion of Section 2.3.1 above.

Consider the system of equations (2.1), (2.43), which is described, after canonization, by:

$$\dot{\mathbf{x}}^* = \mathbf{\Lambda x}^* + \mathbf{B}^*\mathbf{u} \tag{2.45}$$

$$\mathbf{y} = \mathbf{C}^*\mathbf{x}^*; \qquad \mathbf{C}^* = \mathbf{CV}; \qquad \mathbf{V} = \text{eigenvector matrix (as in Section 2.3)} \tag{2.46}$$

The latter system is said to be observable if no column of $\mathbf{C}^*$ is zero, namely, if all $\mathbf{x}_i^*$, $\forall i(1, n)$ appear in $\mathbf{C}^*$. Furthermore, if at least one column of $\mathbf{C}^*$ is zero, the system becomes unobservable.

To prove the latter statement, consider a diagonalized system with distinct eigenvalues, given in discrete form, by:

$$\mathbf{x}(k+1) = \boldsymbol{\phi} \cdot \mathbf{x}(k) + \mathbf{G}\mathbf{u}(k); \qquad k = 0, 1, 2, \ldots \tag{2.47}$$

$$\mathbf{y}(k) = \mathbf{C}\mathbf{x}(k) \tag{2.48}$$

$\boldsymbol{\phi}$ being a diagonal $(n \times n)$ matrix with distinct elements, and $\mathbf{x}$, $\mathbf{u}$, $\mathbf{y}$ being $n$-, $m$-, and $q$-dimensional vectors, respectively, $q \leq n$. Obviously, if all elements $x_i$ of $\mathbf{x}$ appear in $\mathbf{y}$, we may always define a measurable scalar $z$, as follows:

$$z = \mathbf{w}^T\mathbf{y} = w_1 y_1 + w_2 y_2 + \cdots w_q y_q \tag{2.49}$$

by choosing $\mathbf{w}$ such that all elements of $\mathbf{w}^T\mathbf{C}$ are nonzero. Substituting for $\mathbf{y}$ from Equation (2.48) into (2.49) we obtain:

$$z(k) = \mathbf{w}^T\mathbf{C}\mathbf{x}(k) = \mathbf{d} \cdot \mathbf{x}(k) = d_1 x_1 + \cdots d_n x_n; \qquad \mathbf{d} = \mathbf{w}^T\mathbf{C} \triangleq [d_1 \cdots d_n] \tag{2.50}$$

where all $x_i(i = 1 \cdots n)$ appear in $z$.

To derive $x_i(k)\ \forall\ i$ from measurements of $z$ alone, we require $n$ measurements of $z$, at $n$ instants. Denoting these measurements as $z(j)$ for $j = k, \cdots k + r$; $r$ being an integer and $r \geq n - 1$, equations (2.47) and (2.50) yield $n$ independent equations for $x_i(k)$, as follows:

$$z(k) = \mathbf{d}\mathbf{x}(k) \tag{2.51-a}$$

$$z(k+1) = \mathbf{d}\mathbf{x}(k+1) = \mathbf{d}\boldsymbol{\phi}\mathbf{x}(k) + \mathbf{d}\mathbf{G}\mathbf{u}(k) \tag{2.51-b}$$

$$\begin{aligned} z(k+2) = \mathbf{d}\mathbf{x}(k+2) &= \mathbf{d}\boldsymbol{\phi}\mathbf{x}(k+1) + \mathbf{d}\mathbf{G}\mathbf{u}(k+1) \\ \vdots \qquad\qquad &= \mathbf{d}\boldsymbol{\phi}^2\mathbf{x}(k) + \mathbf{d}\boldsymbol{\phi}\mathbf{G}\mathbf{u}(k) + \mathbf{d}\mathbf{G}\mathbf{u}(k+1) \end{aligned} \tag{2.51-c}$$

$$z(k+r) = \mathbf{d}\mathbf{x}(k+r) = \mathbf{d}\boldsymbol{\phi}^r\mathbf{x}(k) + \mathbf{d}\sum_{\mu=0}^{r-1} \boldsymbol{\phi}^\mu\mathbf{G}\mathbf{u}(k+r-\mu) \tag{2.51-d}$$

where $\boldsymbol{\phi}^0 \triangleq \mathbf{I}$.

We define an $n$-dimensional measurement-vector $\mathbf{Z}(k)$, such that,

$$\mathbf{Z}(k) \triangleq [z(k) \cdots z(k+r)]^T \tag{2.52}$$

which contains $n$ elements, only. Hence, Equation (2.51) becomes

$$\mathbf{Z}(k) = \mathbf{P}\mathbf{x}(k) + \sum_{i=0}^{r-1} \boldsymbol{\lambda}_i\,\mathbf{u}(k+i) \tag{2.53}$$

where $\lambda_i$ are derived from Equation (2.51) and:

$$\mathbf{P} \triangleq \begin{bmatrix} \mathbf{d} \\ \mathbf{d}\boldsymbol{\phi} \\ \cdot \\ \cdot \\ \cdot \\ \cdot \\ \mathbf{d}\boldsymbol{\phi}^{n-1} \end{bmatrix} = (n \cdot n) \text{ matrix} \tag{2.54}$$

$\mathbf{u}(k+i)$ of Equation (2.53) are assumed to be measurable and their presence in that equation would therefore not cause unobservability. Subsequently, and since $\boldsymbol{\phi}$ is diagonal with distinct elements, the rows of Equation (2.54) are not linearly dependent and $\mathbf{P}^{-1}$ does exist. Hence, $\mathbf{x}(k)$ may be derived from Equation (2.53) if $\mathbf{Z}(k)$ and $\mathbf{u}(k+i)$ are known. Obviously, if Equation (2.50) does not contain a certain state $x_i$ of $\mathbf{x}$, no information on that $x_i$ is available in $z$ or in $y(k)$ of Equation (2.49), and that state cannot be derived from the measurements of $y(k)$. In the latter case $\mathbf{d}$ is a row vector with $n-1$ elements only (or with even fewer elements if further states do not appear in Equation (2.50)). Hence, $\mathbf{P}$ of Equation (2.54) is singular and cannot be inverted for deriving $\mathbf{x}$ from the measurements.

EXAMPLE 2.7

Consider the system $\dot{\mathbf{x}} = \mathbf{A}\mathbf{x} + \mathbf{B}\mathbf{u}$; $\mathbf{y} = \mathbf{C}\mathbf{x}$, where $\mathbf{A} = \begin{bmatrix} 1 & 2 \\ 4 & 3 \end{bmatrix}$ as in Example 2.5 and $\mathbf{B} = \begin{bmatrix} 3 \\ 4 \end{bmatrix}$, $\mathbf{C} = [1 \quad 1]$. We note from example 2.5 that $\mathbf{V} = \begin{bmatrix} 1 & 1 \\ -1 & 2 \end{bmatrix}$ is an eigenvector matrix of $\mathbf{A}$. For examining the observability of the system of the present example, we thus compute

$$\mathbf{C}^* = \mathbf{C}\mathbf{V} = [1 \quad 1]\begin{bmatrix} 1 & 1 \\ -1 & 2 \end{bmatrix} = [0 \quad 3]$$

Since the first column of $\mathbf{C}^*$ is zero, the system is unobservable.

### 2.4.2 Observability Criterion Based on Expanding exp($\mathbf{A}t$)

The observability criterion, based on a polynomial expansion of the state transition matrix $e^{\mathbf{A}t}$, is analogous to the controllability criterion of Section 2.3.2.

Consider the continuous state and measurement equations of a linear system, as follows:

$$\dot{\mathbf{x}} = \mathbf{Ax} + \mathbf{Bu} \tag{2.55-a}$$

$$\mathbf{y} = \mathbf{Cx} \tag{2.55-b}$$

Since we assume that the input vector $\mathbf{u}(t)$ is measurable, the observability criterion must not be affected by a situation of $\mathbf{u}(t) = \mathbf{0}$. Hence, we assume $\mathbf{u}(t) = \mathbf{0}$ for simplifying the analysis below, to yield:

$$\mathbf{y}(t) = \mathbf{C}e^{\mathbf{A}(t-t_0)}\mathbf{x}(t_0) \tag{2.56}$$

Employing the expression for $e^{\mathbf{A}t}$ as in Equation (2.37), Equation (2.56) becomes:

$$\mathbf{y}(t) = \sum_{i=0}^{n-1} \gamma_i(t-t_0)\mathbf{CA}^i\mathbf{x}(t_0) = \sum_{i=0}^{n-1} \mathbf{CA}^i\gamma_i(t-t_0)\mathbf{x}(t_0) \tag{2.57}$$

Defining

$$\mathbf{L} \triangleq [\mathbf{C}^T; \mathbf{A}^T\mathbf{C}^T; (\mathbf{A}^T)^2\mathbf{C}^T; \ldots; (\mathbf{A}^T)^{n-1}\mathbf{C}^T] \tag{2.58}$$

and:

$$\mathbf{\Gamma} \triangleq [\gamma_0 \cdots \gamma_i \cdots \gamma_{n-1}] \tag{2.59}$$

Equation (2.58) becomes:

$$\mathbf{y}(t) = \mathbf{\Gamma}\mathbf{L}^T\mathbf{x}(t_0) \tag{2.60}$$

We note that $\gamma_i$, and hence $\mathbf{\Gamma}$, obtain different values at different $t$, for the same $t_0$. We thus require, for complete observability of the system of equations (2.55-a, b) (for facilitating a unique derivation of all elements of $\mathbf{x}(t_0)$ from $\mathbf{y}$), that $n$ columns of $\mathbf{L}$ are linearly independent, i.e., that $\mathbf{L}$ be of rank $n$. For deriving $\mathbf{x}(t_0)$, we may further require that measurements be taken at various $t$, as in the case of Section 2.4.1.

### EXAMPLE 2.8

Consider a system having two state variables and one measurement variable, and where the two columns of $\mathbf{L}$ of Equation (2.58) are linearly dependent such that:

$$\mathbf{L} = \begin{bmatrix} l_1; & 3l_1 \\ l_2; & 3l_2 \end{bmatrix}$$

Equation (2.60) thus becomes:

$$y(t) = [\gamma_0; \gamma_1]\begin{bmatrix} l_1 & l_2 \\ 3l_1 & 3l_2 \end{bmatrix}\begin{bmatrix} x_1 \\ x_2 \end{bmatrix}$$

$$= [\gamma_0; \gamma_1]\begin{bmatrix} l_1x_1 + l_2x_2 \\ 3l_1x_1 + 3l_2x_2 \end{bmatrix}$$

$$= \{(\gamma_0)_{t-t_0} \cdot (l_1x_1 + l_2x_2)_{t_0}\} - 3\{(\gamma_1)_{t-t_0} \cdot (l_1x_1 + l_2x_2)_{t_0}\}$$

Since **L** is independent of $t$, the states $x_1$, $x_2$ cannot be uniquely derived, but appear in the combined form of $l_1x_1 + l_2x_2$ even if $y$ is measured (and $\gamma_0; \gamma_1$ are derived) for any number of different time-instances $t$. (See also Problem 2.6.)

## 2.5 THE RELATION BETWEEN STATE SPACE AND TRANSFER FUNCTION FORMULATIONS

The analysis below (Sections 2.5.1, 2.5.2) is concerned with the relations between the state space formulation and the scalar transfer function models, both of which are widely employed in classical control and systems theory. The purpose of this analysis is to facilitate the transformation from one formulation to the other, thus facilitating the application of techniques where one of these formulations is employed to the other formulation. The derivations below are mostly concerned with discrete systems. However, an extension to continuous system is obvious, when the discretization time is assumed to approach zero. When several inputs are concerned, the transformations may be applied to one input at a time.

### 2.5.1 Derivation of State Space Models from Scalar Transfer Functions

We consider in this section a scalar transfer-function formulation, relating a system's output to a single (scalar) input variable. Hence, for cases where several inputs exist, several transfer functions must be derived. Subsequently, for deriving the state space models from scalar transfer functions, we employ the discrete transfer function formulation, which represents the $z$-transformed transfer function. It is, however, possible to derive the continuous formulations by approximating $\dfrac{x(k+1) - x(k)}{\Delta t}$ by $\dfrac{dx(t)}{dt}$ @ $t = k\,\Delta t$; $k = 0, 1, 2, \ldots$.

Let the $z$-transformed transfer-function be given by:

$$G(z) = \frac{b_1z^{-1} + \cdots b_mz^{-m}}{1 + a_1z^{-1} + \cdots a_nz^{-n}} = \frac{y(z)}{u(z)} \tag{2.61}$$

$z^{-1}$ being a back-shift operator[13] such that $z^{-i}y_k \triangleq y_{k-i}$ and $u$, $y$ denoting input and output variables, respectively, $m \leq n$ for realizable systems.

Cross-multiplying Equation (2.61), and noting the definition of $z$, we obtain:

$$y_k + a_1 y_{k-1} + \cdots + a_n y_{k-n} = b_1 u_{k-1} + b_2 u_{k-2} + \cdots b_m u_{k-m} \tag{2.62}$$

Equation (2.62) above may be transformed into:

$$\mathbf{x}(k) = \mathbf{\Phi}\mathbf{x}(k-1) + \mathbf{\Gamma}u(k-1) \tag{2.63}$$

$$y(k) = \mathbf{C}\mathbf{x}(k) \tag{2.64}$$

where $\mathbf{\Phi}$, $\mathbf{\Gamma}$, $\mathbf{C}$ are given by:[14]

$$\mathbf{\Phi} = \left[\begin{array}{c|c} 0 & \\ \cdot & \\ \cdot & \mathbf{I} \\ \cdot & \\ \cdot & \\ 0 & \\ \hline \multicolumn{2}{c}{-a_n;\ -a_{n-1};\ \ldots\ldots -a_1} \end{array}\right] \tag{2.65}$$

$$\mathbf{\Gamma} = \begin{bmatrix} 1 & & & & \mathbf{O} \\ a_1 & 1 & & & \\ a_2 & a_1 & 1 & & \\ \cdot & & & \ddots & \\ \cdot & & & & \\ a_{n-1} & \cdots & a_1 & & 1 \end{bmatrix}^{-1} \cdot \begin{bmatrix} b_1 \\ \cdot \\ \cdot \\ \cdot \\ \cdot \\ b_m \end{bmatrix} = \boldsymbol{\alpha}^{-1}\boldsymbol{\beta} \tag{2.66}$$

$$\mathbf{C} = [1; 0; \ldots 0] \tag{2.67}$$

$\mathbf{\Phi}$ being of a companion matrix form[11], and $\boldsymbol{\alpha}$ of Equation (2.66) being a lower triangular matrix whose inversion is easily performed by substitution.

We note that a nonzero term $b_0 z^0$ in Equation (2.61) would indicate instantaneous transition between input and output, for which Equation (2.63) does not hold. Consequently, if discrete state equations based on finite differencing of $d\mathbf{x}/dt$ are employed to derive the transfer function of Equation (2.61), or vice versa, $b_0$ would not appear in equations (2.61) and (2.62).

The state space formulation of equations (2.63) to (2.67) is shown to satisfy the fomulation of Equation (2.62), and hence the transfer function model of Equation (2.61), as follows:

Let:

$$\mathbf{x} \triangleq [x_1 \cdots x_n]^T \tag{2.68}$$

$$\mathbf{\Gamma} \triangleq [\gamma_1 \cdots \gamma_n]^T \tag{2.69}$$

Employing Equation (2.64) with **C** as in Equation (2.67), we obtain:

$$x_1(k) = y(k) \tag{2.70}$$

Expanding Equation (2.63) when $\mathbf{\Phi}$ is as in Equation (2.65), further yields:

$$x_1(k) = x_2(k-1) + \gamma_1 u(k-1)$$

or, after rearrangement, and noting Equation (2.70):

$$x_2(k) = x_1(k+1) - \gamma_1 u(k) = y(k+1) - \gamma_1 u(k)$$

Similarly:

$$x_i(k) = y(k+i-1) - \sum_{j=2}^{i} \gamma_{j-1} u(k+i-j) \ @ \ i \leq n \tag{2.71}$$

$x_n(k)$ being given by:

$$x_n(k) = y(k+n-1) - \gamma_1 u(k+n-2) - \cdots - \gamma_{n-1} u(k) \tag{2.72}$$

Equating the bottom row of Equation (2.63) with (2.72) when employing $\mathbf{\Phi}$ as in Equation (2.65), we derive:

$$\begin{aligned} -a_n x_1(k-1) - \cdots a_1 x_n(k-1) + \gamma_n u(k-1) \\ = y(k+n-1) - \gamma_1 u(k+n-2) - \cdots - \gamma_{n-1} u(k) \end{aligned} \tag{2.73}$$

Substituting for $x_i(k)\ \forall i = 1, \ldots n-1$ from Equation (2.71) into (2.73) further yields:

$$\begin{aligned} y(k+n-1) &- \gamma_1 u(k+n-2) - \cdots - \gamma_{n-1} u(k) \\ &= -a_n y(k-1) - \cdots - a_1 y(k+n-2) \\ &\quad + a_{n-1}\gamma_1 u(k-1) + a_{n-2}[\gamma_1 u(k) + \gamma_2 u(k-1)] \\ &\quad + \cdots + a_1[\gamma_1 u(k+n-3) + \cdots \gamma_{n-1} u(k-1)] + \gamma_n u(k-1) \end{aligned} \tag{2.74}$$

Subsequently, rearranging Equation (2.74), we derive:

$$\begin{aligned} y(k+n-1) &+ a_1 y(k+n-2) + a_2 y(k+n-3) + \cdots a_n y(k-1) \\ &= a_{n-1}\gamma_1 u(k-1) + a_{n-2}[\gamma_1 u(k) + \gamma_2 u(k-1)] + \cdots \\ &\quad + a_1[\gamma_1 u(k+n-3) + \cdots \gamma_{n-1} u(k-1)] \\ &\quad + \gamma_1 u(k+n-2) + \cdots \gamma_n u(k-1) \\ &= b_1 u(k+n-2) + b_2 u(k+n-3) + \cdots b_m u(k+n-m-1) \end{aligned} \tag{2.75}$$

such that:

$$\left.\begin{aligned} b_1 &= \gamma_1 \\ b_2 &= \gamma_2 + a_1\gamma_1 \\ &\vdots \\ b_m &= \gamma_m + a_1\gamma_{m-1} + \cdots a_{m-1}\gamma_1 \\ 0 &= \gamma_j + a_1\gamma_{j-1} + \cdots a_{j-1}\gamma_1 \ \forall n \geq j > m \end{aligned}\right\} \tag{2.76}$$

Equation (2.76) may be written in matrix form as:

$$\begin{bmatrix} b_1 \\ \cdot \\ \cdot \\ \cdot \\ b_m \\ 0 \\ \cdot \\ \cdot \\ \cdot \\ 0 \end{bmatrix} = \begin{bmatrix} 1 & & & & & & \\ a_1 & 1 & & & \mathbf{O} & & \\ a_2 & a_1 & 1 & & & & \\ a_3 & a_2 & a_1 & 1 & & & \\ \cdot & & & & \cdot & & \\ \cdot & & & & & \cdot & \\ \cdot & & & & & & \cdot \\ a_{n-1} & \cdot & \cdot & \cdot & \cdot & a_1 & 1 \end{bmatrix} \begin{bmatrix} \gamma_1 \\ \gamma_2 \\ \cdot \\ \cdot \\ \cdot \\ \cdot \\ \cdot \\ \cdot \\ \cdot \\ \gamma_n \end{bmatrix} = \boldsymbol{\alpha}\boldsymbol{\Gamma} \tag{2.77}$$

yielding:

$$\boldsymbol{\Gamma} = \boldsymbol{\alpha}^{-1} \begin{bmatrix} b_1 \\ \cdot \\ \cdot \\ \cdot \\ b_m \\ 0 \\ \cdot \\ \cdot \\ \cdot \\ 0 \end{bmatrix} = \boldsymbol{\alpha}^{-1}\boldsymbol{\beta} \tag{2.78}$$

$\boldsymbol{\beta}$ being an $n$-dimensional vector, and $m \leq n$. Since Equation (2.75) satisfies equations (2.65) to (2.67), the derivation of the state space formulation of equations (2.63) to (2.67) is complete.

Example 2.9

To further illustrate the derivation of a state space model from a discrete transfer function, we consider a system given by the following discrete transfer function:

$$G(z) = \frac{0.6z}{z^2 - 1.6z + 1} = \frac{0.6z^{-1}}{1 - 1.6z^{-1} + z^{-2}}$$
$$= \frac{b_1 z^{-1}}{1 + a_1 z^{-1} + a_2 z^{-2}} = \frac{y(z)}{u(z)}$$

$u$, $y$ being the system's input and output, respectively.

To derive a discrete state space model for the above system, as in equations (2.63) and (2.64), with **C** as in Equation (2.67), we compute $\mathbf{\Phi}$, $\mathbf{\Gamma}$ according to equations (2.65) and (2.66), respectively, as follows:

$$\mathbf{\Phi} = \begin{bmatrix} 0 & 1 \\ -1 & +1.6 \end{bmatrix};$$
$$\mathbf{\Gamma} = \begin{bmatrix} 1 & 0 \\ -1.6 & 1 \end{bmatrix}^{-1} \cdot \begin{bmatrix} 0.6 \\ 0 \end{bmatrix}$$
$$= \begin{bmatrix} 1 & 0 \\ 1.6 & 1 \end{bmatrix} \cdot \begin{bmatrix} 0.6 \\ 0 \end{bmatrix} = \begin{bmatrix} 0.6 \\ 0.96 \end{bmatrix}$$

yielding:

$$x_1(k) = x_2(k-1) + 0.6u(k-1)$$
$$x_2(k) = -x_1(k-1) + 1.6x_2(k-1) + 0.96u(k-1)$$

and:

$$y(k) = x_1(k)$$

### 2.5.2 Derivation of Scalar Transfer Functions from State Space Models

When a linear state space model is given for an observable system, its transfer function may be derived by first transforming the state space model to a companion form. For simplicity of the derivation, the state space formulation and the transfer function formulation are considered to be in discrete form. Consequently, direct reference to the analysis of equations (2.61) to (2.78) can be made.

Consider an observable linear system given by a discrete state space model.

$$\mathbf{w}(k+1) = \psi\mathbf{w}(k) + \mathbf{\Omega}u(k) \tag{2.79}$$

$$y(k) = \mathbf{D}\mathbf{w}(k) \tag{2.80}$$

where **w** is the state vector of the system and $u$, $y$ are scalar input and output variables.

The present analysis is concerned with the derivation of a discrete scalar transfer function for the system of equation (2.79), (2.80), which is of the form:

$$G(z) = \frac{y(z)}{u(z)} = \frac{b_1 z^{-1} + b_2 z^{-2} + \cdots b_m z^{-m}}{1 + a_1 z^{-1} + \cdots a_n z^{-n}} \tag{2.81}$$

in similarity to Equation (2.61). Since the highest value of $m$ of Equation (2.81) is $n$ for systems of the form of Equation (2.79), and since the coefficients $a_i$, $b_j$ are unknown, we now assume that $m = n$ (see also the derivation below). Subsequently, cross-multiplying Equation (2.81) yields:

$$y(k) + a_1 y(k-1) + \cdots a_n y(k-n) = b_1 u(k-1) + \cdots b_n u(k-n) \tag{2.82}$$

which is equivalent to Equation (2.62) for $n = m$.

Noting that the system of equations (2.79), (2.80) is observable, its transformation to a companion form may be performed through employing a transformation matrix $\mathbf{T}$ given by Ref. 14:

$$\mathbf{T} \triangleq \begin{bmatrix} \mathbf{D} \\ \mathbf{D\Psi} \\ \cdot \\ \cdot \\ \cdot \\ \mathbf{D\Psi}^{n-1} \end{bmatrix} \tag{2.83}$$

Consequently, the following transformed state space model is derived:

$$\mathbf{w}^*(k+1) = \mathbf{\Psi}^*\mathbf{w}^*(k) + \mathbf{\Omega}^* u(k) \tag{2.84}$$

$$y(k) = \mathbf{D}^*\mathbf{w}^*(k) \tag{2.85}$$

$\mathbf{w}^*$, $\mathbf{\Psi}^*$, $\mathbf{\Omega}^*$, $\mathbf{D}^*$ denoting the transformed $\mathbf{w}$, $\mathbf{\Psi}$, $\mathbf{\Omega}$, $\mathbf{D}$ of equations (2.79), (2.80), such that,

$$\psi^* \triangleq \mathbf{T\Psi T}^{-1} = \left[\begin{array}{c|c} 0 & \\ \cdot & \\ \cdot & \mathbf{I} \\ \cdot & \\ 0 & \\ \hline -\alpha_n \cdots & -\alpha_1 \end{array}\right] \tag{2.86}$$

$$\mathbf{w}^* \triangleq \mathbf{Tw} \tag{2.87}$$

$$\mathbf{\Omega}^* \triangleq \mathbf{T\Omega} \tag{2.88}$$

$$\mathbf{D}^* \triangleq \mathbf{DT}^{-1} \tag{2.89}$$

the matrix at the right-hand-side of Equation (2.86) being of companion form.[11] Substituting $\mathbf{x}$ for $\mathbf{w}^*$, $\boldsymbol{\phi}$ for $\boldsymbol{\Psi}^*$, $\boldsymbol{\Gamma}$ for $\boldsymbol{\Omega}^*$ and $\mathbf{C}$ for $\mathbf{D}^*$ into equations (2.84) and (2.85) yields a set of equations that are identical to equations (2.63) to (2.67). Noting the equivalence of equations (2.84), (2.85) to the state space model of equations (2.63) to (2.67) and the analysis of equations (2.61) to (2.78), the transfer function representing the system of equations (2.84), (2.85) is given by Equation (2.61) for $m = n$. Consequently, the coefficients $a_i$ of Equation (2.81) satisfy:

$$a_i = \alpha_i \qquad \forall i = 1 \cdots n \tag{2.90}$$

$\alpha_i$ being as derived in Equation (2.86) through transforming $\psi$ of Equation (2.79). Furthermore, the coefficients $b_j$ are given by Equation (2.77), to complete the derivation of the transfer function. We also note from equations (2.77), (2.88) that $j \in (1, m)$, $m$ being the dimension of $\boldsymbol{\Omega}$.

EXAMPLE 2.10

The latter derivation of a $z$-transformed transfer function may be further illustrated by considering a system given by equations (2.79), (2.80) with $\psi = \begin{bmatrix} 1 & 2 \\ 4 & 3 \end{bmatrix}$, $\boldsymbol{\Omega} = \begin{bmatrix} 1 \\ 1 \end{bmatrix}$; $\mathbf{D} = [2 \quad 1]$. Its transformation into a $z$-transformed transfer function is performed through first computing $\mathbf{T}$ of Equation (2.83) as follows:

$$\mathbf{T} = \begin{bmatrix} \mathbf{D} \\ \mathbf{D}\psi \end{bmatrix} = \begin{bmatrix} 2 & 1 \\ 6 & 7 \end{bmatrix}$$

such that:

$$\mathbf{T}^{-1} = \begin{bmatrix} 0.875 & -0.125 \\ -0.75 & 0.25 \end{bmatrix}$$

and:

$$\psi^* = \mathbf{T}\psi\mathbf{T}^{-1} = \begin{bmatrix} 2 & 1 \\ 6 & 7 \end{bmatrix} \cdot \begin{bmatrix} 1 & 2 \\ 4 & 3 \end{bmatrix} \cdot \begin{bmatrix} 0.875 & -0.125 \\ -0.75 & 0.25 \end{bmatrix}$$

$$= \begin{bmatrix} 6 & 7 \\ 34 & 33 \end{bmatrix} \cdot \begin{bmatrix} 0.875 & -0.125 \\ -0.75 & 0.25 \end{bmatrix} = \begin{bmatrix} 0 & 1 \\ 5 & 4 \end{bmatrix}$$

$$\boldsymbol{\Omega}^* = \mathbf{T}\boldsymbol{\Omega} = \begin{bmatrix} 2 & 1 \\ 6 & 7 \end{bmatrix} \cdot \begin{bmatrix} 1 \\ 1 \end{bmatrix} = \begin{bmatrix} 3 \\ 13 \end{bmatrix}$$

$$\mathbf{D}^* = \mathbf{D}\mathbf{T}^{-1} = [2 \quad 1] \cdot \begin{bmatrix} 0.875 & -0.125 \\ -0.75 & 0.25 \end{bmatrix} = [1 \quad 0]$$

We observe that $\boldsymbol{\psi}^*$ is in companion form as is $\boldsymbol{\Phi}$ of Equation (2.65). Furthermore, $\mathbf{D}^*$ corresponds to $\mathbf{C}$ of Equation (2.67) and $\boldsymbol{\Omega}^*$ corresponds to $\boldsymbol{\Gamma}$ of Equation (2.77). Consequently, $G(z)$ is obtained directly from equations (2.65), (2.77) such that:

$$\left.\begin{aligned} a_1 &= -4 \\ a_2 &= -5 \end{aligned}\right\} \text{ from Equation (2.65)}$$

$$\begin{bmatrix} b_1 \\ b_2 \end{bmatrix} = \begin{bmatrix} 1 & 0 \\ a_1 & 1 \end{bmatrix} \begin{bmatrix} \Omega_1^* \\ \Omega_2^* \end{bmatrix}$$

$$= \begin{bmatrix} 1 & 0 \\ -4 & 1 \end{bmatrix} \begin{bmatrix} 3 \\ 13 \end{bmatrix} = \begin{bmatrix} 3 \\ 1 \end{bmatrix}$$

according to Equation (2.77); and;

$$G(z) = \frac{3z^{-1} + z^{-2}}{1 - 4z^{-1} - 5z^{-2}}$$

according to Equation (2.61) or (2.81).

**2.5.2-a The continuous case** An analytical derivation of the transfer function for the continuous case is also possible, employing a Laplace-transformed state space model, as follows:

$$s\mathbf{x}(s) = \mathbf{A}\mathbf{x}(s) + \mathbf{B}u(s) \tag{2.91}$$

$$y(s) = \mathbf{C}\mathbf{x}(s) \tag{2.92}$$

$s$ denoting the Laplace transform variable,[13] and $\mathbf{x}$, $u$, $y$ denoting the state vector and scalar input and output variables, respectively. Equation (2.91) yields:

$$(s\mathbf{I} - \mathbf{A})\mathbf{x}(s) = \mathbf{B}u(s) \tag{2.93}$$

and:

$$\mathbf{x}(s) = (s\mathbf{I} - \mathbf{A})^{-1}\mathbf{B}u(s) \tag{2.94}$$

Subsequently, employing Equation (2.92), we derive:

$$y(s) = \mathbf{C}\mathbf{x}(s) = \mathbf{C}(s\mathbf{I} - \mathbf{A})^{-1}\mathbf{B}u(s) \tag{2.95}$$

such that the transfer function $G(s)$ becomes:

$$G(s) = \frac{y(s)}{u(s)} = \mathbf{C}(s\mathbf{I} - \mathbf{A})^{-1}\mathbf{B} \tag{2.96}$$

Since $s$ has no algorithmic value, the latter derivation of a transfer function is not as suitable for machine computation as is the model derived in equations (2.79) to (2.90). However, the simplicity of analytical transfer function derivation according to Equation (2.96) may be illustrated by the following example.

EXAMPLE 2.11

Consider a system given by:

$$\begin{bmatrix} \dot{x}_1 \\ \dot{x}_2 \end{bmatrix} = \begin{bmatrix} 0 & 1 \\ -2 & -3 \end{bmatrix} \begin{bmatrix} x_1 \\ x_2 \end{bmatrix} + \begin{bmatrix} 0 \\ 9 \end{bmatrix} u$$

$$y = x_1$$

yielding:

$$(s\mathbf{I} - \mathbf{A}) = \begin{bmatrix} s & -1 \\ 2 & s+3 \end{bmatrix}$$

and:

$$(s\mathbf{I} - \mathbf{A})^{-1} = \frac{1}{s(s+3)+2} \begin{bmatrix} s+3 & 1 \\ -2 & s \end{bmatrix} = \frac{1}{s^2+3s+2} \begin{bmatrix} s+3 & 1 \\ -2 & s \end{bmatrix}$$

$$= \begin{bmatrix} \dfrac{s+3}{s^2+3s+2} & \dfrac{1}{s^2+3s+2} \\[2ex] \dfrac{-2}{s^2+3s+2} & \dfrac{s}{s^2+3s+2} \end{bmatrix}$$

Consequently:

$$G(s) = [1, 0] \cdot \begin{bmatrix} \dfrac{s+3}{s^2+3s+2} & \dfrac{1}{s^2+3s+2} \\[2ex] \dfrac{-2}{s^2+3s+2} & \dfrac{1}{s^2+3s+2} \end{bmatrix} \cdot \begin{bmatrix} 0 \\ 9 \end{bmatrix}$$

$$= \begin{bmatrix} \dfrac{s+3}{s^2+3s+2} & \dfrac{1}{s^2+3s+2} \end{bmatrix} \begin{bmatrix} 0 \\ 9 \end{bmatrix} = \frac{9}{s^2+3s+2}$$

An analogous derivation may be obtained for discrete state space models, when approximating $\frac{dx(t)}{dt}$ by $\frac{x(k+1) - x(k)}{\Delta t}$ @ $t = k\,\Delta t;\ k = 0, 1, 2 \ldots.$

The example above indicates that when the elements of $\mathbf{B}$ of Equation (2.91) are both nonzero, say, $\mathbf{B} = [1, 9]^T$, $s$ would appear in the numerator of $G(s)$. The latter situation is equivalent to $b_1$, $b_2 \neq 0$; $n = 2$, in Equation (2.81), such that the number of elements $b_i$ is equal to the dimension of $\mathbf{\Omega}$ of Equation (2.79), in the discrete case.

## REFERENCES


1. Sokolnikoff, I. S., and Redheffer, R. M. *Mathematics of Physics and Modern Engineering*, McGraw-Hill, New York, 1966.
2. Mann, J., Marshall, S. A., and Nicholson, H. "A Review of Matrix Techniques in Multivariable Systems Control," *Proc. Inst. Mech. Eng.*, Vol. 179, Pt. 3H, pp. 153–161, London, 1965.
3. Kalman, R. E. "On the General Theory of Control Systems," *Proc. 1st IFAC Congress*, Moscow, 1960.
4. Wonham, W. M. "On Pole Assignment in Multi-Input Controllable Linear Systems," *IEEE Trans.*, Vol. AC-12, No. 6, pp. 660–665, 1967.
5. Gilbert, E. G. "Controllability and Observability in Multivariable Control Systems," *Jour. Soc. Indst. Appl. Math.*, Ser. A., Vol. 1, No. 2, pp. 128–151, 1963.
6. Kuo, B. C. *Automatic Control Systems*, Prentice-Hall, Englewood Cliffs, N.J., 1967.
7. Athans, M., and Falb, P. L. *Optimal Control*, McGraw-Hill, New York, 1966.
8. Koppel, L. B. *Introduction to Control Theory*, Prentice-Hall, Englewood Cliffs, N.J., 1968.
9. Sage, A. P. *Optimum Systems Control*, Prentice-Hall, Englewood Cliffs, N.J., 1968.
10. Elgerd, O. I. *Control Systems Theory*, McGraw-Hill, New York, 1967.
11. Ayres, F. *Theory and Problems of Matrices*, Schaum, New York, 1962.
12. Pipes, L. A. *Matrix Methods for Engineers*, Prentice-Hall, Englewood Cliffs, N.J., 1963.
13. Wilts, C. H. *Principles of Feedback Control*, Addison-Wesley, Reading, Mass., 1960.
14. Lee, R. C. K. *Optimal Estimation, Identification and Control*, M.I.T. Press, Cambridge, Mass., 1964.

## PROBLEMS

1. Transform the system $\dot{\mathbf{x}} = \mathbf{A}\mathbf{x} + \mathbf{u}$ where $\mathbf{A} = \begin{bmatrix} 5 & 7 \\ 3 & 4 \end{bmatrix}$ by a transformation matrix $\boldsymbol{\psi} = \begin{bmatrix} 1 & 8 \\ 3 & 2 \end{bmatrix}$ and find the eigenvalues of **A** and of the transformed $\mathbf{A}^*$.

2. Diagonalize the system $\dot{\mathbf{x}} = \mathbf{A}\mathbf{x} + \mathbf{B}\mathbf{u}$ where $\mathbf{A} = \begin{bmatrix} 0 & 1 \\ -2 & -1 \end{bmatrix}$; $\mathbf{B} = \begin{bmatrix} 0 \\ 2 \end{bmatrix}$.
3. Examine the controllability of the system given by $\dot{\mathbf{x}} = \mathbf{A}\mathbf{x} + \mathbf{B}\mathbf{u}$, where $\mathbf{A} = \begin{bmatrix} 1 & -1 \\ -1 & 1 \end{bmatrix}$; $\mathbf{B} = \begin{bmatrix} 2 \\ 2 \end{bmatrix}$, by transforming the system into canonical form.
4. Examine the controllability of $\dot{\mathbf{x}} = \mathbf{A}\mathbf{x} + \mathbf{B}\mathbf{u}$ where $A = \begin{bmatrix} 2 & 0 \\ -1 & 1 \end{bmatrix}$; $\mathbf{B} = \begin{bmatrix} 1 \\ -1 \end{bmatrix}$, by employing the criterion based on expanding $\exp(\mathbf{A}t)$.
5. Examine the observability of the system of Problem 3, when $\mathbf{C} = [1 \quad 1]$, by transforming the system into canonical form.
6. Check the observability of the system of Problem 4, where $\mathbf{C} = [1 \quad 2]$, by employing the criterion based on expanding $\exp(\mathbf{A}t)$.
7. Derive a discrete state space model, of the form of equations (2.63), (2.64) for a system given by:

$$G(z) = \frac{0.6z^2}{z^3 - 2.5\,z^2 + 1.4z - 0.9} = \frac{y(z)}{u(z)}$$

8. Derive $G(z)$ for a system given by equations (2.79), (2.80) with

$$\boldsymbol{\psi} = \begin{bmatrix} 2 & 4 \\ 8 & 6 \end{bmatrix}, \boldsymbol{\Omega} = \begin{bmatrix} 1 \\ 2 \end{bmatrix}, \mathbf{D} = [1, 0].$$

9. Derive $G(s)$ for a system given by $\dot{\mathbf{x}} = \begin{bmatrix} 1 & 2 \\ 4 & -3 \end{bmatrix}\mathbf{x} + \begin{bmatrix} 1 \\ 2 \end{bmatrix}u$; $y = x_1$.

# 3

# FREQUENCY, STEP, AND IMPULSE RESPONSE METHODS

The earliest methods of control system identification are those based on frequency, step, and impulse responses. Most of these methods apply to linear processes. They may also be applicable to the linearized form of nonlinear ones, as discussed in Appendix 1, if the input levels are kept low. By definition, these methods require the employment of special input signals, namely, of a step input for step-response identification, an impulse input for impulse response identification, and of sine-wave inputs having variable frequencies for frequency-response identification. Since special inputs rather than normal operation inputs are required, it is obvious that the above techniques assume off-line identification. They are therefore applicable only to linear stationary processes where input/output relations obtained for one set of inputs hold for all inputs.

Of the three types of input signals above, the step input is the simplest to apply (it implies a sudden opening or closing of an input-valve or a sudden switching-on or off of an input-voltage), whereas the sinusoidal input requires means of generating sine-wave input disturbances and of varying their frequency over the range of interest. The impulse-response approach often involves realization difficulties, in generating and in applying the impulse-function input. The latter is the only approach of the present chapter that is not applicable to linearized forms of nonlinear systems, since by definition, the impulse amplitude cannot be kept low.

## 3.1 FOURIER TRANSFORM IDENTIFICATION METHODS

In the present chapter Fourier transforms are employed for identification through applying off-line sine-wave inputs (see Section 3.2), step-inputs (see Section 3.3), and impulse-inputs (see Section 3.4). In the next chapter Fourier transforms are further applied to on-line identification based on noise-inputs. We therefore briefly discuss some of the properties of the Fourier transforms, as follows:

Consider an aperiodic time-function $x(t)$. The Fourier transform $X(j\omega)$ of $x(t)$ is given by:

$$F[x(t)] \triangleq X(j\omega) = \int_{-\infty}^{\infty} x(t)e^{-j\omega t}\,dt \tag{3.1}$$

The Fourier transform can be applied to $x(t)$ if it is absolutely integrable, i.e., if:[1]

$$\int_{-\infty}^{\infty} |x(t)|\,dt < \infty \tag{3.2}$$

The latter condition excludes Fourier transform analysis of input functions such as a sine-wave or a step function. This difficulty in applying Fourier transforms to sine or step functions may be overcome if $\int_{-\infty}^{\infty} x(t)e^{-\sigma t}\,dt < \infty$ for some, even very small, positive $\sigma$, such that $x(t)e^{-\sigma t}$ is considered instead of $x(t)$, yielding a Laplace transform, given by:

$$X(s) = L[x(t)] = \int_{-\infty}^{\infty} x(t)e^{-st}\,dt;\; s \triangleq \sigma + j\omega \tag{3.3}$$

Hence, the step-input is considered to represent a very slow asymptotically decreasing step, and the sine-input is considered to be very slightly damped. (A mathematically stronger justification is given in Ref. 2.)

We now derive Fourier and Laplace transformed input/output linear stationary relations as follows:

Consider a linear system $G(s)$, as in Figure 3.1, whose output $x(t)$ is given (for an input $y$) by the following convolution-integral expression:

$$x(t) = \int_0^t y(\tau)g(t-\tau)\,d\tau;\; g(t) = L^{-1}[G(s)] \tag{3.4}$$

$(L^{-1}[\;\;] \triangleq$ inverse Laplace transform)

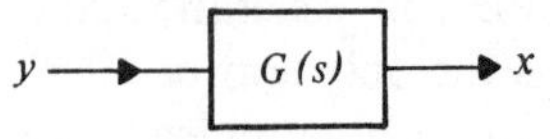


*Figure 3.1* Input/output representation of a linear system.

Equation (3.4) becomes, in Fourier transformed form:

$$X(j\omega) = G(j\omega)Y(j\omega) \tag{3.5}$$

while the Laplace transformation of Equation (3.4) satisfies:

$$X(s) = G(s)Y(s) \tag{3.6}$$

$G(j\omega)$, $G(s)$ being the Fourier and the Laplace transformed transfer-functions of that system, respectively. The term $G(j\omega)$ of Equation (3.5) may be written as $\alpha_\omega + j\beta_\omega = G(j\omega)$ and represents the complex gain of the system for an input of frequency $\omega$. Consequently, $\sqrt{\alpha_\omega^2 + \beta_\omega^2} = |G(j\omega)|$ represents the absolute gain and $\arctan\beta/\alpha$ represents the phase-shift between output and input, the variation of $G(j\omega)$ vs. $\omega$ being the frequency response of the system.

In Section 3.2 of the present chapter we discuss the derivation of $G(j\omega)$ through employing sine-wave inputs. However, the employment of Fourier transforms facilitates the derivation of $G(j\omega)$ by means of other inputs also, as is shown in sections 3.3 and 3.4 of the present chapter and in Chapter 4.

The derivation of $G(j\omega)$ when employing step- or impulse-inputs, by Fourier transform methods, is rather simple, since the Fourier transformed impulse-response is equal to $G(j\omega)$, whereas the Fourier transformed step-response may be given by $G(j\omega)/j\omega$ (considering the comments following Equation (3.2) above). Hence, if a numerical Fourier transformation is applied (say through employing a Fast Fourier Transform algorithm,[3, 4, 5]) to the step or impulse-response, $G(j\omega)$ is easily derived numerically. Furthermore, when considering Equation (3.5), we observe that if a numerical Fourier transform is applied to any convergent input and to the respective output, $G(j\omega)$ may be numerically derived, as follows:

$$G(j\omega) = \frac{X(j\omega)}{Y(j\omega)} = \frac{\text{Output } (j\omega)}{\text{Input } (j\omega)} \tag{3.7}$$

However the latter approach involves a numerical transformation of both output and input, and a division of the resulting two complex values $X(j\omega)$ and $Y(j\omega)$ for many frequencies. Hence, this approach is rather lengthy even if Fast Fourier Transforms are employed. The exceptions to the latter statement are cases of step- or impulse-inputs that have already been mentioned, and cases of noise-inputs to be discussed in Chapter 4. The approach of Chapter 4, where noise-inputs are concerned, employs correlation-function techniques to transform the identification problem into impulse-response identification without actually applying an impulse, thus facilitating on-line identification. Obviously, inputs considered for Fourier transform identification methods should contain all the frequencies that are of interest in the characteristics of the system. If a step-input is realized by an exponentially-rising function of the form of the time-function: $1 - e^{-t/T}$ (see Figure 3.2), the highest frequency which may be adequately identified by a Fourier transformation is of the order of $\omega = 2\pi/T$ (ideally: $T = 0$).

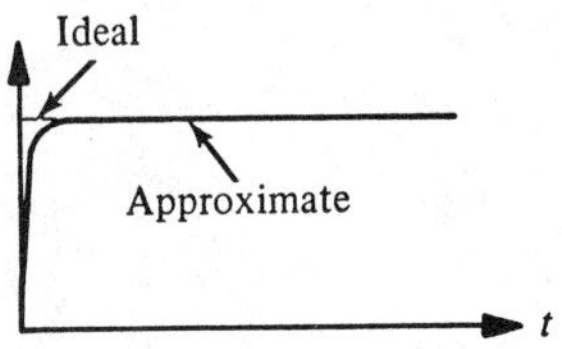


*Figure 3.2* Exponentially rising approximation of a step.

### 3.1.1 Numerical Fourier Transforms

The numerical Fourier transformation requires the approximation of the integral of Equation (3.1) by summation, as follows:

$$X(n) = \Delta t \cdot \sum_{k=0}^{N-1} x(k) e^{-j2\pi(nk/N)} \tag{3.8}$$

where:

$$e^{-j\omega t} = \cos(\omega t) - j\sin(\omega t)$$

$$X(n) \triangleq X(jn\,\Delta\omega);\ n = 0, 1, 2, \ldots$$

$$t_k \triangleq k\,\Delta t;\ k = 0, 1, 2, \ldots (N-1)$$

$$\Delta t \triangleq T/N$$

$$\omega = 2\pi f = 2\pi n/T;\ \Delta\omega = 2\pi/T$$

$$\omega t = \frac{2\pi nk\,\Delta t}{T} = \frac{2\pi nk}{N}$$

Obviously, in a discrete approximation, the limits of the summation in Equation (3.8) are finite. For accuracy, the summation limit $N$ which denotes the time range to be considered, should approach infinity. Consequently, the time interval $T$, in cases of step or impulse-inputs, must be greater than the time required for the response to cease changing above a measurable minimal value. The sampling time interval $\Delta t$ is, of necessity, related to the highest frequency that may be considered in the resulting frequency response, since no frequency above $1/2\Delta t$ *Hz* will be meaningful.

In practice it is best to employ a Fast Fourier Transform procedure[3] for computing Fourier transforms and their inverses. This is faster by a factor of $N/\log_2 N$ than a procedure based on directly computing Equation (3.8) above, and results in a reduced round-off error due to the smaller number of computer operations that is required. The Fast Fourier Transforms are based on a matrix formulation of Equation (3.8), as follows:

$$\mathbf{F} \triangleq \mathbf{W} \cdot \mathbf{X} \tag{3.9}$$

where:

$$\mathbf{F} \triangleq [X(0), \ldots X(n)]^T \tag{3.10}$$

$$\mathbf{X} = [x(0), \ldots x(n)]^T \tag{3.11}$$

and:

$$\mathbf{W} \triangleq \begin{bmatrix} W_0 & W_0 & \cdots & & W_0 \\ W_0 & W_1 & W_2 & \cdots & W_{N-1} \\ W_0 & W_2 & W_4 & \cdots & W_{2(N-1)} \\ \vdots & & & \ddots & \\ W_0 & W_{N-1} & \cdots & & W_{(N-1)(N-1)} \end{bmatrix} \tag{3.12}$$

$W_\mu$ being given by:

$$W_\mu = e^{-j2\pi\mu/N} \tag{3.13}$$

and $\mu$ denoting the product $n \cdot k$ of Equation (3.8). The fast computation features of the Fast Fourier Transform are derived from certain symmetry properties of matrix **W** and of Equation (3.9). These lead to a considerable reduction in the number of arithmetic operations that are involved.

Fast Fourier Transform algorithms are presently available in the major computer languages (such as ALGOL or FORTRAN) in practically every computer library, and are based on the Cooley and Tukey algorithm.[3] A complete ALGOL subroutine for computing the Fast Fourier Transform is given in Ref. 4 and may be adequately employed for this purpose.

Special computational considerations for cases where the frequency response is derived from correlation-functions are discussed in sections 4.3 and 4.4.

## 3.2 FREQUENCY RESPONSE IDENTIFICATION

The frequency-response technique for identifying linear systems is based on the work of Nyquist[6] and of Bode[7] and employs the Bode diagrams of frequency responses.

The frequency response approach implies that sine-wave inputs, whose frequency is varied over the range of interest, are applied to the system. This may lead to considerable practical difficulties in generating sine-wave inputs of various frequencies. The approach is based on the following Laplace transformed convolution relation of input and output (see Figure 3.1):

$$X(s) = G(s) \cdot Y(s) \tag{3.14}$$

or:

$$G(s) = \frac{X(s)}{Y(s)} \tag{3.15}$$

$G(s)$, $X(s)$, and $Y(s)$ being the system's transfer-function, output and input, respectively. The relation between the transfer-function and the state-variable concepts is discussed in Section 2.5 such that a transformation from the transfer-function formulation to the state space formulation and vice versa is possible.

Noting that the Laplace transform variable $s$ is given by:

$$s = \sigma + j\omega \tag{3.16}$$

and since we are only interested in the frequency-dependent behavior of the input/output relations of $G$ of Figure 3.1, we may assume that $\sigma \to 0$, yielding:

$$X(j\omega) = G(j\omega) \cdot Y(j\omega) \tag{3.17}$$

Equation (3.17) above represents a valid Fourier-transform formulation for convergent $g(t)$, $x(t)$, and $y(t)$, where:

$$\begin{aligned} g(t) &= L^{-1}[G(s)] \\ x(t) &= L^{-1}[X(s)] \\ y(t) &= L^{-1}[Y(s)] \end{aligned} \tag{3.18}$$

$G(j\omega)$ thus denotes the gain of the system to components of the frequency $\omega$ [rad/sec] in the input $y$. Since $G(j\omega)$ is complex, it may be considered in terms of absolute gain (modulus) of $G(j\omega)$ and of argument (or phase shift), such that for:

$$G(j\omega) = \alpha(\omega) + j\beta(\omega) \tag{3.19}$$

we derive that:

$$|G(j\omega)| = \sqrt{\alpha^2(\omega) + \beta^2(\omega)} \tag{3.20}$$

and:

$$\psi(\omega) = \text{Arg}[G(\omega)] = \arctan \frac{\beta(\omega)}{\alpha(\omega)} \tag{3.21}$$

The output $x(t)$ of a linear system is of the same frequency as its input $y(t)$ when $y(t)$ is a pure sine-wave input of a single frequency $\omega$. In that case, the amplitude of $x(t)$ is amplified by $|G(j\omega)|$ with respect to the input $y(t)$ and its phase is shifted by $\psi(\omega)$ with respect to $y(t)$, such that for:

$$y(t) = M \cdot \sin(\omega t) \tag{3.22}$$

we obtain that:

$$x(t) = N \cdot \sin(\omega t + \psi) \tag{3.23}$$

where:

$$\frac{N}{M} = |G(j\omega)| \tag{3.24}$$

and:

$$\psi = \mathrm{Arg}[G(j\omega)] \tag{3.25}$$

The measurement of $G(j\omega)$ for obtaining a frequency-response is performed by applying sine-wave inputs $M \cdot \sin(\omega t)$ for various $\omega$ and recording the respective outputs $N \cdot \sin(\omega t + \psi)$. The values of $M/N$ and $\psi$ are thus recorded for each frequency $\omega$ that is considered, to yield the required frequency response.

We observe that a Fourier transform method has been employed for an analysis based on sine-wave inputs. Theoretically, the Fourier transforms do not hold for a nonconvergent input $y(t)$, when $\int_{-\infty}^{\infty} |y(t)|\, dt \to \infty$. However, we already mentioned in Section 3.1 that the sine-wave input may be considered to be slight damped, such that:

$$y(t) = \sin(\omega t)e^{-\sigma t} \tag{3.26}$$

where $\sigma$ is of a very small positive value.

The Bode diagrams of frequency-response, that are widely employed in classical control theory,[8] consist of one diagram for the modulus (absolute value) of $G(j\omega)$ and one for its argument (phase), $G(j\omega)$ obviously being complex. From plotting the modulus of the measured frequency-response of stable linear systems in units of $20 \cdot \log_{10}|G(j\omega)|$ vs. $\log(\omega)$, we may directly identify these systems. The limitation to stable systems is not only theoretical, but also practical, since no practical frequency-response of unstable systems can be measured. The general form of $G(s)$ is as follows:

$$G(s) = \frac{\alpha_m s^m + \alpha_{m-1}s^{m-1} + \cdots \alpha_0}{\beta_n s^n + \beta_{n-1}s^{n-1} + \cdots \beta_0} = \frac{Ks^q \cdot \prod_{i=1}^{p}(\tau_i s + 1) \cdot \prod_{\rho=1}^{r}(T_\rho^2 s^2 + 2T_\rho \xi_\rho s + 1)}{s^\mu \cdot \prod_{h=1}^{\gamma}(\tau_h s + 1) \cdot \prod_{\eta=1}^{\lambda}(T_\eta^2 s^2 + 2T_\eta \xi_n s + 1)} \tag{3.27}$$

where:

$$q + p + 2r = m = \text{order of the polynomial of } s \text{ in the numerator}$$

$$\mu + \gamma + 2\lambda = n = \text{order of the polynomial of } s \text{ in the denominator}$$

Consequently, $\log|G(j\omega)|$ and $\operatorname{Arg}[G(j\omega)]$ are given by:

$$\begin{aligned}\log|G(j\omega)| &= \log K + q \cdot \log \omega + \sum_{i=1}^{p} \log|j\tau_i \omega + 1| \\ &+ \sum_{\rho=1}^{r} \log|1 - \omega^2 T_\rho^2 + 2jT_\rho \xi_\rho \omega| - \mu \cdot \log \omega \\ &- \sum_{h=1}^{\gamma} \log|j\tau_h \omega + 1| - \sum_{\eta=1}^{\lambda} \log|1 - \omega^2 T_\eta^2 + 2T_\eta \xi_\eta \omega|\end{aligned} \tag{3.28}$$

$$\begin{aligned}\operatorname{Arg}[G(j\omega)] &= \psi(\omega) = q \cdot \pi/2 + \sum_{i=1}^{p} \operatorname{Arg}(j\tau_i \omega + 1) \\ &+ \sum_{\rho=1}^{r} \operatorname{Arg}(1 - \omega^2 T_\rho^2 + 2jT_\rho \xi_\rho \omega) - \mu \cdot \pi/2 \\ &- \sum_{h=1}^{\gamma} \operatorname{Arg}(j\tau_h \omega + 1) - \sum_{\eta=1}^{\lambda} \operatorname{Arg}(1 - \omega^2 T_\eta^2 + 2T_\eta \xi_\eta \omega)\end{aligned} \tag{3.29}$$

(We note that for all $A$, $B$: $\operatorname{Arg}(A \cdot B) = \operatorname{Arg} A + \operatorname{Arg} B$; $\operatorname{Arg}(A/B) = \operatorname{Arg} A - \operatorname{Arg} B$; $\operatorname{Arg} jD = \operatorname{Arg} j + \operatorname{Arg} D = \pi/2 + \operatorname{Arg} D = \pi/2$ for all real values of $D$.)

Equations (3.28), (3.29) indicate that any system $G(s)$ may be partitioned into products of elements of the form of $k_i$; $(\tau_i s + 1)$; $(T_i^2 s^2 + 2T_i \xi_i s + 1)$; $s^{\pm v}$; $\dfrac{1}{(\tau_j s + 1)}$; $\dfrac{1}{(T_j^2 s^2 + 2T_j \xi_j s + 1)}$.

These may be asymptotically approximated in the Bode diagram as is shown in Table 3.1.

The dependence of the logarithmic frequency response (Bode plot) of an element $(T_i^2 s^2 + 2\xi T_i s + 1)^{\pm 1}$ on $\xi$ is shown in Figure 3.3. The frequency response of the argument (phase) of $G(j\omega)$ may also be asymptotically approximated, as in Table 3.2.

The argument for $(T_i^2 s^2 + 2\xi T_i s + 1)^{\pm 1}$ near $\omega = 1/T$ is also dependent on $\xi$, as shown in Figure 3.4.

The frequency responses of the various elements listed in tables 3.1, 3.2 are illustrated in figures 3.5, 3.6 for modulus and argument (phase), respectively. A very important result of the discussion above is that the frequency responses of first and second order elements may be plotted in terms of a normalized frequency $T\omega$ or $\tau\omega$, thus being independent of the value $T$ may take.

**TABLE 3.1 Amplitudes vs. $\omega$ in the Bode Diagram.**

| *Element* | $\omega \ll 1/T$ | $\omega = 1/T$ | $\omega \gg 1/T$ |
|---|---|---|---|
| $K$ | $20 \log_{10} K$[db] | $20 \log_{10} K$[db] | $20 \log_{10} K$[db] |
| $s^n$ | $n \cdot 20$[db/decade] | $n \cdot 20$[db/decade] | $n \cdot 20$[db/decade] |
| $Ts+1$ | 0[db] | +3[db] | +20[db/decade] |
| $\frac{1}{Ts+1}$ | 0[db] | −3[db] | −20[db/decade] |
| $T^2s^2+2\xi Ts+1$ | 0[db] | depending on $\xi$ | +40[db/decade] |
| $\frac{1}{T^2s^2+2\xi Ts+1}$ | 0[db] | depending on $\xi$ | −40[db/decade] |
| $\exp(-Ts)$ | 0[db] | 0[db] | 0[db] |

1 db $= 20 \cdot \log_{10} 10$; decade $\triangleq$ decade of $\omega$

$T_i^2s^2 + 2\xi T_i s + 1 \triangleq s^2/\omega_i^2 + 2\xi s/\omega_i + 1$

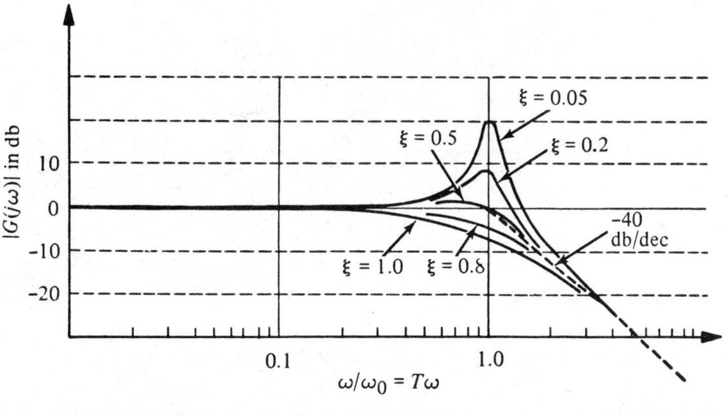


*Figure 3.3* Frequency response of modulus for second order system.

The approximations of tables 3.1 and 3.2 facilitate the approximate identification of any stable linear system $G(j\omega)$ from its measured frequency response. Identification may be performed from the modulus response alone, as long as all the coefficients of the polynomial of $s$ at the numerator of $G(s)$ in Equation (3.27) are known to have the same sign. Otherwise, both the modulus and the phase response are required for unique identification.

We illustrate the identification from frequency responses by means of the following example.

**TABLE 3.2 Argument vs. $\omega$ in the Bode Diagram.**

| *Element* | $\omega \ll T^{-1}$ | $\omega = T^{-1}$ | $\omega \gg T^{-1}$ |
|---|---|---|---|
| $K$ | 0° | 0° | 0° |
| $s^{\pm n}$ | $\pm 90° \cdot n$ | $\pm 90° \cdot n$ | $\pm 90°$ |
| $Ts+1$ | 0° | 45° | 90° |
| $\frac{1}{Ts+1}$ | 0° | −45° | −90° |
| $T^2s^2+2\xi Ts+1$ | 0° | 90° | 180° |
| $\frac{1}{T^2s^2+2\xi Ts+1}$ | 0° | −90° | −180° |
| $e^{-Ts}$ (pure time delay) | $-T\omega \cdot \frac{180°}{\pi}$ | $-T\omega \cdot \frac{180°}{\pi}$ | $-T\omega \cdot \frac{180°}{\pi}$ |

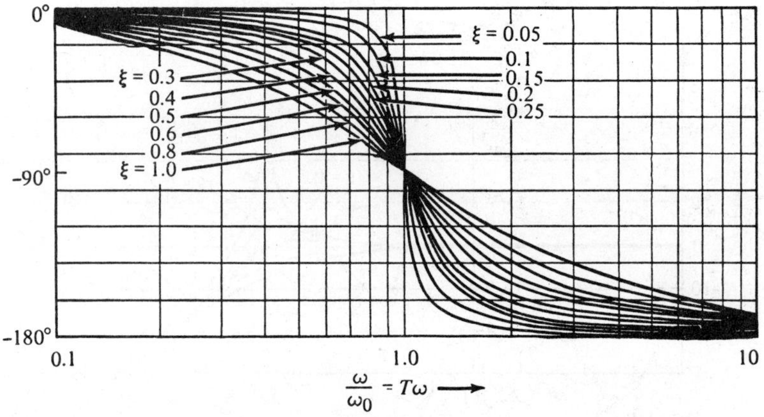


*Figure 3.4* Frequency response of phase for second order systems.

EXAMPLE 3.1

Consider a modulus frequency response as in Figure 3.7. The initial slope at low frequencies indicates that $G(s)$ contains an element of $s^{-2}$ (low-frequency slope of $-20 \cdot n = -40$ db/dec). Subsequently, we have at $\omega_1 = 1/T_1 = 6$ a bending point of a second order element of the form of $(T_1^2s^2 + 2\xi_1T_1s + 1)$ where $\xi_1$ appears to be close to 1, due to the lack of amplitude-overshoot near $\omega_1$ (see Figure 3.3). The slope added by the modulus of the latter element, for $\omega_1 \ll 1/T$, is 0 db/dec and for $\omega \gg 1/T_1$ the slope added is +40 db/dec, thus

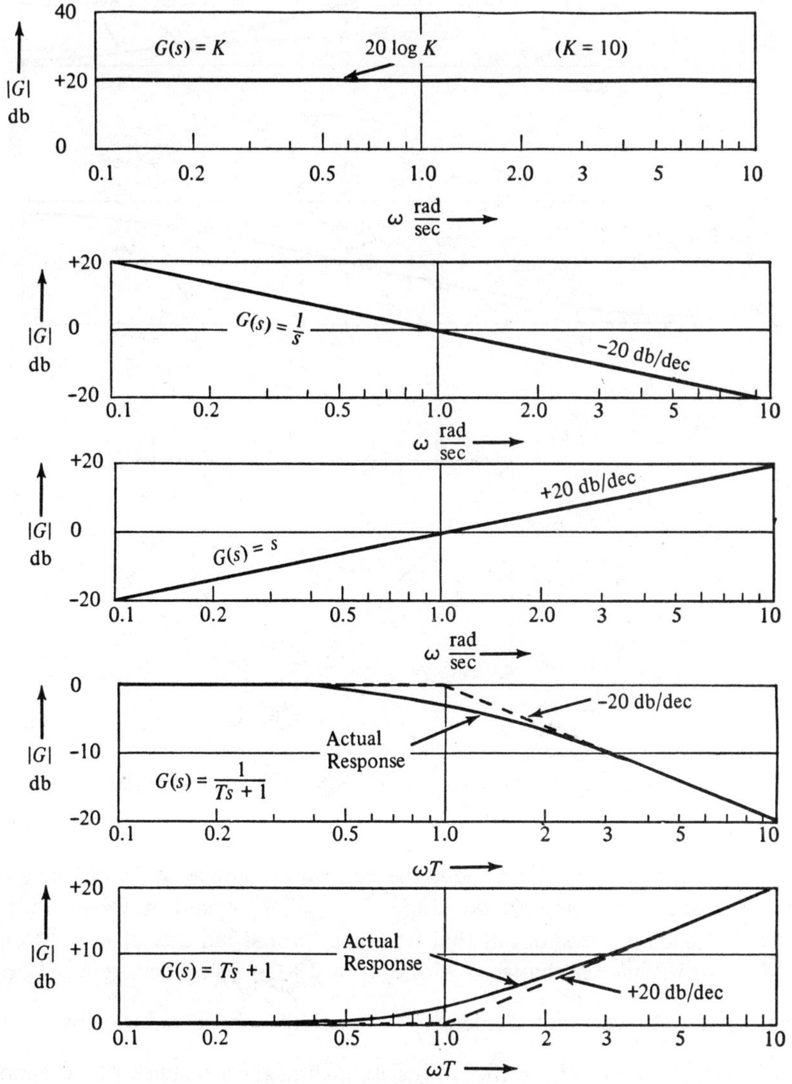


*Figure 3.5* Frequency response of modulus for various elements.

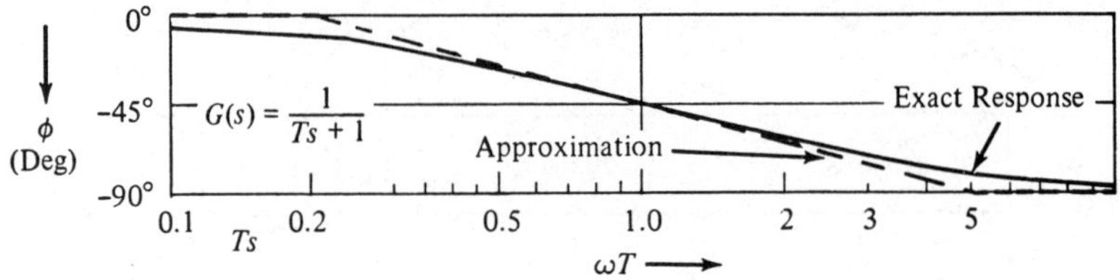


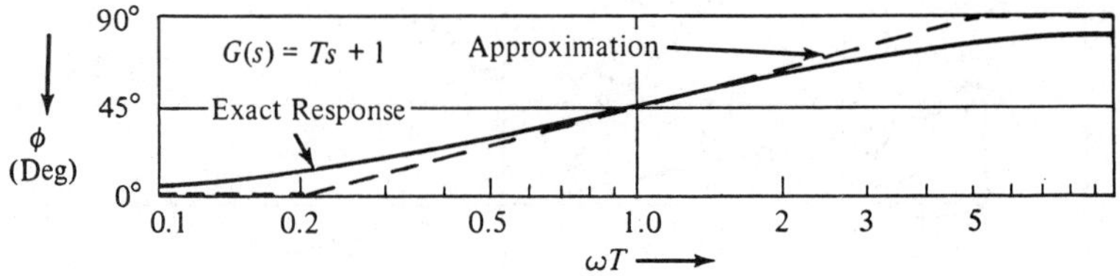


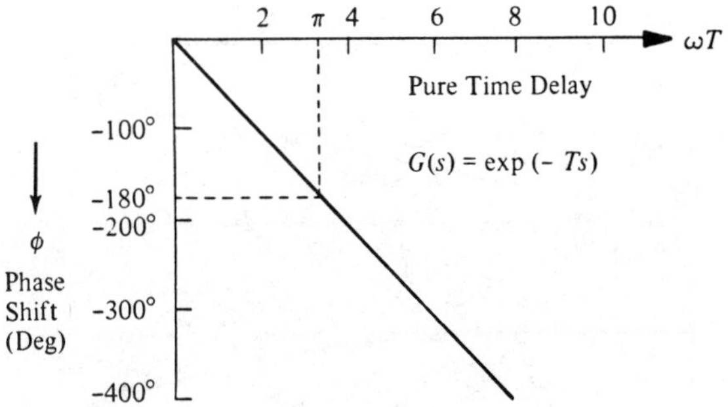


*Figure 3.6* Frequency response of phase for various elements.

cancelling the negative slope due to the element $s^{-2}$ above. We note that a very gradual and slow change in the slope at $\omega_1 = 1/T_1$ would, however, indicate $\xi_1 > 1$. while an overshoot at that frequency would indicate $\xi_1 < 1$. At $\omega_2 = 1/T_2 = 60$ we have a change in slope from 0 to $-20$ db/dec, representing a first order time-constant element $\frac{1}{T_2 s + 1}$. The slope is reduced by another 20 db/dec beyond $1/T_3 = 1000$, thus indicating the existence of an element $\frac{1}{T_3 s + 1}$. Consequently, $G(s)$ may be described as the product of the elements stated above, as follows:

$$G(s) = \frac{K(T_1 s + 1)^2}{s^2(T_2 s + 1)(T_3 s + 1)}$$

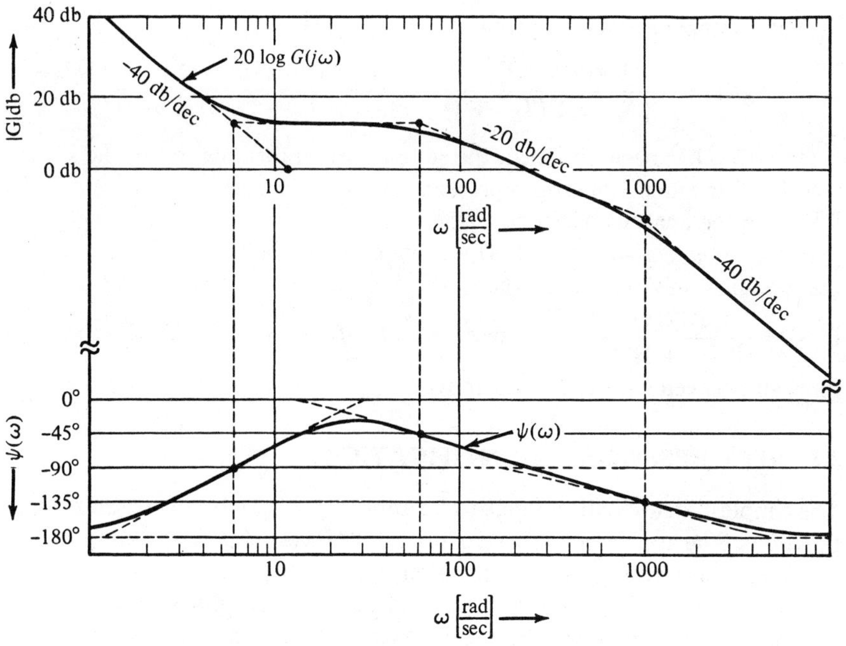


*Figure 3.7* Identification from frequency responses.

In all cases, where $\xi$ significantly differs from 1, an examination according to Figure 3.3 is required. This examination should, in fact, be performed according to its mirror diagram, since we are presently concerned with an element $(T^2s^2 + 2\xi Ts + 1)$, whereas Figure 3.3 deals with the reciprocal of that element.

The gain $K$ in the example above is obtained from continuing the low-frequency slope up to the zero–db axis. The intersection-frequency $\omega_0$ at $0 \cdot$ db is related to the gain as follows:

$$\log \frac{K}{(j\omega_0)^n} = 0 \tag{3.30}$$

Hence:

$$\frac{K}{\omega_0^n} = 1 \tag{3.31}$$

and:

$$K = \omega_0^n = 12^2 = 144 \tag{3.32}$$

$G(s)$ of Example 3.1 is thus given by:

$$G(s) = \frac{144(T_1 s + 1)^2}{s^2(T_2 s + 1)(T_3 s + 1)} = \frac{144(0.167s + 1)^2}{s^2(0.0167\,s + 1)(0.001\,s + 1)}$$

Once $G(s)$ has been obtained, the state-equation formulation of the system (i.e., its differential-equation representation) may be further computed when following the analysis of Section 2.5.

In the latter derivation of $G(s)$ we made use of the frequency response of the modulus only. However, the same modulus response is possible also for $G'(s) = \dfrac{K(T_1 s - 1)^2}{s^2(T_2 s + 1)(T_3 s + 1)}$, and the phase response is required to distinguish between $G(s)$ and $G'(s)$ above.

## 3.3 STEP RESPONSE IDENTIFICATION

The simplest identification input to be applied is certainly this based on step functions. The application of a step input to a process may be accomplished by say, a sudden opening (or closing) of an input valve, a sudden switching-on (or off) of input voltage or current, etc. ..., as is almost always possible without special instrumentation. An ideal step consists of a zero-duration rise-time, which is physically impossible since it involves infinite initial velocity. Consequently, all practical step inputs are only approximations of the ideal step. However, if the initial rise-time is of a duration that is much shorter than the period of the highest frequency of interest in the identification, the resulting identification-error is negligible. In noisy processes, or where measurements contain noise (as they usually do, to some degree), adequate filtering of noise is essential.

As has been stated earlier in this chapter, step-response identification is an off-line technique, thus applicable to stationary processes only. However, since step disturbances are applied to many (if not to most) processes also during normal operation or at start-up, step responses may be recorded without disturbing normal operation, thus adding attraction to this technique. Obviously, the identification results in the latter case still assume process stationarity, since identification is assumed to be valid also after the application of the step. They further assume linearity within the amplitude range of the step.

### 3.3.1 Analysis of Step Responses

The relationship between input, process characteristics, and output in the time domain involves convolution, as in Equation (3.4). However, in Laplace transformed form the above relationship merely involves multiplication, as indicated by Equation (3.6). Hence, Laplace transforms may be employed to analyze step responses, as follows:

Consider a system whose Laplace transformed transfer-function is $G(s)$, where:

$$G(s) = \frac{X(s)}{Y(x)} \tag{3.33}$$

$s$ being the Laplace transform variable and $X$, $Y$ denoting the process output and input, respectively (see Figure 3.1).

The Laplace transform of a unit step at $t = 0$ is:[9]

$$L[\text{Unit Step at } t = 0] = \frac{1}{s} \tag{3.34}$$

Consequently, the step response $X(s)$ of any linear system $G(s)$ becomes:

$$X(s) = \frac{G(s)}{s} \tag{3.35}$$

which, according to the Laplace transform theory, represents the Laplace transform of the time-integral $\int g(t)\,dt$, where $g(t)$ denotes the inverse Laplace transform of the transfer function $G(s)$, as follows:

$$g(t) = L^{-1}[G(s)] \tag{3.36}$$

$$s \cdot X(s) = G(s) \tag{3.37-a}$$

and:

$$L^{-1}[s \cdot X(s)] = \frac{dx(t)}{dt} = g(t) \tag{3.37-b}$$

### 3.3.2 Fourier Transformation of Step Responses

The results of Equation (3.34) or (3.37) are of direct use in step-response identification. We note that *the identification required for control purposes is that which provides sufficient information to facilitate adequate prediction of the state of the system in some future time* $(t + \tau)$, assuming that the present state and control-input are given. Consequently, and knowing the required state at $t + \tau$, we can compute the required control for reaching the required future state, from the identification information above. Furthermore, for the identification to be effective, we require that $\tau$ be such that at $t + \tau$ we can again update identification and compute a new control for adequate performance at another interval ahead. Obviously, this identification that facilitates accurate prediction to *any* lead time $\tau$ ($@\tau \to \infty$) is best, but practically impossible. In stationary processes, knowledge of the transfer-function $G(s)$ or of the transition and the control matrices **A, B** of Equation (2.1), facilitates, in theory, identification to any lead time ($G(s)$ and **A, B** being interrelated as in Section 2.5). Considering equations (3.34) and (3.37), we note that $x(t)$ or $dx(t)/dt$ can be transformed into the transfer-function form of $G(s)$, by applying a Fourier transformation (preferably, a Fast Fourier Transform algorithm[3,4]) to $x(t)$ or to $dx(t)/dt$. The application of Fourier transforms has been discussed at length in Section 3.1 above. However, for the completeness of the discussion, we state that once $dx(t)/dt$ is transformed into $F[g(t)] = G(j\omega)$, $F$ being the Fourier-transform operator, we may plot $G(j\omega)$ vs. $\omega$. We note that $G(j\omega)$ is complex; hence, both its modulus and argument must be considered. From the behavior of $G(j\omega)$, we may obtain $G(s)$ in exactly the same manner as has been described in Section 3.2 above, and subsequently we may derive the system's state space model according to Section 2.5. We observe that the Fourier transform may be applied either to $dx(t)/dt$, yielding $G(j\omega)$, or to $x(t)$, yielding $X(j\omega)$ from which $G(j\omega)$ must be further derived. Furthermore, a Fourier transform is theoretically restricted to absolutely integrable time-functions, i.e., to convergent time-functions,[10] as has been discussed in Section 3.1. This theoretical consideration introduces certain difficulties when employing Fourier transforms in identification, as has also been discussed in Section 3.1.

The following example provides further insight to the Fourier transform identification using step-responses.

EXAMPLE 3.2

Consider a system $G(s)$, where:

$$G(s) = \frac{1}{Ts + 1}$$

The step response $X(s)$ of $G(s)$ is given by:

$$X(s) = \frac{1}{s(Ts + 1)}$$

and the well-known inverse Laplace transform of the latter expression yields:

$$x(t) = L^{-1}[X(s)] = 1 - e^{-t/T}$$

For deriving the system's transfer function $G(s)$, we may write:

$$s \cdot x(s) = \frac{1}{Ts + 1} = G(s)$$

$$\frac{dx(t)}{dt} = g(t) = \frac{1}{T} e^{-t/T}$$

Since $e^{-t/T}$ is convergent, we may apply a Fourier transform to it, as follows:

$$F[g(t)] = \int_{-\infty}^{\infty} g(t)e^{-j\omega t}\,dt = G(j\omega)$$

We note that $g(t)$ is in fact equal to 0 for $t \leq 0$ and equal to $e^{-t/T}$ for $t > 0$. Consequently, the integral in the latter Fourier transform may be rewritten as:

$$G(j\omega) = \int_{-\infty}^{0} 0 \cdot e^{-j\omega t}\,dt + \int_{0}^{\infty} \frac{1}{T} e^{-t/T} \cdot e^{-j\omega t}\,dt = \frac{1}{T}\int_{0}^{\infty} e^{-(j\omega T+1)t/T}\,dt$$

$$= -\frac{1}{j\omega T + 1} e^{-(j\omega T+1)t/T}\Big|_{0}^{\infty} = \frac{1}{j\omega T + 1}$$

yielding for $j\omega = s$:

$$G(s) = \frac{1}{Ts + 1}$$

as is required.

Approaching the problem of the above example by transforming $x(t)$ instead of $dx(t)/dt$, we derive:

$$X(j\omega) = \int_{-\infty}^{0} 0 \cdot e^{-j\omega T}\,dt + \int_{0}^{\infty} (1 - e^{-t/T})e^{-j\omega t}\,dt$$

$$= \int_{0}^{\infty} e^{-j\omega t}\,dt - \int_{0}^{\infty} e^{-(j\omega T+1)t/T}\,dt$$

$$= \frac{-1}{j\omega} e^{-j\omega t}\Big|_{0}^{\infty} + \frac{T}{j\omega t + 1} e^{-(j\omega t+1)t}\Big|_{0}^{\infty}$$

$$= \frac{1}{j\omega} - \frac{T}{j\omega T + 1} = \frac{j\omega T + 1 - j\omega T}{j\omega(j\omega T + 1)} = \frac{1}{j\omega(j\omega T + 1)}$$

However, the Fourier transform of a unit-step is approximately equal to $1/j\omega$. (We say "approximately" since a step function is not absolutely integrable,[1] its time integral from $-\infty$ to $\infty$ being $\infty$.) Consequently, if this step is approximated by $e^{-\sigma t}$ $\forall t > 0$, where $\sigma$ is a positive real value that is very close to 0, we derive:

$$F[\text{unit step}(t)] \cong \int_{-\infty}^{0} 0 \cdot e^{-j\omega t}\,dt + \int_{0}^{\infty} e^{-\sigma t} \cdot e^{-j\omega t}\,dt = \int_{0}^{\infty} e^{-(\sigma + j\omega)t}\,dt$$

$$= \frac{1}{\sigma + j\omega} e^{-(\sigma + j\omega)t}\Big|_{0}^{\infty} \Rightarrow \frac{1}{\sigma + j\omega} = \frac{1}{j\omega} \quad @ \text{ small positive } \sigma \tag{3.38}$$

Employing the transformed convolution theorem,[1] as follows:

$$X(j\omega) = G(j\omega)Y(j\omega) \tag{3.39}$$

$$G(j\omega) = \frac{X(j\omega)}{Y(j\omega)} \tag{3.40}$$

where $X(j\omega)$, $Y(j\omega)$ represent output and input respectively, as in Figure 3.1 and noting from Equation (3.38) that the transformed input of Example 3.2 is given by:

$$Y(j\omega) = \frac{1}{j\omega}$$

we obtain:

$$G(j\omega) = \frac{j\omega}{j\omega(j\omega T + 1)} = \frac{1}{j\omega T + 1}$$

which corresponds with the result obtained above in the example.

### 3.3.3 Graphical Parameter Identification from Step Responses

It is often possible to derive the transfer function of a system from a recording of its step response. This derivation is discussed below for the most common types of linear systems, namely for first and second order systems and for aperiodic systems of high order.

**3.3.3-a First order systems** The most fundamental of the graphical step-response techniques is concerned with *first order* processes, as in Figure 3.8.

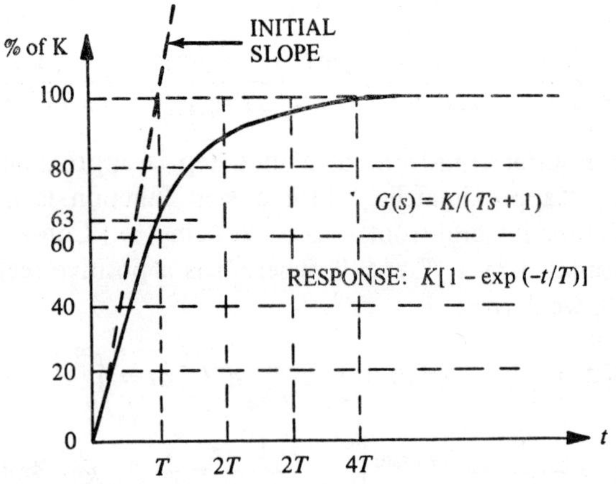


*Figure 3.8* Step response of first order process.

The step response of a first order system is given by:

$$x(t) = K(1 - e^{-t/T}) \tag{3.41}$$

or, in Laplace transformed form:

$$X(s) = L[x(t)] = G(s)\,Y(s) = \frac{G(s)}{s} = \frac{K}{s(Ts + 1)} \tag{3.42}$$

where:

$$G(s) = K/(Ts + 1) \tag{3.43}$$

is the transfer function of the first order system, and:

$$Y(s) = 1/s = L[\text{unit step}] \tag{3.44}$$

is the step-input. We observe that for $t = T$, $x(t)$ is given by:

$$x(t) = K(1 - e^{-1}) = K(1 - 0.37) = 0.63K \tag{3.45}$$

Hence, the time-constant parameter $T$ of a first order system is the time at which the step response reaches 63% of its steady state value. The gain $K$ is obviously the (usually dimensional) relation between the steady state value of the output and the step amplitude.

The time-constant $T$ may be alternatively derived by continuing the initial slope (the tangent at $t = 0$) of the step response until it reaches the steady-state amplitude value, as in Figure 3.8. The resulting point of intersection is reached at time $T$ after the beginning of the step response, since the slope of $x$ at $t = 0$ is given by:

$$\frac{dx}{dt_{t=0}} = \frac{K}{T} e^{-t/T}\bigg|_{t=0} = K/T \tag{3.46}$$

The behaviour of the above slope-line vs. time, therefore, follows the relation:

$$\text{initial slope} \triangleq \Phi(t) = \frac{+Kt}{T} \tag{3.47}$$

which reaches the value $K$ for $t = T$.

**3.3.3-b Pure time delays** If any step response is delayed by a delay time $\tau$ such that it remains zero up to a time $\tau$ after the application of the step, as in Figure 3.9, we assume that the system contains a (pure) time delay term,

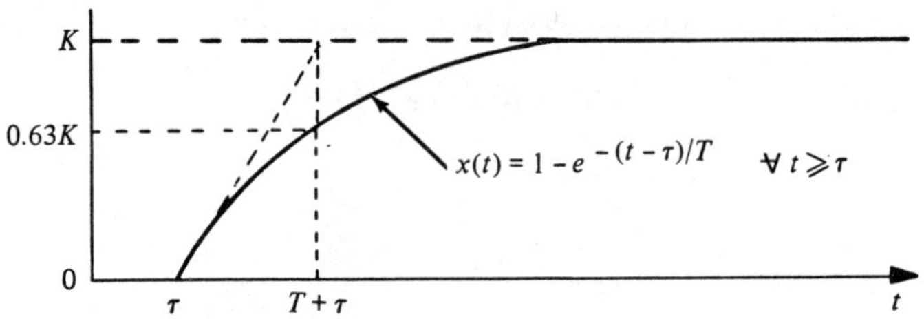


*Figure 3.9* Step response of system with pure time-delay.

given, in Laplace transformed form, by $e^{-\tau s}$. Consequently, if the step response of the system is given by:

$$x(t) = \begin{cases} 0; & \forall t \leq \tau \\ K(1 - e^{-(t-\tau)/T}); & \forall t > \tau \end{cases} \tag{3.48}$$

its transfer function becomes:

$$G(s) = \frac{K \cdot e^{-\tau s}}{Ts + 1} \tag{3.49}$$

as results from applying a Laplace transform to Equation (3.48).

**3.3.3-c Aperiodic second order systems** Naslin[11,12] describes a graphical method of identifying systems from their step responses, to derive the parameters of second order transfer functions approximating these systems, as follows.

Consider a system $G(s)$, where:

$$G(s) = \frac{1.25}{(s + 2.5)(s + 0.5)}$$

and whose step-response is given by:

$$x(t) = 1 - 1.25e^{-0.5t} + 0.25e^{-2.5t}$$

as is illustrated in Figure 3.10*A*. The behavior of $x(\infty) - x(t)$ for the latter system is subsequently plotted, as in Figure 3.10*B*. We note that $x(\infty) - x(t) = 1 - x(t) = 1.25e^{-0.5t} - 0.25e^{-2.5t}$. Hence, for large $t$ where $e^{-2.5t} \to 0$, the term $[x(\infty) - x(t)]$ is approximated by $1.25e^{-0.5t}$, as in Figure 3.10*A*, and the slope of $\log_{10}[x(\infty) - x(t)]$ (see Figure 3.11) is approximately given by:

$$\frac{d[\log_{10}(1.25e^{-0.5t}])}{dt} = \frac{d[\log_{10} 1.25 - 0.5t \cdot \log_{10} e]}{dt} = -0.5 \log_{10} e = -0.21$$

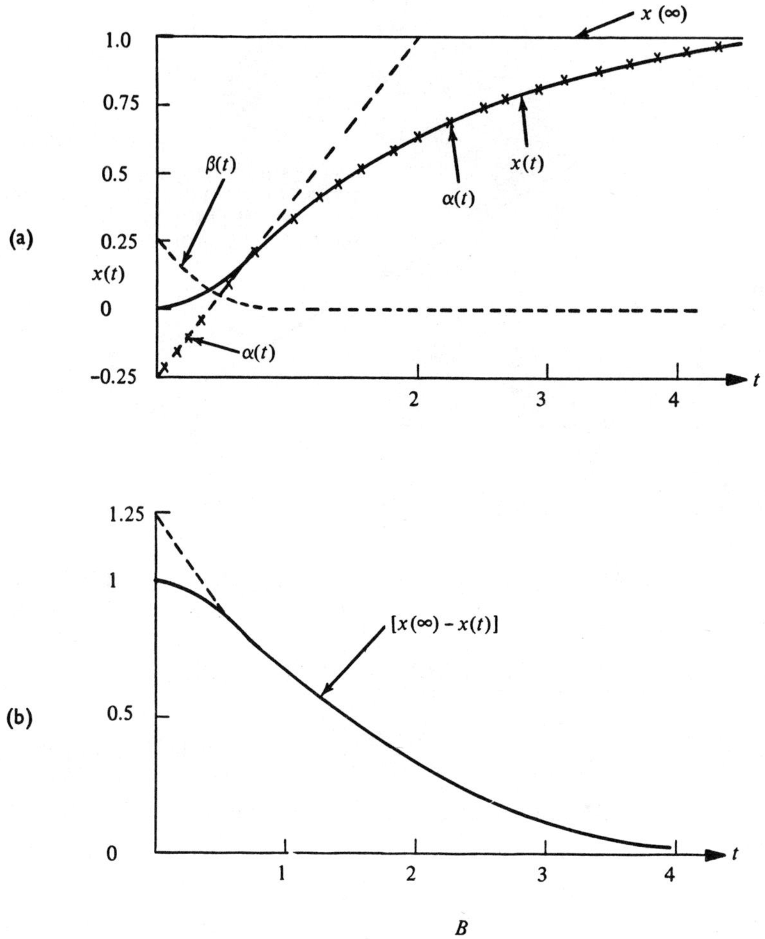


*Figure 3.10* Responses of aperiodic second order system.

Hence, the approximation of $x(t)$ for large $t$ becomes $\alpha(t) = (1 - 1.25e^{-0.5t})$, whereas for small $t$ another term $\beta(t)$ is required, which for $t = 0$ should be $\beta(0) = 0.25$. This second term is thus of the form of $\beta(t) \triangleq 0.25e^{-rt}$. Returning to Figure 3.10$A$, we plot $\alpha(t) \triangleq (1 - 1.25e^{-0.5t})$, marking $\alpha(0) = -0.25$. From $\alpha(0)$ we continue with the initial slope $\frac{d\alpha(0)}{dt} = .625$, and connect the latter smoothly with $x(t)$. The difference between $x(t)$ and $\alpha(t)$ now (approximately) yields $\beta(t)$, which is also plotted in Figure 3.10$A$, and $\log_{10} \beta(t)$ is

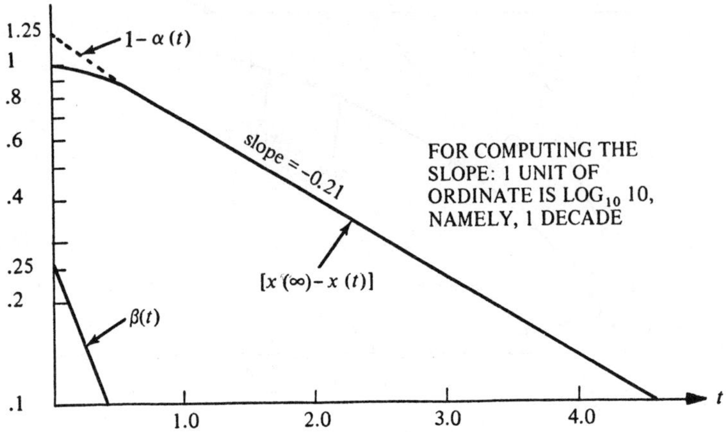


*Figure 3.11* **Logarithmic step response of aperiodic second order system.**

subsequently plotted in Figure 3.11. The slope of $\log_{10} \beta(t)$ in Figure 3.11 is thus given by:

$$\frac{d[\log \beta(t)]}{dt} = \frac{d[\log 0.25e^{-rt}]}{dt} = \frac{d[\log 0.25 - r \cdot t \cdot \log e]}{dt}$$

$$= -r \cdot \log e = -0.42 \cdot r$$

from which $r$ may be derived to be equal to 2.5. Consequently, $x(t)$ is approximated by:

$$1 - 1.25e^{-0.5t} + 0.25e^{-rt}$$

and $G(s)$ becomes:

$$G(s) = \frac{K}{(s+a)(s+r)} = \frac{K}{(s+0.5)(s+r)}$$

$K$ is determined to satisfy the steady state value of the response $x(t)$, where:

$$X(s) = G(s)/s = \text{step-response} \tag{3.50}$$

and, by the final value theorem:

$$\lim_{t\to\infty} x(t) = \lim_{s\to 0} s \cdot X(s) = \lim_{s\to 0} s \cdot \frac{G(s)}{s} = \frac{K}{a \cdot r} \tag{3.51}$$

Since $x(0) = 1$, as has been measured, we obtain that $K = 0.5 \cdot r$, where $r$ has already been determined above.

**3.3.3-d Periodic second order systems** Periodic second order systems may always be described by:

$$G(s) = \frac{K}{(s/\omega_0)^2 + 2\xi s/\omega_0 + 1} = \frac{K}{(Ts)^2 + 2\xi Ts + 1} \tag{3.52}$$

where $0 < \xi < 1$ and $T \triangleq 1/\omega_0$, as is well-known from classical control theory.[8] Consequently, the determination of only $\omega_0$, $\xi$, and $K$ is required for identifying periodic second order systems, $K$ being the ratio of output to input at steady state. The damping coefficient $\xi$ is directly related to the *overshoot* that is always present in oscillatory second order systems, as is shown in Figure 3.12. The relation between $\xi$ and the overshoot (as a percentage of the steady state step response) is given in Figure 3.13. Once

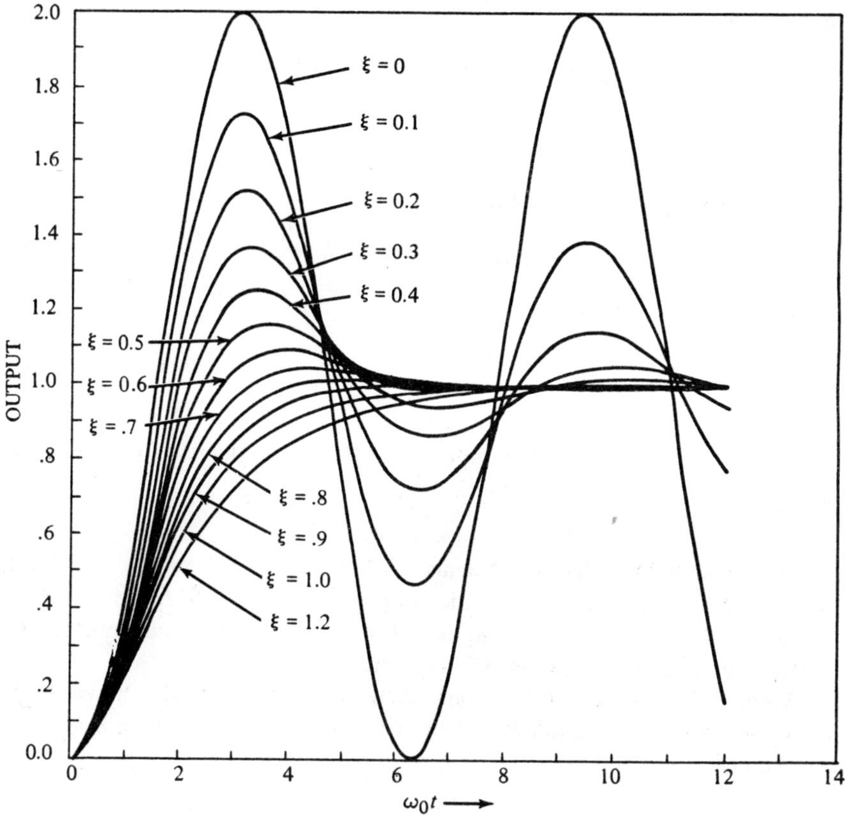


*Figure 3.12* Step response of periodic second order systems.

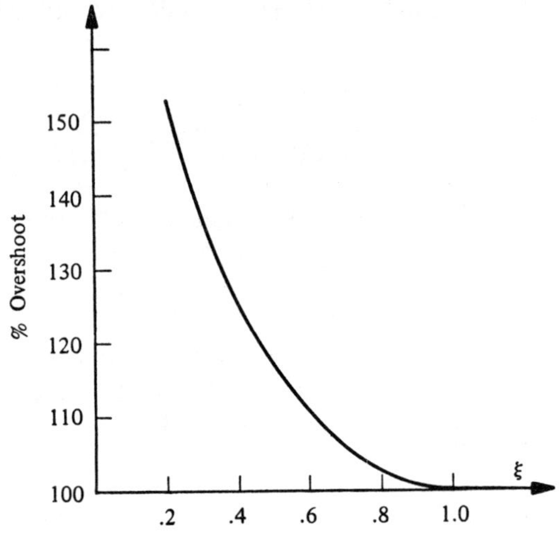


*Figure 3.13* Overshoot vs. damping.

$\xi$ is graphically determined, according to Figure 3.13, the natural frequency $\omega_0$ may be obtained as follows:

$$\omega_0 = \omega/\sqrt{1-\xi^2} \tag{3.53}$$

where:

$$\omega = \frac{2\pi}{\theta} \tag{3.54}$$

$\theta$ being the period of the damped oscillations in the step response (see Figure 3.12).

**3.3.3-e Aperiodic high order systems** A simple graphical identification technique for high order aperiodic processes is due to Strejc.[12,13] Strejc's method is based on the notation, as in Figure 3.14, where a generalized high order aperiodic step response is illustrated.

According to Strejc, an aperiodic system with $n$ different time constants may be adequately approximated by a transfer function having $n$ identical time constants as follows:

$$G(s) = \frac{K}{(T_1 s + 1)(T_2 s + 1) \cdots (T_n s + 1)} \cong \frac{K}{(\tau s + 1)^n} \tag{3.55}$$

where $K$ represents the steady state gain. The identification problem is thus restricted to identifying $\tau$ and $n$. For this purpose Strejc tabulated the relations of $n$ and $T_a/T_b$; $T_e/T_b$; as in Table 3.3. The point of inflexion $Q$ in Figure 3.14, which is required for determining $T_a \cdots T_e$, is that where $d^2x/dt^2$ is zero. Once $n$ is obtained from $T_a/T_b$ (and verified by $T_e/T_b$), then $\tau$ of Equation (3.55) may be derived from $T_a/\tau$ (and verified by $T_b/\tau$; $T_d/\tau$; $T_e/\tau$) according to Table 3.4.

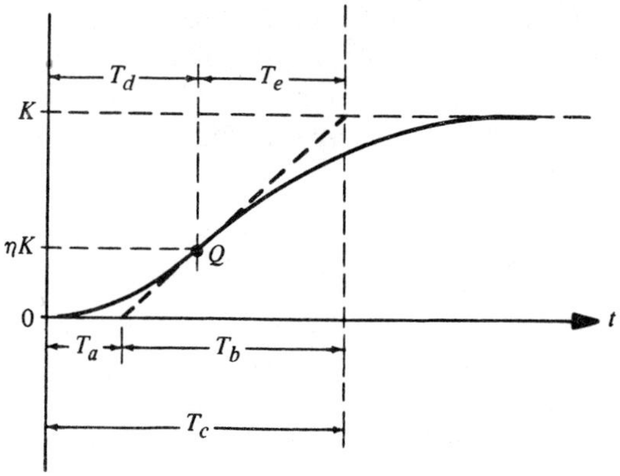


*Figure 3.14* Step response of aperiodic high order process.

**TABLE 3.3**

| $n$ | 1 | 2 | 3 | 4 | 5 | 6 | 7 | 8 | 9 | 10 |
|---|---|---|---|---|---|---|---|---|---|---|
| $T_a/T_b$ | 0 | 0.104 | 0.218 | 0.319 | 0.410 | 0.493 | 0.570 | 0.642 | 0.709 | 0.773 |
| $T_e/T_b$ | 1 | 0.736 | 0.677 | 0.647 | 0.629 | 0.616 | 0.606 | 0.599 | 0.593 | 0.587 |
| $\eta$ | 0 | 0.264 | 0.323 | 0.353 | 0.371 | 0.384 | 0.394 | 0.401 | 0.407 | 0.413 |

**TABLE 3.4**

| $n$ | 1 | 2 | 3 | 4 | 5 | 6 | 7 | 8 | 9 | 10 |
|---|---|---|---|---|---|---|---|---|---|---|
| $T_a/\tau$ | 0 | 0.282 | 0.805 | 1.425 | 2.1 | 2.811 | 3.549 | 4.307 | 5.081 | 5.869 |
| $T_b/\tau$ | 1 | 2.718 | 3.695 | 4.463 | 5.119 | 5.699 | 6.226 | 6.711 | 7.164 | 7.59 |
| $T_d/\tau$ | 0 | 1 | 2 | 3 | 4 | 5 | 6 | 7 | 8 | 9 |
| $T_e/\tau$ | 1 | 2 | 2.5 | 2.888 | 3.219 | 3.51 | 3.775 | 4.018 | 4.245 | 4.458 |

## 3.4 IMPULSE RESPONSE IDENTIFICATION

The identification of linear processes by means of their impulse responses follows very similar lines to the identification by means of step responses. Impulse response identification requires the application of an impulse (delta function) input to the system that is to be identified, and is therefore an off-line identification technique. By definition, a delta function is a pulse of zero width and of unit area (see Figure 3.15) and, hence, of an infinite amplitude. Obviously, delta functions cannot be realized, because of their infinite amplitudes. They can, however, be approximated by pulses of finite width $\theta \to 0$ and of unit area, with a resulting amplitude of $1/\theta \to \infty$, thus yielding inaccuracies in the response that is obtained, as is illustrated in Figure 3.16.

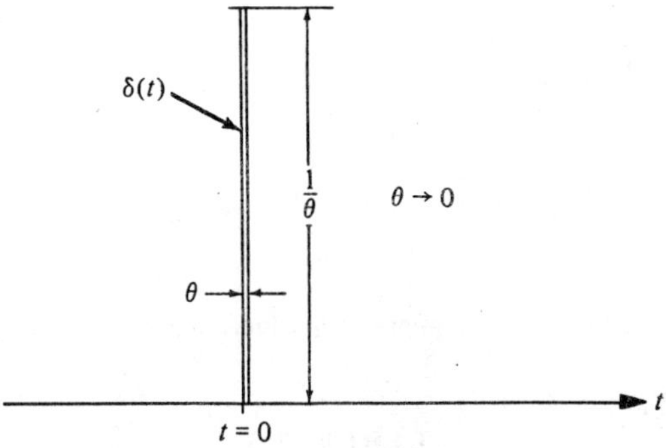


*Figure 3.15* An impulse function.

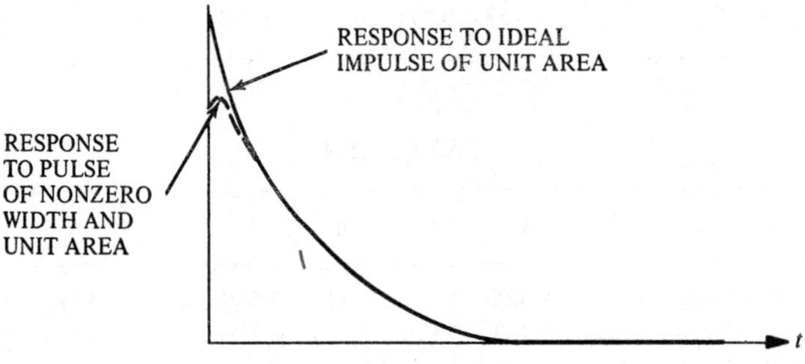


*Figure 3.16* Responses to ideal and approximate impulses.

### 3.4.1 Impulse Response Analysis

Consider a system $G(s)$, as in Figure 3.1, where:

$$X(s) = G(s)Y(s) \tag{3.56}$$

$x$ and $y$ being the system's output and input, respectively, and the input $y$ being a unit impulse, whose Laplace transform is given by:

$$Y(s) = L[\delta(t)] = 1 \tag{3.57}$$

Consequently, the Laplace transformed output becomes:

$$X(s) = G(s)L[\delta(t)] = G(s) \cdot 1 = G(s) \tag{3.58}$$

and:

$$x(t) = L^{-1}[X(s)] = L^{-1}[G(s)] = g(t) \tag{3.59}$$

Equations (3.58), (3.59) imply that the impulse response of a linear system is identical to the inverse Laplace transform of its transfer function $G(s)$. The latter result is, obviously, of major importance for identification.

If, however, the input $y(t)$ to the process is a finite width pulse, whose width $\theta$ is sufficiently small, we may describe the latter pulse as the sum of a positive unit step at $t = 0$ and a negative unit step at $t = \theta$, as is shown in Figure 3.17, yielding:

$$L[y(t)] = Y(s) = \frac{1 - e^{-\theta s}}{s} \tag{3.60}$$

$1/s$ being the Laplace transformed unit step at $t = 0$ and $e^{-\theta s}/s$ representing the negative unit step at $t = \theta$.

*Figure 3.17* Finite width pulse.

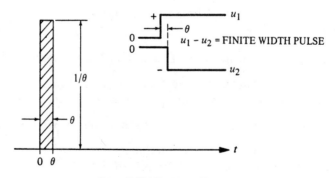

Employing a Taylor series expansion, Equation (3.60) becomes:

$$Y(s) = \frac{1}{s} - \frac{1}{s}\left(1 - s\theta + \frac{s^2\theta^2}{2!} - \frac{s^3\theta^3}{3!} \pm \cdots\right) \tag{3.61}$$

yielding, for $\theta \to 0$:

$$Y(s) \cong \frac{1}{s} - \frac{1}{s}(1 - \theta s) = \theta \tag{3.62}$$

If the amplitude of the pulse is $1/\theta$, then $Y(s)$ of Equation (3.62) becomes:

$$Y(s) = \frac{1}{\theta}\left[\frac{1}{s} - \frac{1}{s}(1 - \theta s)\right] = 1 \tag{3.63}$$

as in the case of a pure $\delta$-function.

Comparing the impulse function above and the step function as in Section 3.3, we observe that the $\delta$-function is, in fact, the time derivative of an ideal step function (this derivative being infinity at the zero-duration rise time of the step, and zero elsewhere). In the Laplace transform domain we again observe this relationship (noting that the Laplace transform variable $s$ represents $d/dt$), as follows:

$$s \cdot L[\text{unit step}] = s \cdot \frac{1}{s} = 1 \tag{3.64}$$

Consequently, if $x(t)$ represents the step response of a system, we obtain that $dx/dt$ is given by:

$$s \cdot X(s) = s \cdot \frac{G(s)}{s} = G(s) \tag{3.65}$$

$\frac{G(s)}{s}$ being the step response, as in Equation (3.35). Comparing equations (3.58) and (3.65), we observe that the time derivative of the step response is identical to the impulse response of the system. Again, the integral of the impulse response $\frac{1}{s}G(s)$, is identical to the step response. We thus conclude that impulse response identification techniques may be applied to step responses if the latter responses are differentiated. Furthermore, step response identification techniques are applicable to impulse responses if the behavior of the time integral of the latter is considered.

### 3.4.2 Fourier Transformation of Impulse Responses

As in the case of step response identification (Section 3.3.2), the transfer function $G(s)$ may be derived by applying a Fourier transformation to the impulse response $g(t)$. Once $G(s)$ has been derived, the differential-equation formulation of the system can be obtained, as in Section 2.5.

Since the impulse function $\delta(t)$ is integrable ($\int_{-\infty}^{\infty} |\delta(t)|\,dt = 1 < \infty$), a Fourier transform analysis of its convergent response is theoretically possible. According to Equation (3.1), the Fourier transform of $\delta(t)$ is thus given by:

$$
\begin{aligned}
F[\delta(t)] = Y(j\omega) &= \int_{-\infty}^{\infty} \delta(t) e^{-j\omega t}\,dt \\
&= \lim_{\theta \to 0} \left[ \int_{-\infty}^{0} 0 \cdot dt + \int_{0}^{\theta} \frac{1}{\theta} e^{-j\omega t}\,dt + \int_{\theta}^{\infty} 0 \cdot dt \right[ \\
&= \lim_{\theta \to 0} \left[ 0 + \int_{0}^{\theta} \frac{1}{\theta} e^{-j\omega t} + 0 \right] \\
&= \lim_{\theta \to 0} \frac{1}{j\omega\theta} \left[ 1 - \left( 1 - j\omega\theta + \frac{(j\omega\theta)^2}{2!} \mp \cdots \right) \right] = 1
\end{aligned}
\tag{3.66}
$$

Noting Equation (3.66), the Fourier transform of the impulse response $x(t)$ is thus given by:

$$X(j\omega) = G(j\omega) \cdot Y(j\omega) = G(j\omega) \cdot 1 \tag{3.67}$$

Consequently, if $X(j\omega)$ is plotted vs. $\omega$, the frequency response $G(j\omega)$ of the system is obtained. $G(s)$ may now be derived from $G(j\omega)$ by exactly the same frequency response analysis as in Section 3.2, employing Bode diagram techniques.

### 3.4.3 Graphical Identification from Impulse Responses

Direct identification from the time behavior of the impulse response can be performed in full analogy to the identification from the time behavior of the step response, as has been described in Section 3.3.3. For this purpose, the impulse response may be integrated to provide the time behavior of the step response.

Alternatively, identification relations analogous to these of Section 3.3.3 may be derived for impulse responses, some of which are discussed below.

**3.4.3-a First order processes** A first order process is given, in a generalized form, by the following transfer function:

$$G(s) = \frac{K}{Ts + 1} \tag{3.68}$$

Consequently, its impulse response is as follows:

$$g(t) = L^{-1}[G(s)] = \frac{K}{T}e^{-t/T} \tag{3.69}$$

and is graphically presented in Figure 3.18; $T$ and $K$ are thus derived from the graphical response such that the initial amplitude is $\frac{K}{T} = \frac{K}{T}e^{-0/T}$, and

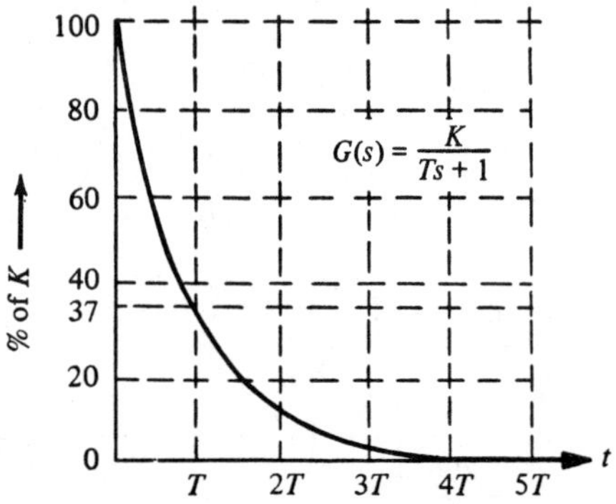


*Figure 3.18* Impulse response of first order system.

the time by which $g(t)$ reaches $0.37 \cdot \frac{K}{T}\left(= \frac{K}{T}e^{-T/T} = \frac{K}{T}e^{-1}\right)$ is $T$. $T$ may also be obtained from continuing the initial slope of $g(t)$ until it reaches zero amplitude, since, according to Equation (3.69):

$$\frac{dg(0)}{dt} = -\frac{K}{T^2} \tag{3.70}$$

and:

$$\frac{K}{T} - \frac{K}{T^2}t = 0 \ @ \ t = T \tag{3.71}$$

In practice, the input to a system is only an approximate impulse. Hence, $g(t)$ never does start at $K/T$. The actual derivation of $K$, $T$ is thus performed as in Figure 3.19, where the maximum slope near (though not *at*) $t = 0$ is extrapolated backwards up to $t = 0$ to yield $K/T$.

**3.4.3-b Impulse responses of periodic second order systems** Impulse responses of second order periodic systems are derived as follows:

$$G(s) = \frac{K}{(s/\omega_0)^2 + 2\xi s/\omega_0 + 1} \qquad \forall 0 < \xi < 1 \tag{3.72}$$

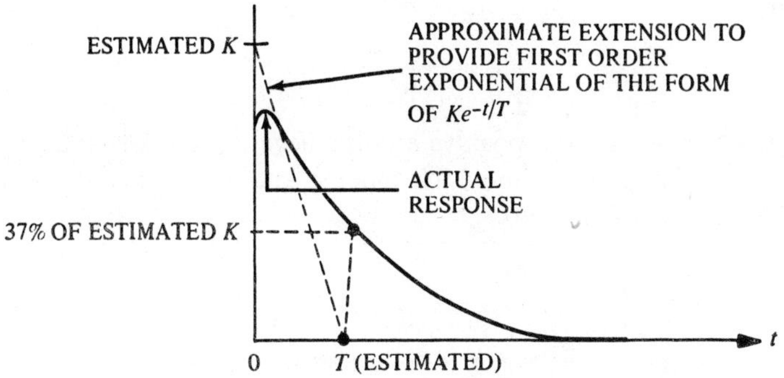


*Figure 3.19* Practical first order impulse response identification.

yielding:

$$g(t) = \frac{K}{\omega_0\sqrt{1-\xi^2}}\, e^{-\xi\omega_0 t} \cdot \sin \omega_0 t\sqrt{1-\xi^2} \tag{3.73}$$

and are described in Figure 3.20. Hence:

$$\omega_0 \triangleq \frac{\omega}{\sqrt{1-\xi^2}}; \qquad \omega \triangleq \frac{2\pi}{\theta} \tag{3.74}$$

$\theta$ being the period of one oscillation and $\xi$ being derived from the following relation:[14]

$$\frac{A(+)}{A(-)} = e^{\pi\xi/\sqrt{1-\xi^2}} \triangleq R \tag{3.75}$$

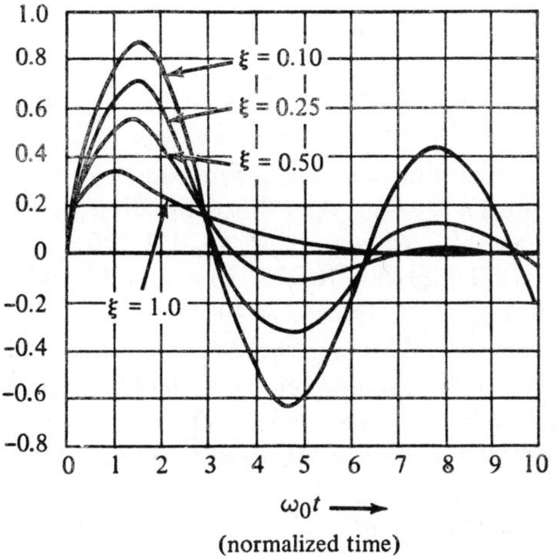


*Figure 3.20* Impulse responses of second order periodic systems.

yielding:

$$\xi = \frac{\ln R}{\sqrt{\pi^2 + (\ln R)^2}} \tag{3.76}$$

where $A(+)$, $A(-)$ are the positive and the negative successive areas of this impulse response, as in Figure 3.21. Once $\xi$ and $\omega_0$ are known, $K$ may be derived from Equation (3.73).

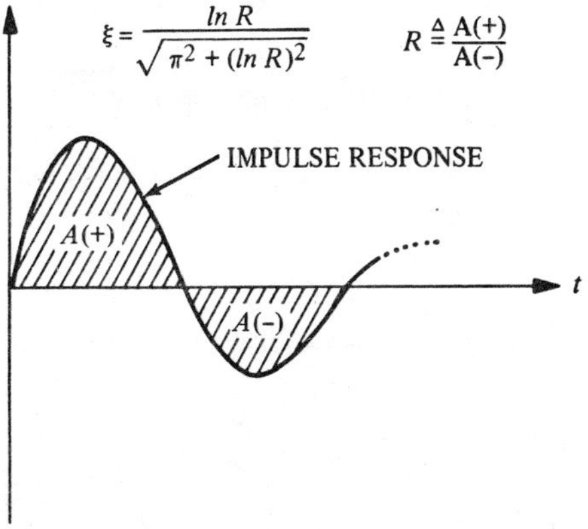


*Figure 3.21* Derivation of $\xi$ from area ratios.

## REFERENCES


1. Miller, K. S. *Engineering Mathematics*, Dover, New York, 1963 (Sections 4.6, 5.1).
2. Papoulis, A. *The Fourier Integral and Its Applications*, McGraw-Hill, New York, 1962.
3. Cooley, J. W., and Tukey, J. W. "An Algorithm for the Machine Calculation of Complex Fourier Series," *Jour. Math. Comput.*, Vol. 19, pp. 297–301, 1965.
4. Singleton, R. C. "Algorithm 338 (Algol Procedures for the Fast Fourier Transform), and: Algorithm 339 (An Algol Procedure for the Fast Fourier Transform with Arbitrary Factors)," *Comm. ACM*, pp. 773–779, 1968.
5. Brigham, E. O., and Morrow, R. E. "The Fast Fourier Transform," *IEEE Spectrum*, Vol. 4, pp. 63–70, December 1967.
6. Nyquist, H. "Regression Theory," *Bell Sys. Jour.*, Vol. 11, pp. 126–147, 1932.
7. Bode, H. W. *Network Analysis and Feedback Amplifier Design*, D. Van Nostrand, (Van Nostrand Reinhold,), New York, 1945.
8. Wilts, C. H. *Principles of Feedback Control*, Addison-Wesley, Reading, Mass., 1960.
9. Churchill, R. V. *Modern Operational Mathematics in Engineering*, McGraw-Hill, New York, 1944.
10. Sokolnikoff, I. S., and Redheffer, R. M. *Mathematics of Physics and Modern Engineering*, McGraw-Hill, New York, 1966.

11. Naslin, P. *Variable Arrangements in Linear and Nonlinear Systems*, Dunod, Paris, 1962.
12. Chaussard, R. "Use of Methods of Transient Analysis and of the Criterion of Naslin for the Regulation of Thermal Power Station Boilers," *Proc. Inst. Mech. Eng.*, Vol. 179 Pt. 3H, pp. 74–81, London, 1965.
13. Strejc, V. "Approximate Determination of the Control Characteristics of an Aperiodic Response Process," *Automatisme*, March 1960.
14. Thaler, G. J., and Pastel, M. P. *Analysis and Design of Nonlinear Feedback Control Systems*, McGraw-Hill, New York, 1967.

## PROBLEMS

**1.** Plot the Bode diagram (modulus and phase) for a system given by

$$G(s) = \frac{4e^{-2s}(s+10)}{s(s^2+0.5s+0.3)(s+1)}$$

**2.** Identify the system whose step response is described in Figure 3.22, in terms of a second order transfer function, using the approach of Section 3.3.3-c.

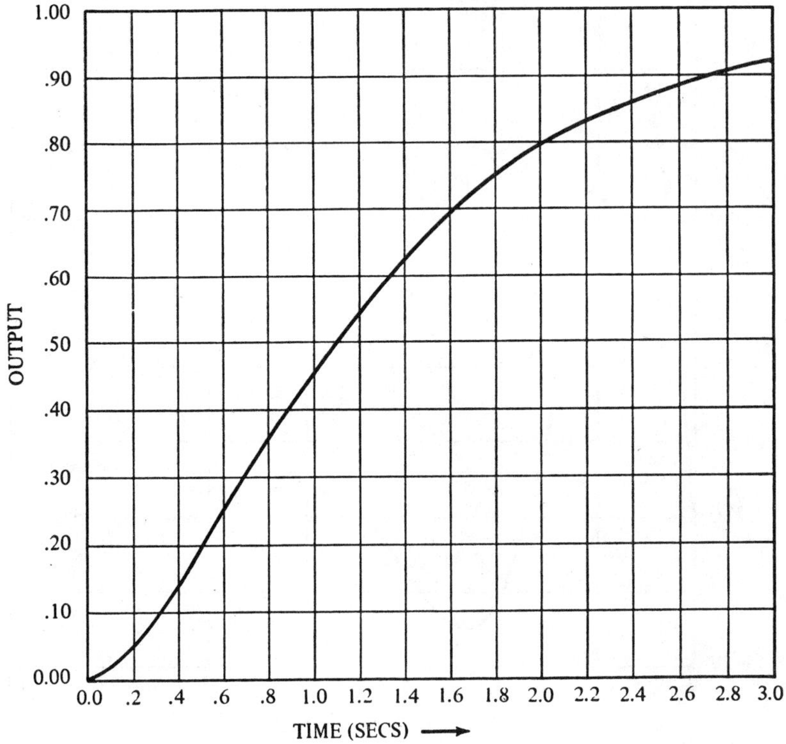


*Figure 3.22* Step response of a second order system.

3. Identify the system whose step response yields an overshoot of 1.35, and whose period is measured (between two crossings of the steady state value) to be of 13 msec. The steady state gain of the response has been measured to be 2.7.
4. Identify a high order linear system whose step response is as in Figure 3.14 and where the following values have been measured:

$$T_a = 24 \text{ msec}$$
$$T_b = 72 \text{ msec}$$
$$T_d = 48 \text{ msec}$$
$$k = 100 \text{ per unit of input}$$
$$\eta = 0.34$$

   You may employ Tables 3.3 and 3.4.
5. Identify the second order system whose impulse response is given in Figure 3.23, through computing the area ratio according to Equation (3.75) and through comparing the response with responses in Figure 3.20.

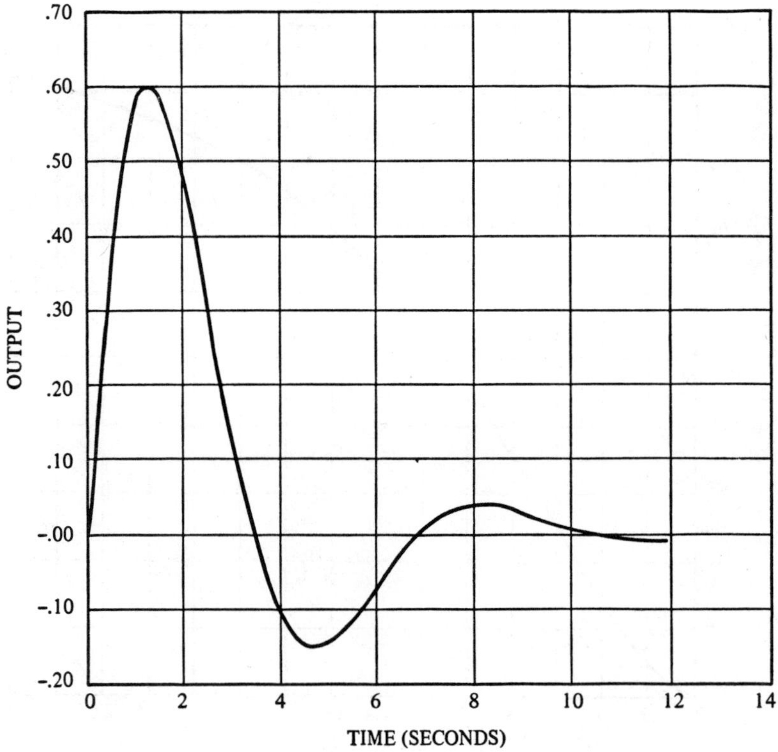


*Figure 3.23* Impulse response of a second order system.

# 4

# CORRELATION FUNCTION TECHNIQUES

The correlation function approach to identifying linear processes facilitates both on-line and off-line identification. It is based on applying a white noise input to the process (namely, an uncorrelated random input having an infinite flat frequency spectrum and zero mean). Although no such input exists in practice, it can be approximated to provide noise whose features satisfy the identification requirements of the correlation function identification approach. If this noise is of a sufficiently low amplitude, it may be superimposed on the normal-operation input to the system without affecting performance, and can therefore be applied on-line. Furthermore, it will be shown below that the normal-operation input usually does not affect the identification procedure.

The identification procedure requires processing of input and output over a wide (theoretically infinite) time range, before identification can be performed. Consequently, the correlation function approach assumes process stationarity (namely, that the process parameters, which are the coefficients of its transfer function or of its state equations, are time-invariant).

## 4.1 CONVOLUTION AND CORRELATION INTEGRALS

The output $x(t)$ of a linear process having an input $y(t)$ is given by the convolution-integral expression as follows:

$$x(t) = \int_{-\infty}^{t} g(t-\tau)y(\tau)\,d\tau = \int_{0}^{\infty} g(\tau)y(t-\tau)\,d\tau \tag{4.1}$$

where $g(t)$ is the impulse response $L^{-1}$ $[G(s)]$ of the system, as has been discussed in Chapter 3 (see Figure 3.1). If $y(t) = 0 \ \forall t < 0$, Equation (4.1) becomes:

$$x(t) = \int_{0}^{t} g(t-\tau)y(\tau)\,d\tau = \int_{0}^{t} g(\tau)y(t-\tau)\,d\tau \tag{4.2}$$

The physical interpretation of equations (4.1), (4.2) may be understood if we consider $y(t)$ to be a sequence of pulses of width $\theta \to 0$ and of amplitude $y(t)$, such that their strength (area) is $\theta \cdot y(t)$, these pulses being applied at $t = 0$, $\theta$, $2\theta$, .... We further consider $x_i(t)$ to denote the response of the system at time $t$ to the $i$'th impulse only (namely, to the impulse applied at $t = (i-1)\theta$. Consequently, $x_1(t_1)$ denotes the response at $t = t_1$, to the first impulse that has been applied at $t = 0$ and whose strength is $\theta \cdot y$ (0), such that:

$$x_1(t_1) = g(t_1) \cdot \theta \cdot y(0) \tag{4.3}$$

$g(t_1)$ being the impulse response at $t_1$ units of time after the application of the respective impulse. Similarly, $x_2(t_1)$ denotes the response at $t = t_1$ to the next impulse (which has been applied at $t = \theta$) and whose strength is $\theta \cdot y(\theta)$, such that:

$$x_2(t_1) = g(t_1 - \theta) \cdot \theta \cdot y(\theta) \tag{4.4}$$

Similarly, the response $x_i$ to the $i$'th impulse, which has been applied at time $t = (i-1)\theta$, is given by:

$$x_i(t_1) = g[t_1 - (i-1)\theta] \cdot \theta \cdot y[(i-1)\theta] \tag{4.5}$$

$g[t_1 - (i-1)\theta]$ being the impulse response at $t_1 - (i-1)\theta$ units of time after the respective impulse has been applied. Since a train of $n$ impulses has been applied from $t = 0$ to $t = t_1$, $n$ being $t_1/\theta$, we may consider $x(t_1)$ as the sum of $n$ responses $x_1(t_1)$; $x_2(t_1)$; ... $x_n(t_1)$, yielding:

$$x(t_1) = \sum_{i=1}^{n} x_i(t_1) = \sum_{i=1}^{n} g[t_1 - (i-1)\theta] \cdot \theta \cdot y[(i-1)\theta] \tag{4.6}$$

At the limit, where $\theta \to d\tau \to 0$ and where $i\theta = \tau$, $x(t_1)$ is therefore given by the convolution-integral expression of Equation (4.2), whose Laplace transform is:

$$X(s) = G(s) \cdot Y(s) \tag{4.7}$$

We now define a cross-correlation function $\phi_{xy}(\theta)$ which describes the summarized product-relations between each value of a signal $x(t)$ at time $t$ and each value of another signal $y(t-\theta)$ at another time $(t-\theta)$, where $t$ may vary from $-T$ to $T$, as follows:

$$\phi_{xy}(\theta) \triangleq \lim_{T\to\infty} \frac{1}{2T} \cdot \int_{-T}^{T} x(t) \cdot y(t-\theta)\, dt \tag{4.8}$$

We similarly define an autocorrelation function $\phi_{yy}(\theta)$ as the summarized product-relations between each value of a signal $y(t)$ and each value of the same signal at another time $(t-\theta)$, where $t$ may vary from $-T$ to $T$, as follows:

$$\phi_{yy}(\theta) \triangleq \lim_{T\to\infty} \frac{1}{2T} \cdot \int_{-T}^{T} y(t)y(t-\theta)\, dt \tag{4.9}$$

### 4.1.1 Cross-Correlation and Impulse Responses

Substituting $x(t)$ from Equation (4.1) into (4.8), we derive:

$$\phi_{xy}(\theta) = \lim_{T\to\infty} \frac{1}{2T} \int_{-T}^{T} \left[ y(t-\theta) \int_{0}^{\infty} g(\tau) \cdot y(t-\tau)\, d\tau \right] dt \tag{4.10}$$

Reversing the order of integration, as is possible since $t$ and $\theta$ are independent of $\tau$, Equation (4.10) becomes:

$$\phi_{xy}(\theta) = \int_{0}^{\infty} g(\tau) \cdot \left[ \lim_{T\to\infty} \frac{1}{2T} \int_{-T}^{T} y(t-\theta) \cdot y(t-\tau)\, dt \right] d\tau \tag{4.11}$$

However, the expression in the square brackets of Equation (4.11) may be written as:

$$\lim_{T\to\infty} \frac{1}{2T} \int_{-T}^{T} y(t-\theta) \cdot y(t-\tau)\, dt$$

$$= \lim_{T\to\infty} \frac{1}{2T} \int_{-T}^{T} y(t') \cdot y(t'-\theta')\, dt' = \phi_{yy}(\theta') = \phi_{yy}(\theta-\tau) \tag{4.12}$$

where:

$$t' \triangleq t - \tau \tag{4.13-a}$$

$$\theta' \triangleq \theta - \tau \tag{4.13-b}$$

$\phi_{yy}(\theta-\tau)$ being the autocorrelation function of the input $y$. Hence, Equation (4.11) becomes:

$$\phi_{xy}(\theta) = \int_{0}^{\infty} g(\tau) \cdot \phi_{yy}(\theta-\tau)\, d\tau \tag{4.14}$$

The cross-correlation function of Equation (4.14) thus describes, in analogy to Equation (4.1), the hypothetical response of a system whose impulse response is $g(t)$ but whose input is $\phi_{yy}(t)$ rather than $y(t)$. We may now consider a white-noise input function $y(t)$, whose autocorrelation integral is (due to its uncorrelated randomness properties) a delta function, namely:

$$\phi_{yy}(\theta) = \lim_{T\to\infty} \frac{1}{2T} \int_{-T}^{T} y(t) \cdot y(t-\theta)\, dt = \delta(\theta) \tag{4.15}$$

The cross-correlation function $\phi_{xy}(\theta)$ of the system with the latter white noise input thus becomes, in full analogy to Equation (4.1):

$$\phi_{xy}(\theta) = \int_{0}^{\infty} g(\tau) \cdot \delta(\theta - \tau)\, d\tau = g(\theta) \tag{4.16}$$

$g(\theta)$ being the impulse response of that system. Furthermore, since $y(\theta) = 0$ $\forall \theta < 0$, the second integral in Equation (4.10) may go from 0 to $\theta$. Hence Equation (4.16) becomes:

$$\phi_{xy}(\theta) = \int_{0}^{\theta} g(\tau) \cdot \delta(\theta - \tau)\, d\tau = g(\theta) \tag{4.17}$$

$\phi_{xy}(\theta)$ describing the system's response $g(t)$ to an impulse at $t = \theta$.

### 4.1.2 Identification by White Noise Inputs

In practice, ideal white noise inputs $y(t)$ cannot be realized, since they were shown to imply uncorrelated randomness with an infinite frequency spectrum. However, the autocorrelation integral may approximate a delta function if $y(t)$ is random noise with a flat frequency spectrum that is much wider than that of the system, or if it is a pseudo-random binary sequence of periodic nature, as discussed in the next section (Section 4.2).

To facilitate on-line identification, the random or pseudo-random input (whose autocorrelation integral approximates a delta function), must be superimposed on the normal-operation input to the system. Hence, the input to system becomes $Y(t) = R(t) + y(t)$ and the actual output $x(t)$ is a response to $Y(t)$ and not to $y(t)$. Cross-correlation for identification purposes is, however, performed between the output $x(t)$ and the random or pseudo-random part $y(t)$ of the total input, as is illustrated in Figure 4.1. Since we are concerned with a linear system, we may define:

$$x(t) \triangleq x_R(t) + x_y(t) \tag{4.18}$$

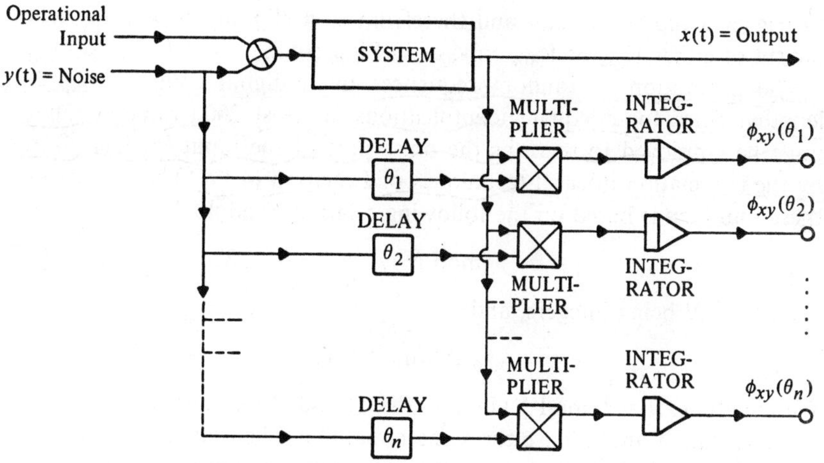


*Figure 4.1* Cross-correlation in system with noise superimposed on input.

$x_R(t)$ and $x_y(t)$ being the part of the output due to the operational (nonrandom) part $R(t)$ and to the random part $y(t)$ of the input, respectively.

Substituting for $x(t)$ from Equation (4.18) into (4.8) we thus derive:

$$\phi_{xy}(\theta) = \lim_{T\to\infty} \frac{1}{2T} \left[ \int_{-T}^{T} x_R(t) \cdot y(t-\theta)\, dt + \int_{-T}^{T} x_y(t) \cdot y(t-\theta)\, dt \right] \quad (4.19)$$

where, according to the derivation of equations (4.9) to (4.16), only the second term in the square brackets of Equation (4.19) is equal to $g(\theta)$. However, the operational input $R(t)$ is usually nonrandom and of a narrow frequency range, whereas $y(t)$ is random of a wide and flat frequency spectrum. Consequently, $R(t)$ and $y(t)$ are hardly correlated, and so are also $x_R(t)$ and $y(t)$. The first term in the square brackets of Equation (4.19) is therefore negligible and the cross-correlation integral $\phi_{xy}(\theta)$ between $y$ and $x$ yields $g(\theta)$, even if $y(t)$ is superimposed on $R(t)$. The latter result permits on-line identification as long as the amplitude of $y(t)$ is low enough compared with $R(t)$, such that $y(t)$ does not affect normal performance.

## 4.2 GENERATION OF RANDOM AND PSEUDO-RANDOM SEQUENCES

### 4.2.1 Random Number Generators

Generation of white noise may be performed by employing a noise source such as a radioactive sample which excites a Geiger counter. Binary white noise may subsequently be obtained if the output of the Geiger tube is fed to trigger a flip-flop circuit and therefrom to a clipping circuit, to yield an output of either $V_{max}$ or $V_{min}$ only, as in Figure 4.2.

The generation of random sequences by a digital computer is rather lengthy, since for adequate identifications, at least 2000 random numbers must be employed to serve as the noise part of the input for identification by the correlation integral techniques of Equation (4.19). The generation of these numbers is based on the following relation, modulo $N$:

$$y_{i+1} \equiv a \cdot y_i (\text{mod } N); \qquad i = 0, 1, 2 \ldots \tag{4.20}$$

$y_i$, $a$, and $N$ being integers, and:

$$y_0 \not\equiv 0(\text{mod } N) \tag{4.21}$$

We note that: $A \equiv B(\text{mod } N)$ implies that $A$ and $B$ are congruent modulo $N$, namely, that $A$ and $B$ have the same remainder when divided by $N$. Hence, for an initial choice of $y_0$, the random numbers $y_i$ are the products of the multiplication according to Equation (4.20), each product being reduced modulo $N$ (i.e., to its remainder after dividing it by $N$). Equation (4.20) implies that the resulting random numbers are distributed between 0 and $N$. Usually $N$ is chosen as $b^k$, $b$ being the base of the computer word (10 in decimal machines and 2 in binary machines), and $k$ being an integer; $y_0$ is conveniently chosen as 1, whereas $a$ should always be large. An often recommended value for $a$ is $7^9$ in decimal machines.[1] The sequence generated according to Equation (4.20) is, in fact, periodic. However, for a convenient choice of $a$, $N$, and $k$, the period may be very long (of $5 \cdot 10^7$ numbers for $a = 7^9$, $N = 10^{10}$).

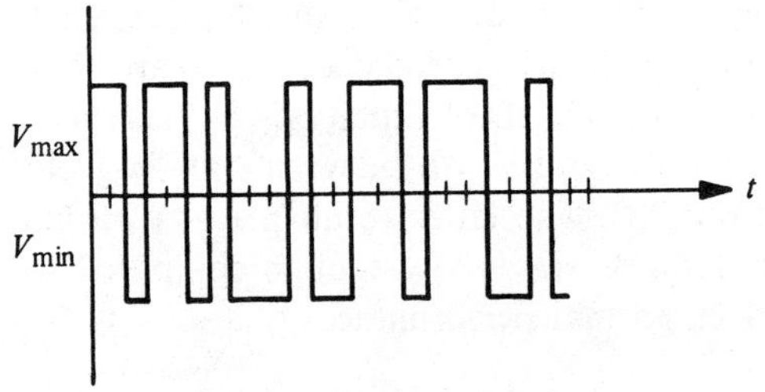


*Figure 4.2* Binary noise signal.

### 4.2.2 Generation of pseudo-random Binary Sequences

Pseudo-random binary sequences (PRBNS) are probably the most convenient inputs for purposes of identification by correlation integral techniques. These sequences are of periodic nature, their periods being relatively short, and yet their autocorrelation integral provides a satisfactory approximation of a delta function. Due to their periodic character, they require very limited computer storage and computer time for their generation, as compared with random sequences of similar length. Furthermore, their autocorrelation integral yields a better approximation to a delta function than with random sequences of similar length (say a sequence of 150 elements produced by a pseudo-random code having a 15-element cycle, compared with a random sequence of an infinite cycle length). Consequently, the resulting identification accomplished when using PRBNS is more accurate (see Figure 4.3).

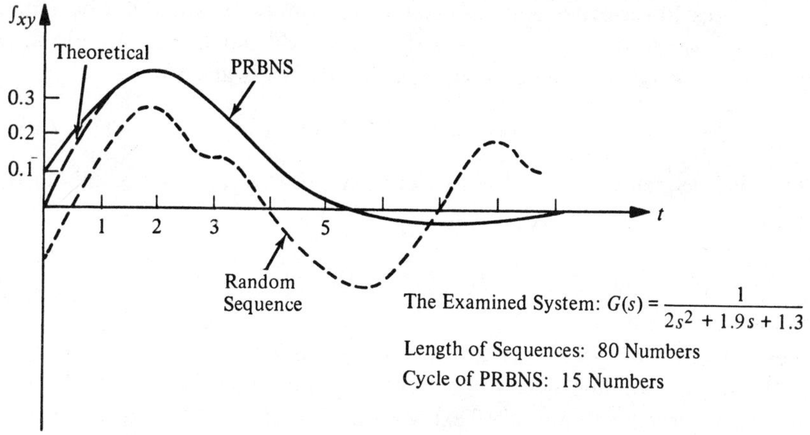


*Figure 4.3* Comparison of identification results based on random and on PRBN input sequences of equal lengths.

**4.2.2-a Maximum-length pseudo-random sequences** Maximum-length null-sequences are binary sequences with pseudo-random properties of a near-delta-function autocorrelation integral, and may therefore be employed as noise inputs in correlation integral identification procedures. These sequences are easily generated with shift-registers, or by using a simple digital algorithm.

The maximum-length null sequences[2] satisfy a linear difference-equation (modulo 2), as follows:

$$D^m x \oplus D^{m-1} x \oplus \cdots Dx \oplus x \equiv Y \tag{4.22}$$

$D^m$ denoting a delay of $m$ intervals, such that $D^m x_i = x_{i-m}$, $i$ being the sampling instance, and $\oplus$ denoting a modulo 2 addition (such that: $0 \oplus 0 \equiv 0$; $0 \oplus 1 \equiv 1 \oplus 0 \equiv 1$; $1 \oplus 1 \equiv 0$, and therefore, $(D \oplus D)x \equiv 0\ \forall x$).

Equation (4.22) may be rewritten as:

$$(D^m \oplus D^{m-1} \oplus \cdots \oplus D \oplus I)x \equiv Y \tag{4.23}$$

$I$ being the identity operator. A delay-sequence $\{x_i\}$ of order $m$ as in Equation (4.22) with $Y \equiv 0$, is called a *null-sequence*. The solutions satisfying a null-sequence are of a periodic nature. The maximum number of elements in a null-sequence of order $m$ is $2^m - 1$, and the resulting sequence is called a *maximum-length null-sequence* (MLNS).

A polynomial equation of the form:

$$(D^m \oplus \cdots + D \oplus I)x \equiv 0 \tag{4.24}$$

that yields an MLNS, must be irreducible (i.e., it should not be a product of two or more lower-order polynomials). Furthermore, it should not be a factor modulo 2 of $D^n \oplus 1$ @ $n < 2^m - 1$ (i.e., it should not divide modulo 2, the expression $D^m \oplus 1$). Hence, for $m = 5$, the MLNS is given by:

$$(D^5 \oplus D^3 \oplus I)x \equiv 0 \tag{4.25}$$

which is a sequence of $2^5 - 1 = 31$ elements. However, a polynomial of order 5, such as:

$$(D^5 \oplus D^4 \oplus D^3 \oplus D^2 \oplus I)x \equiv 0 \equiv \frac{D^6 \oplus I}{D \oplus I} \tag{4.26}$$

does not yield MLNS sequences since it divides $D^6 \oplus I$.

MLNS polynomials up to order 11 are given in Table 4.1.[3] (Note that since we are concerned with modulo 2 expressions, Equation (4.25) may be rewritten as: $(D^5 \oplus D^3)x = x$.) A shift-register generator of an MLNS is shown in Figure 4.4 for $m = 7$, where, according to Table 4.1, the outputs of the fourth and seventh delay element are added (modulo 2) to yield $x$. Hence, the latter outputs are to be fed back into the first stage of the shift-register. The initial logic values in the $m$ stages of the shift cannot all be zero. Otherwise, the shift-register will remain stuck with zeros only.

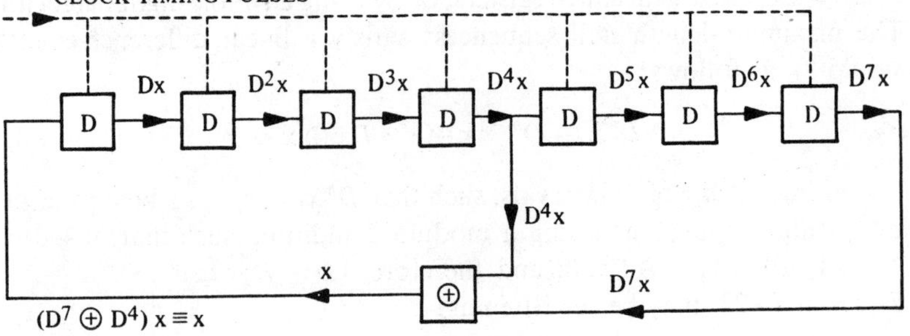


*Figure 4.4* Seven-stage shift-register for generating MLNS.

TABLE 4.1

| $n$ | *MLNS polynomial* |
|---|---|
| 2 | $(D^2 \oplus D)x \equiv x$ |
| 3 | $(D^3 \oplus D)x \equiv x$ |
| 4 | $(D^4 \oplus D^3)x \equiv x$ |
| 5 | $(D^5 \oplus D^3)x \equiv x$ |
| 6 | $(D^6 \oplus D^5)x \equiv x$ |
| 7 | $(D^7 \oplus D^4)x \equiv x$ |
| 8 | $(D^8 \oplus D^4 \oplus D^3 \oplus D^2)x \equiv x$ |
| 9 | $(D^9 \oplus D^5)x \equiv x$ |
| 10 | $(D^{10} \oplus D^7)x \equiv x$ |
| 11 | $(D^{11} \oplus D^9)x \equiv x$ |

The MLNS code is a sequence of 0's and 1's, whose average is, for $N = 2^m - 1$, approximately $N/2$. The latter average is certainly not a random property and yields an autocorrelation integral that is different from an impulse in its average (for example, consider the MLNS of period 15: 111100010011010). Consequently, a preferable MLNS is that whose elements are 1, − 1, instead of 1, 0, yielding an autocorrelation integral as in Figure 4.5. The latter sequence is termed the *MLNSN* (MLNS-Negative) sequence.

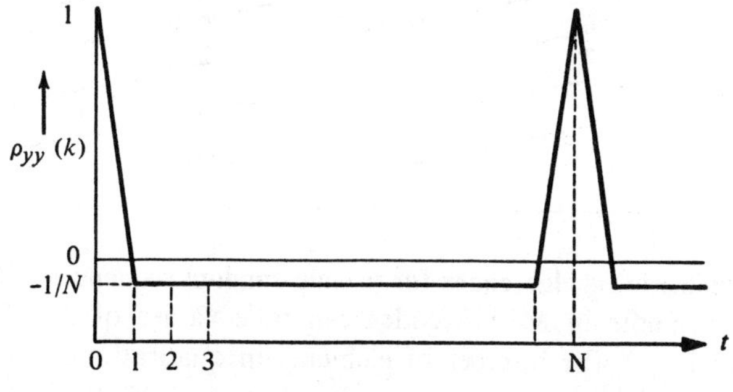


*Figure 4.5* Autocorrelation function of MLNSN.

EXAMPLE 4.1

To illustrate the generation of an MLNS sequence, we consider a three-stage shift-register. Initially, all its stages are at logic state 1. For obtaining an MLNS sequence, feedback is taken from the first and the third stage of the register to the logic modulo-2 adder, according to Table 4.1. Consequently, the adder output will initially be $x(1) \equiv 1 \oplus 1 \equiv 0$. The sequence generated at the adder output and at the various stages may thus be tabulated as shown in Table 4.2. In the table $Y_1$ at interval $i + 1$ is in the state of $X$ at interval $i$, namely, $Y_1 \equiv DX$. Similarly $Y_2$ at interval $i + 1$ is $Y_1$ at interval $i$ and $Y_3$ at $i + 1$ is $Y_2$ at $i$. We observe that all states at the eighth interval ($8 = 2^3$, 3 being the number of stages of the shift-register) are identical to the first (initial) interval ($i = 1$). Hence, the present shift-register is shown to generate a sequence of $7 = 2^3 - 1$ elements given by: 0, 1, 0, 0, 1, 1, 1.

An alternative pseudo-random sequence with an average that is even closer to zero than that of the MLNSN is the inverse-repeat MLNSN, where the sign of every other element of the MLNSN is inverted. Since the period of the MLNSN is odd, the *inverse-repeat MLNSN* has a period of $2N$ (i.e., twice that of the MLNSN). The resulting autocorrelation function is as in Figure 4.6.

**TABLE 4.2**

| $i =$ *Timing Interval* | *Adder output* $X \equiv Y_1 + Y_3$ | *Stage 1* $Y_1 \equiv DX$ | *Stage 2* $Y_2 \equiv DY_1$ | *Stage 3* $Y_3 \equiv DY_2$ |
|---|---|---|---|---|
| 1 | 0 | 1 | 1 | 1 |
| 2 | 1 | 0 | 1 | 1 |
| 3 | 0 | 1 | 0 | 1 |
| 4 | 0 | 0 | 1 | 0 |
| 5 | 1 | 0 | 0 | 1 |
| 6 | 1 | 1 | 0 | 0 |
| 7 | 1 | 1 | 1 | 0 |
| 8 | 0 | 1 | 1 | 1 |

**4.2.2-b Quadratic-residue codes for pseudo-random sequences** Whereas the number of elements in MLNS codes can take values of $2^i - 1$ only (say, 3, 7, 15, 31, 63, ...), the number of elements in quadratic-residue sequences can take values that are much closer together (3, 7, 11, 19, 23, ...). Consequently, sequences of intermediate length between two possible lengths of MLNS may be chosen. The number of elements of quadratic-residue pseudo-random sequences is given by:

$$N = 4K - 1; \qquad K = \text{integer}, \qquad N = \text{prime number} \tag{4.27}$$

The quadratic-residue sequences (see Table 4.3) are generated as follows:[3] The element of the sequence whose serial number $q$ is equal to any $q^2 \bmod N$ is given the value of $+1$, whereas all other elements are given the value of $-1$.

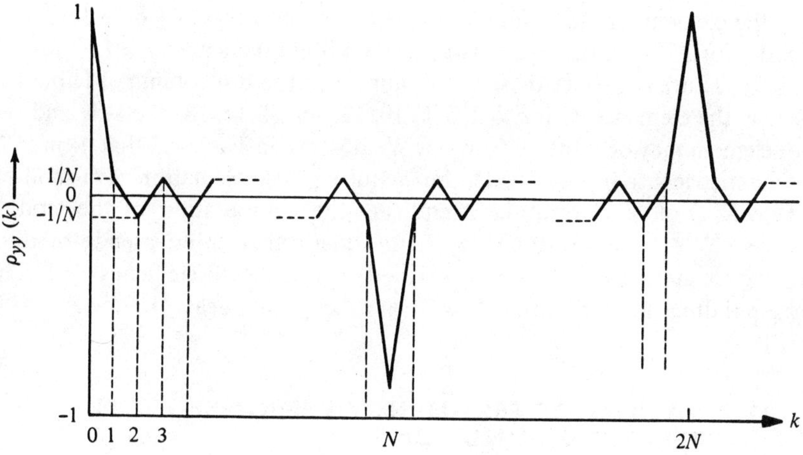


*Figure 4.6* Autocorrelation function for inverse-repeat MLNSN.

**TABLE 4.3 Quadratic Residue Sequences: $N = 19$**

| $q$ | $q^2$ | *Closest Multiple of N, below $q^2$* | $q^2$ *modulo N* |
|---|---|---|---|
| 1 | 1 | 0 | 1 |
| 2 | 4 | 0 | 4 |
| 3 | 9 | 0 | 9 |
| 4 | 16 | 0 | 16 |
| 5 | 25 | 19 | 6 |
| 6 | 36 | 19 | 17 |
| 7 | 49 | 38 | 11 |
| 8 | 64 | 57 | 7 |
| 9 | 81 | 76 | 5 |
| 10 | 100 | 95 | 5 |
| 11 | 121 | 114 | 7 |
| 12 | 144 | 133 | 11 |
| 13 | 169 | 152 | 17 |
| 14 | 196 | 190 | 6 |
| 15 | 225 | 209 | 16 |
| 16 | 256 | 247 | 9 |
| 17 | 289 | 285 | 4 |
| 18 | 324 | 323 | 1 |

Only the element whose serial number is $N$ may be either $+1$ or $-1$. Consequently, for $N = 19$, the elements whose serial numbers are: $q = 1, 4, 5, 6, 7, 9, 11, 16, 17$ are $+1$, since these values appear in the last column of Table 4.1, whereas the elements with $q = 2, 3, 8, 10, 12, 13, 14, 15, 18$, are $-1$, and the 19th element may be either $+1$ or $-1$. We observe in Table 4.3 that $q^2 \bmod N$ are symmetrical to $q = \frac{1}{2}(N-1)$, thus requiring the calculation of ($1 \bmod N$) to ($\frac{1}{2}(N-1) \bmod N$) only, i.e., requiring the computation of the mod $N$ of only $\frac{1}{2}(N-1)$ terms. For $N = 7$, the quadratic-residue pseudo-random sequence is given by: $1, 1, -1, 1, -1, -1, 1$, if the $N$'th element is $+1$. The corresponding MLNSN for $N = 7$ is exactly identical ($1, 1, -1, 1, -1, -1, 1$).

## 4.3 DERIVATION OF FREQUENCY RESPONSE FROM CORRELATION FUNCTIONS

The correlation-integral identification technique of the present chapter yields the impulse response $g(t)$ of the system that is being identified, thus providing impulse response identification. For obtaining the transfer function $G(s)$ of the system or its state equations coefficients, we must employ the methods discussed in Section 3.4 that deal with deriving $G(s)$ from a recording of $g(t)$. We note that the graphical description $g(t)$ may be obtained if $g(\theta)$ of Equation (4.15) is computed for an appropriate number of values of $\theta$.

Observing the cross-correlation integral of Equation (4.14), we again consider this integral as a convolution integral where:

$$\phi_{xy}(\theta) \triangleq \xi(\theta) \tag{4.28-a}$$

and:

$$\phi_{yy}(\theta) \triangleq \eta(\theta) \tag{4.28-b}$$

yielding:

$$\xi(\theta) = \int_0^\infty g(\tau) \cdot \eta(\theta - \tau)\, d\tau \tag{4.29}$$

The Laplace and Fourier transforms of a convolution integral of the form of Equation (4.29) are known to be given by:[4]

$$\xi(s) = G(s) \cdot \eta(s) \tag{4.30-a}$$

$$\xi(j\omega) = G(j\omega) \cdot \eta(j\omega) \tag{4.30-b}$$

Hence, $G(j\omega)$ is obtained according to:

$$G(j\omega) = \xi(j\omega)/\eta(j\omega) \tag{4.31}$$

where:

$$\xi(j\omega) \triangleq F[\phi_{xy}(\theta)] = \Phi_{xy}(j\omega) \tag{4.32}$$

$$\eta(j\omega) \triangleq F[\phi_{yy}(\theta)] = \Phi_{yy}(j\omega) \tag{4.33}$$

the two latter Fourier transforms being computable by Fast Fourier Transforms, as discussed in Section 3.1.1. Since a white-noise input $y(t)$, or a pseudo-random input, satisfies:

$$\phi_{yy}(\theta) \cong \delta(\theta) \tag{4.34}$$

we obtain:

$$\Phi_{yy}(j\omega) \cong 1 \tag{4.35}$$

yielding:

$$G(j\omega) = \xi(j\omega)/1 = \xi(j\omega) \tag{4.36}$$

## 4.4 COMPUTATIONAL CONSIDERATIONS

For identifying $g(\theta)$, we must compute the cross-correlation function of Equation (4.8), which becomes, in discrete form:

$$\phi_{xy}(k) = \frac{1}{(2M+1)} \sum_{i=-M}^{M} x_i \cdot y_{i-k} \quad @ \quad \begin{aligned} k &= 0, 1, \dots (M-1) \\ k\,\Delta t &\triangleq \theta \\ M\,\Delta t &\triangleq T \end{aligned} \tag{4.37}$$

However, since $x(t) = 0 \;\; \forall t \leq 0$, $\phi_{xy}$ becomes:

$$\phi_{xy}(k) = \frac{1}{(M-k)} \sum_{i=1}^{M-k} x_{i+k}\, y_i \tag{4.38}$$

If $G(j\omega)$ is derived from Equation (4.29), we must also compute $\phi_{yy}(k)$, which is given by:

$$\phi_{yy}(k) = \frac{1}{(M-k)} \sum_{i=1}^{M-k} y_i\, y_{i+k} \quad @ \quad k = 0, 1, \dots (M-1) \tag{4.39}$$

and therefrom derive the Fourier transforms $\Phi_{xy}(j\omega)$ of $\phi_{xy}(k)$ and $\Phi_{yy}(j\omega)$ of $\phi_{yy}(k)$, as in Equation (3.8) of Section 3.1.1. A much faster derivation of $\Phi_{xy}(j\omega)$, $\Phi_{yy}(j\omega)$ and thus of $G(j\omega)$ is possible when the Fourier transforms $X(j\omega)$ of $x(t)$ and $Y(j\omega)$ of $y(t)$ are first computed, and where no computation of $\phi_{xy}(k)$, $\phi_{yy}(k)$ is required at all. The latter derivation which also reduces the round-off errors, is based on:

$$\Phi_{xy}(j\omega) = X(j\omega)Y^*(j\omega); \qquad Y^* = \text{conjugate of } Y \tag{4.40}$$

$$\Phi_{yy}(j\omega) = Y(j\omega)Y^*(j\omega) \tag{4.41}$$

where $X(j\omega)$ and $Y(j\omega)$ are derived by applying a Fast Fourier Transform procedure to $x(t)$, $y(t)$, as discussed in Section 3.1.1. Even when $\phi_{xy}(k)$, $\phi_{yy}(k)$ are required in themselves, their calculation could be performed by first computing the Fast Fourier Transforms of equations (4.40) and (4.41) and subsequently applying an inverse Fast Fourier Transform to these. The latter approach would again result in reduced round-off errors and in speeding up the computation by a factor of several hundreds compared with a derivation of $\phi_{xy}(k)$, $\phi_{yy}(k)$ according to Equations (4.38), (4.39), if long records of $x(t)$, $y(t)$ are considered.

Equations (4.40) and (4.41) are derived from applying a Fourier transform to $\phi_{xy}(\theta)$ of Equation (4.8), as follows:

$$\begin{aligned}\Phi_{xy}(j\omega) &= F[\phi_{xy}(\theta)] = \int_{-\infty}^{\infty} \phi_{xy}(\theta) \cdot e^{-j\omega\theta}\, d\theta \\ &= \int_{-\infty}^{\infty} \left[\int_{-\infty}^{\infty} x(t)y(t-\theta)\, dt\right] e^{-j\omega\theta}\, d\theta \\ &= \int_{-\infty}^{\infty} x(t)\left[\int_{-\infty}^{\infty} y(t-\theta)e^{-j\omega\theta}\, d\theta\right] dt\end{aligned} \tag{4.42}$$

Substituting:

$$t' \triangleq t - \theta \tag{4.43}$$

we obtain (after change of limits and of sign of inner integral):

$$\begin{aligned}\Phi_{xy}(j\omega) &= \int_{-\infty}^{\infty} x(t)\left[\int_{-\infty}^{\infty} y(t')e^{-j\omega(t-t')}\, dt'\right] dt \\ &= \int_{-\infty}^{\infty} x(t)e^{-j\omega t}\left[\int_{-\infty}^{\infty} y(t')e^{j\omega t'}\, dt'\right] dt\end{aligned} \tag{4.44}$$

We observe that the term in the last square brackets of Equation (4.44) is $Y^*(j\omega)$. Consequently, Equation (4.40) is satisfied.

Substitution of $\Phi_{xy}(j\omega)$, $\Phi_{yy}(j\omega)$ from equations (4.40) and (4.41) into Equation (4.31) yields:

$$G(j\omega) = \frac{X(j\omega) \cdot Y^*(j\omega)}{Y(j\omega) \cdot Y^*(j\omega)} = \frac{X(j\omega)}{Y(j\omega)} \tag{4.45}$$

Hence, $G(j\omega)$ could have been derived by only computing $X(j\omega)$, $Y(j\omega)$ and dividing these according to Equation (4.45). However, the latter division is rather inconvenient, compared with the computation of $\Phi_{xy}(j\omega)$. Therefore, and noting that $\Phi_{yy}(j\omega) = 1$ for white-noise inputs $y(t)$, as in Equation (4.35), a derivation of $G(j\omega)$ from Equation (4.36) where division is avoided, is considerably faster. We further note from comparing Equation (4.41) with Equation (4.35) that:

$$|Y(j\omega)| = \sqrt{\Phi_{yy}(j\omega)} = 1 \tag{4.46}$$

Substituting the latter result into Equation (4.45) implies that through dividing $X(j\omega)/Y(j\omega)$ the phase information is lost.

For an input sequence of $N$ elements with length $N\Delta t$, the interval $\Delta t$ determines the highest frequency that can be observed in the resulting frequency response if $G(j\omega)$ is computed according to Equation (4.31) or (4.36).

The limits of $i$ and $k$ of equations (4.38) and (4.39) yield that the length $N$ of the input sequence should be at least $2M$, $M\Delta t$ being the range of interest in the record of $g(t)$. In case of inverse-repeat MLNS codes, as described in Section 4.2.2-a, whose period is of $2N$ elements, it is required that $N \geq 2M$, $N$ being one-half of the $2N$ period of inverse-repeat MLNS inputs, to avoid effects of the second peaks in the autocorrelation functions of the noise sequences, as in Figures 4.5 and 4.6.

## REFERENCES


1. Scheid, F. *Numerical Analysis*, Schaum-McGraw-Hill, New York, 1968.
2. Briggs, P. A. N., Hammond, P. H., Hughes, M. T. G., and Plumb, G. O. "Correlation Analysis of Process Dynamics Using Pseudo-Random Binary Test Perturbation," *Proc. Inst. Mech. Eng.*, Vol. 179, Pt. 3H, pp. 37–51, London, 1965.
3. Godfrey, K. R. "The Theory of the Correlation Method of Dynamic Analysis and its Application to Industrial Processes and Nuclear Power Plant," *Measurement and Control*, Vol. 2, pp. T65–T72, May 1969.
4. Miller, K. S. *Engineering Mathematics*, Dover, New York, 1963 (Chapter 5).


## PROBLEMS

**1.** Generate a sequence of numbers according to Equation (4.20) when $a = 13$; $y_0 = 1$; $N = 100$. Notice the periodicity of the sequence.

**2.** Compute the autocorrelation function of the sequence of Problem 1 according to Equation (4.39) and plot it against the subscript of $y$. You may add elements to the sequence such that the number of elements considered for $\phi_{yy}(k)$ is the same for all $k$, and compare the solution with the case where the number of elements considered decreases with $k$ when $M$ of Equation (4.39) is fixed.

3. Generate an MLNS sequence of 31 elements (using a five-stage shift-register).
4. Compute the autocorrelation function $\psi_{xx}(k)$ for an MLNSN sequence of 15 elements, and show that for an MLNSN of any length $\psi_{xx}(0) = 1$.
5. Generate a quadratic residue sequence with $N = 11$.
6. Write a computer program where a quadratic residue sequence of $N = 19$ is fed to a linear system given by $G(s) = \dfrac{0.8s + 1}{s^2 + s + 0.8}$. Subsequently, compute the output of the system, cross-correlate between input and output and compare the latter cross-correlation with the analytical $g(t)$. Choose the interval between the noise bits as 0.01. Use the Fast Fourier Transform in this problem.
7. Repeat Problem 6 when the noise is superimposed on an input function of $25 \cdot e^{-t} \cdot \sin t$. Note that for autocorrelation purposes you consider only the noise input. Use the Fast Fourier Transform in this problem.
8. Consider the inputs and outputs of Problem 6 and derive $G(j\omega)$ according to Equation (4.45), using a Fast Fourier Transform procedure. Compare the latter $G(j\omega)$ with that obtained from an analytical Bode diagram.

# 5

# IDENTIFICATION BY REGRESSION TECHNIQUES

Regression analysis is by now a classical statistical tool.[1] Due to the wide range of applicability of regression techniques to process identification, it has been naturally adopted in systems engineering, though its applications to multi-variable on-line identification[2-7] became accepted only with the advancement and availability of fast digital computers.

Identification techniques based on least-squares regression procedures are applicable to both linear and nonlinear processes, and facilitate identification with respect to several inputs simultaneously. Furthermore, the regression techniques are based on input/output measurements that may be obtained during normal process operation, thus facilitating on-line identification as long as a transient appears in the measurements.

Stationarity or quasi-stationarity of the identified process parameters is assumed over the period where measurements are collected for regression identification, this period being at least equal to $mT$, $T$ being the sampling interval and $m$ being the number of parameters to be identified (see sections 5.1 and 5.2 below). If identification of $m$ coefficients is required in each of $n$ simultaneous equations of the form:

$$x_j = a_{0j} + a_{1j}u_1 + a_{2j}u_2 + \cdots + a_{mj}u_m \; (j = 1, 2, \ldots n) \tag{5.1}$$

and if the same $u_i$ ($i = 1, 2, \ldots m$) appear in all $n$ equations, all $a_{ij}$ $\forall i, j$ may be identified over $m + 1$ measurement instances. Hence, the coefficients of the above $n$ equations may be identified simultaneously, as is shown in Section 5.3 below.

We noted above that the regression techniques of the present chapter require the accumulation of non-steady state input/output data over at least $m + 1$ sampling intervals before regression can be performed. Hence, at the $i$'th time interval, the regression-identification is based on the data from the ($i$-$m$-$p$)'th interval ($p \geq 0$) up to the $i$'th interval. Similarly, at the $(i + 1)$'th interval, it is based on the data from the ($i$-$m$-$p$ + 1)'th interval to the $(i + 1)$'th interval, thus facilitating detection of nonstationarities.

The derivation of the regression parameters is shown below to require matrix inversion, if more than one parameter requires identification. A sequential formulation of the regression techniques of the present chapter, which avoids matrix inversion, is discussed in Chapter 6. Regression techniques are further considered in the present text in Chapter 8, dealing with quasi-linearization methods of identification; in Chapter 10, dealing with predictive identification; and in Chapter 12, concerning the identification of predictor parameters.

## 5.1 THE SINGLE-OUTPUT STATIC PROBLEM

Consider a linear static system, as in Figure 5.1, having $m$ inputs $U_1 \cdots U_m$ and one output $X$. This system may be described by the linear equation:

$$X = a_0 + a_1 U_1 + a_2 U_2 + \cdots a_m U_m \tag{5.2}$$

Taking $r$ sets of measurements of $X$, $U_j$ ($j = 0, 1, 2, \ldots m$), we may derive $a_i$ as follows: First, the $r$ sets of measurement of $X$ and of $U_j$ are stored. Subsequently, these $r$ sets of measurement are employed to compute $\bar{X}$ and $\bar{U}$, $\bar{X}$ being the average of $X$ and $\bar{U}$ being the average of $U$, over the above $r$ sets of measurement. Defining:

$$x \triangleq X - \bar{X} \tag{5.3}$$

$$u \triangleq U - \bar{U} \tag{5.4}$$

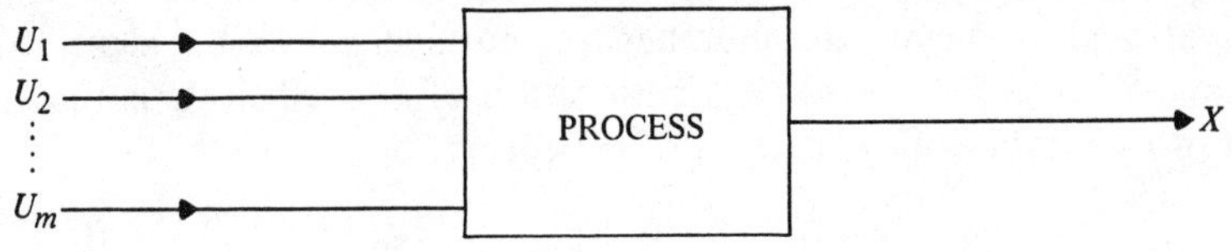


*Figure 5.1* Single output process.

Equation (5.1) becomes:

$$x = a_1 u_1 + a_2 u_2 + \cdots a_m u_m \tag{5.5}$$

or in vector form:

$$x = \mathbf{u}^T \mathbf{a} \tag{5.6}$$

**u, a** being column vectors with elements of $u_j$, $a_j$ respectively. Consequently, the $r$ sets of measurement satisfy:

$$\begin{aligned} x_{(1)} &= \mathbf{u}_{(1)}^T \cdot \mathbf{a} \\ &\vdots \\ x_{(\mu)} &= \mathbf{u}_{(\mu)}^T \cdot \mathbf{a} \\ &\vdots \\ x_{(r)} &= \mathbf{u}_{(r)}^T \cdot \mathbf{a} \end{aligned} \tag{5.7}$$

$(\mu)$ indicating the $\mu$'th set of measurement of $x, \mathbf{u}^T$; $(\mu = 1, 2, \ldots r)$. We further define a vector $\boldsymbol{\chi}$ and a matrix $\mathbf{U}$ as follows:

$$\boldsymbol{\chi} \triangleq [x_{(1)} \cdots x_{(\mu)} \cdots x_{(r)}]^T \tag{5.8}$$

$$\mathbf{U} \triangleq \begin{bmatrix} \mathbf{u}_{(1)}^T \\ \cdot \\ \cdot \\ \cdot \\ \mathbf{u}_{(\mu)}^T \\ \cdot \\ \cdot \\ \cdot \\ \mathbf{u}_{(r)}^T \end{bmatrix} = \begin{bmatrix} u_{1(1)} & \cdot & \cdot & \cdot & u_{j(1)} & \cdot & \cdot & \cdot & u_{m(1)} \\ \cdot & & & & & & & & \\ \cdot & & & & & & & & \\ \cdot & & & & & & & & \\ u_{1(\mu)} & & \cdot & & \cdot & & \cdot & & u_{m(\mu)} \\ \cdot & & & & & & & & \\ \cdot & & & & & & & & \\ \cdot & & & & & & & & \\ u_{1(r)} & & \cdot & & \cdot & & \cdot & & u_{m(r)} \end{bmatrix} \tag{5.9}$$

Hence, Equation (5.7) may be written, in vector form:

$$\boldsymbol{\chi} = \mathbf{U} \cdot \mathbf{a} \tag{5.10-a}$$

Assuming that the elements of **a** of Equation (5.10-a) are estimates $\hat{\mathbf{a}}$ of the true **a**, Equation (5.10-a) yields estimates $\hat{\boldsymbol{\chi}}$ of $\boldsymbol{\chi}$ such that:

$$\hat{\boldsymbol{\chi}} = \mathbf{U} \cdot \hat{\mathbf{a}} \tag{5.10-b}$$

we may define a scalar sum $S$ of the squared errors in estimation, as follows:

$$S \triangleq (\boldsymbol{\chi} - \mathbf{U}\hat{\mathbf{a}})^T (\boldsymbol{\chi} - \mathbf{U}\hat{\mathbf{a}}) = \mathrm{tr}[(\boldsymbol{\chi} - \mathbf{U}\hat{\mathbf{a}}) (\boldsymbol{\chi} - \mathbf{U}\hat{\mathbf{a}})^T] \tag{5.11}$$

tr[$\cdots$] indicating the trace of the matrix [$\cdots$]. The best estimate of **a**, in a least-squares sense, must therefore satisfy the expression:

$$\frac{\partial S}{\partial \hat{a}_i} = 0 \qquad \forall i \in (1, m) \tag{5.12}$$

or in vector form:

$$\frac{\partial S}{\partial \hat{\mathbf{a}}} = \frac{\partial \operatorname{tr}[(\chi - \mathbf{U}\hat{\mathbf{a}})(\chi - \mathbf{U}\hat{\mathbf{a}})^T]}{\partial \hat{\mathbf{a}}}$$

$$= \frac{\partial \operatorname{tr}(\chi\chi^T + \mathbf{U}\hat{\mathbf{a}}\hat{\mathbf{a}}^T\mathbf{U}^T - \mathbf{U}\hat{\mathbf{a}}\chi^T - \chi\hat{\mathbf{a}}^T\mathbf{U}^T)}{\partial \hat{\mathbf{a}}} = 0 \tag{5.13}$$

According to the matrix calculus of trace functions[8,9,10] outlined in Appendix 2, Equation (5.13) becomes:

$$\frac{\partial \operatorname{tr}(\chi\chi^T + \mathbf{U}\hat{\mathbf{a}}\hat{\mathbf{a}}^T\mathbf{U}^T - \mathbf{U}\hat{\mathbf{a}}\chi^T - \chi\hat{\mathbf{a}}^T\mathbf{U}^T)}{\partial \mathbf{a}}$$

$$= \mathbf{0} + 2\mathbf{U}^T\mathbf{U}\hat{\mathbf{a}} - \mathbf{U}^T\chi - \mathbf{U}^T\chi \tag{5.14}$$

$$= 2(\mathbf{U}^T\mathbf{U}\hat{\mathbf{a}} - \mathbf{U}^T\chi) = \mathbf{0}$$

Consequently, the best estimate $\hat{\mathbf{a}}^*$ of **a**, in a least-squares sense, satisfies:

$$\mathbf{U}^T\mathbf{U}\hat{\mathbf{a}}^* = \mathbf{U}^T\chi \tag{5.15}$$

such that:

$$\hat{\mathbf{a}}^* = (\mathbf{U}^T\mathbf{U})^{-1}\mathbf{U}^T\chi = [\hat{a}_1^*, \hat{a}_2^*, \ldots \hat{a}_m^*]^T \tag{5.16}$$

yielding the linear least-squares-regression identification of **a**. We note that $(\mathbf{U}^T\mathbf{U})^{-1}$ exists only if no column of **U** is a linear combination of other columns. Furthermore, we require that $r \geq m$, in order to balance all rows in Equation (5.16), $r$ denoting the number of measurements of $x$ and of **u**. However, if $r = m$, the estimated $\hat{\chi}$ would not smooth the measurement-noise at all; we thus require that $r \geq m + 1$ rather than $r \geq m$. The latter requirement implies that for adequate identification at least $(m + 1)$ measurement instances (sampling intervals) must be considered, and over this period stationarity is assumed.

## 5.2 THE MULTI-INPUT-MULTI-OUTPUT STATIC PROBLEM

A multi-input-multi-output process having $m$ inputs and $n$ outputs, as in Figure 5.2, may be described, in analogy to the single-output processes, by the following set of equations:

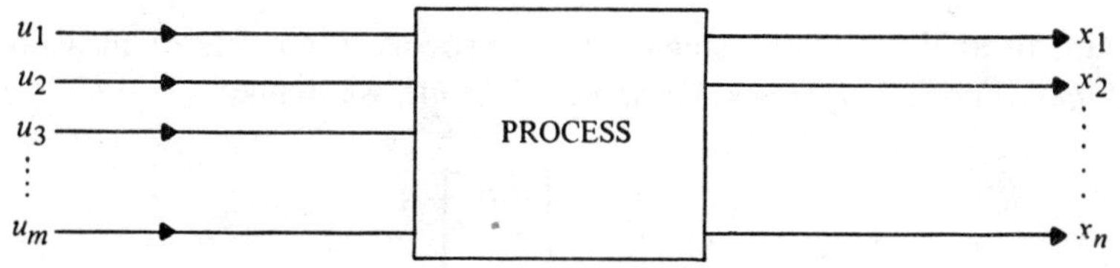


*Figure 5.2* Multi-input-multi-output process.

$$\begin{aligned}
x_1 &= a_{11}u_1 + \cdots a_{1j}u_j + \cdots a_{1m}u_m \\
&\vdots \\
x_i &= a_{i1}u_1 + \cdots a_{ij}u_j + \cdots a_{im}u_m \\
&\vdots \\
x_n &= a_{n1}u_1 + \cdots a_{nj}u_j + \cdots a_{nm}u_m
\end{aligned} \tag{5.17}$$

or, in vector form:

$$\mathbf{x} = \mathbf{A}\mathbf{u} \tag{5.18}$$

where:

$$\mathbf{x} \triangleq (x_1 \cdots x_i \cdots x_n)^T \tag{5.19}$$

$$\mathbf{u} \triangleq (u_1 \cdots u_j \cdots u_m)^T \tag{5.20}$$

and:

$$\mathbf{A} \triangleq \begin{bmatrix} a_{11} & \cdots & a_{1m} \\ \vdots & & \\ a_{n1} & \cdots & a_{nm} \end{bmatrix} \tag{5.21}$$

Each row of equations (5.17) or (5.18) is of exactly the same form as equations (5.5) or (5.6) of the single-output problem. Consequently, we may write the $i$'th row of Equation (5.17) as follows:

$$x_i = \mathbf{u}^T\mathbf{a}_i \tag{5.22}$$

where:

$$\mathbf{a}_i \triangleq [a_{i1}\ a_{i2} \cdots a_{ij} \cdots a_{im}]^T \tag{5.23}$$

Again, in analogy to the single-output process, for $r$ sets of measurement ($r \geq m+1$) of $x_i$, $u_j$ ($i = 1, \ldots n; j = 1, \ldots m$), we define:

$$\chi_i \triangleq \begin{bmatrix} x_{i(1)} \\ \cdot \\ \cdot \\ \cdot \\ x_{i(\mu)} \\ \cdot \\ \cdot \\ \cdot \\ x_{i(r)} \end{bmatrix} \tag{5.24}$$

$$\mathbf{U} \triangleq \begin{bmatrix} u_{1(1)} & \cdot & \cdot & \cdot & u_{m(1)} \\ \cdot & & & & \\ \cdot & & & & \\ \cdot & & & & \\ u_{1(\mu)} & \cdot & \cdot & \cdot & u_{m(\mu)} \\ \cdot & & & & \\ \cdot & & & & \\ \cdot & & & & \\ u_{1(r)} & \cdot & \cdot & \cdot & u_{m(r)} \end{bmatrix} = \begin{bmatrix} \mathbf{u}^T_{(1)} \\ \cdot \\ \cdot \\ \cdot \\ \mathbf{u}^T_{(r)} \end{bmatrix} \tag{5.25}$$

the bracketed subscript ($\mu$) denoting the $\mu$'th set of measurement ($\mu = 1, 2, \ldots r$) and $\mathbf{u}$ being as in Equation (5.9). Consequently, the $r$ sets of measurement above satisfy for the $i$'th output:

$$\begin{aligned} x_{i(1)} &= \mathbf{u}^T_{(1)}\,\mathbf{a}_i \\ &\;\;\vdots \\ x_{i(\mu)} &= \mathbf{u}^T_{(\mu)}\,\mathbf{a}_i \\ &\;\;\vdots \\ x_{i(r)} &= \mathbf{u}^T_{(r)}\,\mathbf{a}_i \end{aligned} \tag{5.26-a}$$

or, in matrix form:

$$\chi_i = \mathbf{U}\mathbf{a}_i \tag{5.26-b}$$

Since Equation (5.26) is fully analogous to Equations (5.7), (5.8) for the single output case, the best estimates $\hat{a}_i^*$ of $a_i$ $\forall i$, in a least-squares regression sense, satisfy:

$$\hat{\mathbf{a}}_i^* = (\mathbf{U}^T\mathbf{U})^{-1} \cdot \mathbf{U}^T\chi_i = (\hat{a}^*_{1i} \cdots \hat{a}^*_{mi}) \tag{5.27}$$

The derivation of Equation (5.27) is therefore identical to that of Equation (5.16) above, when all $\mathbf{a}$; $\chi$ of equations (5.6) to (5.16) are replaced by $\mathbf{a}_i$; $\chi_i$ ($\mathbf{a}_i$, $\chi_i$ being defined in equations (5.23) and (5.24)).

The identification of $\hat{\mathbf{a}}_i^*$ according to Equation (5.27) implies that $r \geq m + 1$, as in the single output case of Section 5.1. Since the same measurements-matrix $\mathbf{U}$ is considered for all $i$ ($i$ denoting the $i$'th row of Equation (5.18)), we may fully identify all elements of $\mathbf{A}$ in $(m + 1)$ measurement instances, $\mathbf{a}_i$ being identified simultaneously for all $i$.

## 5.3 REGRESSION IDENTIFICATION OF LINEAR DYNAMIC PROCESSES

Linear dynamic systems may be described by the following state equation:

$$\dot{\mathbf{x}} = \boldsymbol{\alpha}\mathbf{x} + \boldsymbol{\beta}\mathbf{u} \tag{5.28}$$

$\mathbf{x}$, $\mathbf{u}$ being an $n$-dimensional state vector and an $m$-dimensional control (input) vector, respectively. In discrete form, Equation (5.28), may be written as:

$$\mathbf{x}_{k+1} = \mathbf{A}\mathbf{x}_k + \mathbf{B}\mathbf{u}_k \tag{5.29}$$

where $t = k\,\Delta t$, and:

$$\mathbf{A} = \begin{bmatrix} a_{11} & \cdot & \cdot & \cdot & a_{1n} \\ \cdot & & & & \\ \cdot & & & & \\ \cdot & & & & \\ a_{n1} & \cdot & \cdot & \cdot & a_{nn} \end{bmatrix} \cong \mathbf{I} + \Delta t \cdot \boldsymbol{\alpha}$$

$$\mathbf{B} = \begin{bmatrix} b_{11} & \cdot & \cdot & \cdot & b_{1m} \\ \cdot & & & & \\ \cdot & & & & \\ \cdot & & & & \\ b_{n1} & \cdot & \cdot & \cdot & b_{nm} \end{bmatrix} \cong \Delta t \cdot \boldsymbol{\beta}$$

We now define:

$$\mathbf{w}_k \triangleq (x_{1,k} \cdots x_{n,k};\, u_{1,k} \cdots u_{m,k})^T \triangleq (w_{1,k} \cdots w_{n+m,k})^T \equiv (n + m) \cdot 1 \text{ vector} \tag{5.30}$$

$$\boldsymbol{\Phi} \triangleq \begin{bmatrix} a_{11} & \cdot & \cdot & \cdot & a_{1n};\, b_{11} & \cdot & \cdot & \cdot & b_{1m} \\ \cdot & & & & & & & & \\ \cdot & & & & & & & & \\ \cdot & & & & & & & & \\ a_{n1} & \cdot & \cdot & \cdot & a_{nn};\, b_{n1} & \cdot & \cdot & \cdot & b_{nm} \end{bmatrix} = \begin{bmatrix} (\boldsymbol{\Phi}_1)^T \\ \cdot \\ \cdot \\ \cdot \\ (\boldsymbol{\Phi}_n)^T \end{bmatrix} \tag{5.31}$$

Consequently, Equation (5.29) becomes:

$$\mathbf{x}_{k+1} = \mathbf{\Phi} \cdot \mathbf{w}_k \tag{5.32}$$

which is of the same form as Equation (5.18) of Section 5.2. If we store $r$ sets of measurement ($r \geq n + m + 1$) of $\mathbf{x}_{k+1}$, $\mathbf{w}_k$ (i.e., of $\mathbf{x}_{k+1}$; $\mathbf{x}_k$; $\mathbf{u}_k$), the elements of $\mathbf{\Phi}$ may be identified by the least-squares linear regression procedure of Sections 5.1 and 5.2. Hence, the $i$'th row of the least-squares estimate $\hat{\mathbf{\Phi}}_i^*$ of $\mathbf{\Phi}$ ($i = 1, \dots n$) is given by:

$$(\hat{\mathbf{\Phi}}_i^*)^T = [(\mathbf{W}_k)^T\mathbf{W}_k]^{-1}(\mathbf{W}_k)^T\chi_{i,k+1} = [a_{1i} \cdots a_{ni}; b_{1i} \cdots b_{mi}] \tag{5.33}$$

where, in analogy to Equation (5.25):

$$\mathbf{W}_k \triangleq \begin{bmatrix} w_{1(1)k} & \cdots & w_{m+n(1)k} \\ \cdot & & \\ \cdot & & \\ \cdot & & \\ w_{1(r)k} & \cdots & w_{m+n(r)k} \end{bmatrix} = \begin{bmatrix} x_{1(1)k} & \cdots & x_{n(1)k}; & u_{1(1)k} & \cdots & u_{m(1)k} \\ \cdot & & \cdot & \cdot & & \\ \cdot & & \cdot & \cdot & & \\ \cdot & & \cdot & \cdot & & \\ x_{1(r)k} & \cdots & x_{n(r)k}; & u_{1(r)k} & \cdots & u_{m(r)k} \end{bmatrix} \tag{5.34}$$

$$\chi_{i,k+1} = [x_{i,(1)k+1} \cdots x_{i(\mu)k+1} \cdots x_{i(r)k+1}]^T \tag{5.35}$$

$x_{i(\mu)k+1}$ denoting the $\mu$'th measurement of the $i$'th state of $\mathbf{x}_{k+1}$ ($\mu = 1, 2, \dots r$) and $r$ being the number of sets measurement of $\mathbf{W}_k$, $\mathbf{x}_{k+1}$. We observe that for identifying $\mathbf{\Phi}$ we must store $r$ sets of $\mathbf{x}_{k+1}$ and $r$ sets of measurement of vectors $\mathbf{x}_k$, $\mathbf{u}_k$ belonging to one integration interval $\Delta t$ earlier (denoted as $\mathbf{w}_k$). It may be possible to measure and store several sets of $\mathbf{x}$, $\mathbf{u}$ during an interval $\Delta t$, such that the sampling (or the measuring) interval $\tau$ is $v \cdot \Delta t$ ($1/v$ = integer), as long as at each sampling interval the present $\mathbf{x}_k$ is paired with $\mathbf{w}_k$ belonging to $v$ sampling intervals earlier, to yield $\mathbf{x}_{k+1}$ and $\mathbf{x}_k$, $\mathbf{u}_k$, as is required for identifying $\mathbf{\Phi}$. Hence, $u_{j,(\mu),k}$ belongs to a set of measurements taken $(r - \mu)$ sampling intervals earlier than $u_{j,(r),k}$, and $(v + r - \mu)$ sampling intervals earlier than $x_{i,(r),k+1}$. In total, the storage of $2 \cdot r$ sets of measurement of $\mathbf{x}$ and of $r$ sets of measurement of $\mathbf{u}$ is required for identification of $\mathbf{A}$, $\mathbf{B}$ according to Equation (5.33).

In the derivation above it is assumed that measurements of the state vector $\mathbf{x}$ are obtainable. In the general case only measurements of an output vector $\mathbf{y}$ are possible, where:

$$\mathbf{y} = \mathbf{C}\mathbf{x} + \mathbf{n}; \qquad \mathbf{n} = \text{noise vector} \tag{5.36}$$

Consequently, and noting the observability analysis of Chapter 2, if certain elements of $\mathbf{C}$ of Equation (5.36) are zero, direct identification of $\mathbf{A}$, $\mathbf{B}$ from $\mathbf{y}$ may not be possible. However, since the system to be identified is assumed to be observable, **A**, **B** may be identified from an input/output relationship as in Section 5.4 below, and a transformation into **A**, **B** may subsequently be performed according to the algorithm of Section 2.5. Furthermore, if the dimension $n$ of the state vector $\mathbf{x}$ is a priori unknown, the transfer function approach of Section 5.4 may yield this dimension of $\mathbf{x}$ after transformation according to Section 2.5. Effect of the noise are discussed in Section 5.4.2.

## 5.4 DERIVATION OF TRANSFER FUNCTION MODELS OF INPUT-OUTPUT SYSTEMS

### 5.4.1 Input-Output Models

The regression identification of Section 5.3 is concerned with a state-space formulation of the system, as in equations (5.28) and (5.29). If identification of a transfer-function model is required, a transformation of the state-space model, which is identified as in Section 5.3, into a transfer-function formulation is possible, following the outline of Section 2.5. An alternative identification, which is directly concerned with a transfer function formulation, is also possible where the process is assumed to obey a transfer function of the following generalized form[11]:

$$G_i(s) = \frac{e^{\tau_i s}(b_m s^m + b_{m-1}s^{m-1} + \cdots b_0)_i}{(a_n s^n + a_{n-1}s^{n-1} + \cdots 1)_i} = \frac{x}{u_i} \tag{5.37}$$

for some inputs $u_i$, $x$ being a measurable output.

Although the present discussion is concerned with deterministic inputs and outputs, the transfer function formulation of Equation (5.37) is also valid for stochastic systems, where $u$ is an unmeasurable noise sequence. In that case, the discrete version of Equation (5.37) yields a model that is known in the literature as the mixed autoregressive-moving-average model,[12] which is later employed in Section 5.4.2 for input-output-noise identification and is further discussed in Chapter 12.

In the present section, transfer function models will be considered in discrete form, as is more suitable for digital computer analysis. Consequently, discretization methods based on z-transforms, will be applied to Equation (5.37) to yield a discrete transfer function model to be identified below.

Consider the system of Equation (5.37) in its time domain formulation (for $u_i \triangleq u$), where:

$$a_n \cdot \frac{d^n x(t)}{dt^n} + a_{n-1}\frac{d^{n-1}x(t)}{dt^{n-1}} + \cdots a_1\frac{dx(t)}{dt} + x(t)$$

$$= b_m \frac{d^m u(t-\tau)}{dt^m} + \cdots b_1 \frac{du(t-\tau)}{dt} + b_0 u(t-\tau) \tag{5.38}$$

Equation (5.38) may be approximated by employing a finite difference formulation such that $dx/dt$ is represented by $[x(t) - x(t-T)]/T$. Noting from Section 2.5.1 that $z^{-1}$ is a back-shift operator, we may write that:

$$\frac{x(t) - x(t-T)}{T} = \frac{(1 - z^{-1})x(t)}{T} \tag{5.39}$$

Employing the back-shift operator notation of Box, Jenkins and Bacon[12,13] where:

$$B \triangleq z^{-1} \tag{5.40}$$

Equation (5.39) becomes:

$$\frac{x(t) - x(t-T)}{T} = \frac{(1 - B)x(t)}{T} \tag{5.41}$$

Consequently, and substituting:

$$\tau \triangleq pT \tag{5.42}$$

Equation (5.38) may be approximated by:

$$\begin{aligned}(\alpha_n B^n + \alpha_{n-1}B^{n-1} + \cdots \alpha_1 B + 1)x(t)\\ = B^p(\beta_m B^m + \beta_{m-1}B^{m-1} + \cdots \beta_1 B + \beta_0)u(t)\end{aligned} \tag{5.43}$$

The relations between $\alpha_i$ ($\forall i = 1, \ldots n$); $\beta_j$ ($\forall j = 0, \ldots m$) and $a_i$ ($\forall i = 1, \ldots n$); $b_j$ ($\forall j = 0, \ldots m$) are now easily derived.

In cases where several inputs exist, models of the form of Equation (5.43) may be established per each input, such that $u_i(t)$ is considered instead of $u(t)$ in that equation. When the process consists of several noninteracting inputs, the model of Equation (5.43) is still adequate per each output. We prove below that this model is also adequate for cases of several interacting outputs, as follows.

Consider a system having two interacting outputs $x_1(t)$, $x_2(t)$. The discrete transfer function model for that system is given by:

$$\begin{aligned}x_1(t) = \alpha_1 x_1(t-1) + \beta_1 x_2(t-1) + \gamma_1 u(t-1) + \alpha_2 x_1(t-2)\\ + \beta_2 x_2(t-2) + \gamma_2 u(t-2) + \alpha_3 x_1(t-3) + \cdots\end{aligned} \tag{5.44-a}$$

$$\begin{aligned}x_2(t) = \delta_1 x_1(t-1) + \varepsilon_1 x_2(t-1) + \eta_1 u(t-1) + \delta_2 x_1(t-2)\\ + \varepsilon_2 x_2(t-2) + \eta_2 u(t-2) + \delta_3 x_1(t-3) + \cdots\end{aligned} \tag{5.44-b}$$

Substituting for $x_2$ from Equation (5.44-b) into Equation (5.44-a), we obtain:

$$\begin{aligned}(1 - \alpha_1 B - \alpha_2 B^2 - \cdots)x_1 = \frac{(\delta_1 B + \delta_2 B^2 + \cdots)x_1}{1 - \varepsilon_1 B - \varepsilon_2 B^2 - \cdots}\\ + \left(\gamma_1 B + \gamma_2 B^2 + \cdots + \frac{\eta_1 B + \eta_2 B^2 + \cdots}{1 - \varepsilon_1 B - \varepsilon_2 B^2 - \cdots}\right)u\end{aligned} \tag{5.45}$$

yielding:

$$(1 + \xi_1 B + \xi_2 B^2 + \cdots)x_1 = (\omega_1 B + \omega_2 B^2 + \cdots)u \tag{5.46}$$

the latter representing $x_1$ in terms of its own history and of the input history only, just as in the single output case.

It is important to observe that the powers $n$, $m$, and $p$ above should be specified. However, in the general case, we may assume a certain highest possible order $N$ for $n$ and $M$ for $(m + p)$. We thus compute the regression coefficients of the equation:

$$(\alpha_n B^n + \alpha_{n-1} B^{n-1} + \cdots \alpha_1 B + 1)x(t)$$
$$= (\gamma_{m+p} B^{m+p} + \gamma_{m+p-1} B^{m+p-1} + \cdots \gamma_1 B + \gamma_0)u(t) \tag{5.47}$$

to identify the parameters of the transfer-function model from measured $x(t)$, $u(t)$. The orders $m$, $n$, $p$ of Equation (5.47) are evaluated through identifying $\alpha_i$, $\gamma_j$ in terms of some $m$, $n + p$ which are subsequently iterated until a (near) minimum of the sum of the squared errors between the measured output and the output predicted by a model of given $m$, $n + p$ is obtained for the lowest $m + n + p$. Finally, after dividing the left-hand-side and the right-hand-side polynomials of Equation (5.47), $n$, $m$, and $p$ are obtained such that when:

$$\gamma_j = 0 \qquad \forall j = 0 \cdots q \tag{5.48-a}$$

is satisfied, the order $p$ is given by:

$$p = q + 1 \tag{5.48-b}$$

and $\beta_m$ of Equation (5.43) are derived from:

$$\beta_\mu = \gamma_{q+1+\mu} \qquad \forall \mu = 0, 1, \ldots m \tag{5.48-c}$$

For initially assumed highest orders $n_0$, $m_0 + p_0$, the maximum number of required iterations will be $1 + \log_2(m_0 + n_0 + p_0)$, when the range of $n_0$ or $(m_0 + p_0)$ is halved at each iteration.

We note that the terminology of mixed autoregressive-moving-average models is directly related to Equation (5.47), where, for $\gamma_1 = \cdots \gamma_{m+p} = 0$, the remaining equation may be viewed as a regression equation of $x$ and its past values, such that $\alpha_i$ are (auto)regression coefficients. However, for $\alpha_i = 0 \; \forall i$ and $\gamma_j \neq 0$, the equation becomes a moving-average equation, $\gamma_j$ being moving-average coefficients when $u(t)$ is nondeterministic.

Box and Jenkins discuss the identification of discrete transfer function models above in further detail in Ref. 12. Their main effort is, however, concerned with the derivation of mixed autoregressive-moving-average prediction models (relating, in a $z$-transformed form, the message that is to be predicted, namely, the output of a system, to an unmeasurable uncorrelated random noise input). Approaches leading to similar predictor models, and which aim at yielding identification procedures for on-line implementation, are discussed in Section 12.6 of the present text. The extension of the above models to certain nonstationary sequences and input/output systems, as suggested by Box and Jenkins,[12] is also discussed in Chapter 12 (Section 12.7 below).

### 5.4.2 Input-Output-Noise Models

The models considered earlier in Section 5.4.1 are in terms of input-output relations only, $u(t)$ being a measurable input. We shall now discuss a case where identification is required for an invertible* system given by:

$$(\alpha_R B^R + \cdots \alpha_1 B + 1)x_k = (\gamma_m B^m + \cdots \gamma_0)u_k + v_k \tag{5.49-a}$$

$x_k$, $u_k$ being the measurable output and input, respectively, and $v_k$ being a noise sequence that is uncorrelated with $u_k$. Equation (5.49-a) may be rewritten in operator form as:

$$x_k = \eta(B)u_k + \Omega(B)v_k = \eta(B)u_k + \omega_k \tag{5.49-b}$$

The identification problem where $u_k$ of Equation (5.49-b) is zero is that discussed in Sections 12.6, 12.7 below, where a consistent identification (namely, where the probability of reaching the true parameters, for $k \to \infty$, is 1) is derived to express unmeasurable $v_k$ in terms of a white noise sequence $n_k$, such that:

$$(\alpha_R B^R + \cdots \alpha_1 B + 1)x_k = (\delta_s B^s + \cdots \delta_0)n_k \tag{5.49-c}$$

whereas our present problem is that of identifying $\alpha_i$; $\gamma_j$; $\delta_v$ in:

$$(\alpha_R B^R + \cdots 1)x_k = (\gamma_m B^m + \cdots \gamma_0)u_k + (\delta_s B^s + \cdots \delta_0)n_k \tag{5.49-d}$$

The identification in cases where both a measurable input $u_k$ and an unmeasurable random input $v_k$ exist may be solved consistently through first identifying $\eta_i$ by the procedure outlined in Section 5.4.1 (when disregarding $\delta_v$), and subsequently identifying $\delta_v$ from the residual $r_k$ of the former model, where:

$$r_k \triangleq x_k - \hat{x}_k \tag{5.50-a}$$

$$\hat{x}_k = (\eta_p B^p + \ldots \eta_0)u_k \tag{5.50-b}$$

Hence, the identification procedure for the residue sequence $r_k$ is equivalent to that for Equation (5.49-c), namely the procedure of Section 12.6.

The latter combined identification procedure for the parameters of the input-output-noise model of Equation (5.49-d) may be shown to be consistent as long as the identification of the input-output part alone, namely of $\eta(B)$ is consistent, as follows:

*See Section 12.6.1 for a discussion of invertibility.

We first note that the identification of $\alpha_i$; $\beta_j$ earlier in Section 5.4.1 was assumed to be consistent, since a least squares error for the model of Equation (5.47) has been reached. The latter minimum error is obviously $r_k = \omega_k$ of Equation (5.49-b). However, if $\eta(B)$ of Equation (5.49-b) is wrongly identified to be $\eta'(B)$, the error would become:

$$r_k = \omega_k + [\eta(B) - \eta'(B)]u_k \tag{5.51}$$

The expected squared prediction error for accurate identification of $\eta$ is thus given by:

$$J' = \frac{1}{h} \sum_{k=1}^{h} \omega_k^2 \tag{5.52-a}$$

whereas, for the case of Equation (5.51) it becomes:

$$J'' = \frac{1}{h} \sum_{k} \{\omega_k + [\eta(B) - \eta'(B)]u_k\}^2 \tag{5.52-b}$$

and since $u_k$ is uncorrelated with $\omega_k$:

$$J'' = \frac{1}{k} \sum_{k} \{\omega_k^2 + [[\eta(B) - \eta'(B)]u_k]^2\} = J' + \Delta J' \tag{5.52-c}$$

$\eta(B)$, $\eta'(B)$ having constant coefficients, and $\Delta J' \geq 0$. Consequently, if $r_k$ of Equation (5.51) is correlated with $u_k$ (in case of wrong identification), the expected error increases in comparison to the case of accurate identification. Furthermore, when identification of $\varepsilon_\mu$, $\delta_v$ is performed for the residue model of:

$$(\varepsilon_Q B^Q + \cdots \varepsilon_1 B + 1)r_k = (\delta_s B^s + \cdots \delta_0)n_k \tag{5.53}$$

using the procedure of Sections 12.6, 12.7, we show in Section 12.6 that the expected squared prediction error for that model is given by $\frac{1}{h} \sum_{i=1}^{h} n_k^2$ as long as $r_k = \omega_k$. However, if $r_k$ contains also terms of $u_k$ as in Equation (5.51), which are uncorrelated with $\omega_k$, the identification problem becomes that of identifying the predictors of two uncorrelated sequences, one being $\omega_k$ and the other being $[\eta(B) - \eta'(B)]u_k$. The prediction error of the model for $[\eta(B) - \eta'(B)]u_k$ is obviously uncorrelated with the white noise sequence $n_k$ which is the prediction error for the model of $\omega_k$. Hence, the expected squared prediction error, for erroneous identification of $\eta(B)$ is given by $\frac{1}{h} \sum_{k=1}^{h} n_k^2 + \Delta J''$, where $\Delta J'' \geq 0$. Since the error in predicting the residue is the total prediction error of the input-output-noise model, we have shown that any error in identifying $\eta(B)$ regardless of the parameters of the residue model, increases the total expected prediction error, such that consistent identification of the input-output model alone, followed by a consistent identification of the residue model, is a consistent combined method when the same data are employed throughout. In Section 12.6 we further show that the identification of the noise model above is consistent regardless of the distribution of the noise that is considered, though, for non Gaussian noise it is valid only when a linear model is assumed.

## 5.5 MINIMUM-VARIANCE IDENTIFICATION AND LIKELIHOOD FUNCTIONS

Consider a system given by:

$$\mathbf{z} = \mathbf{x} + \mathbf{n} \tag{5.54-a}$$

**z** and **n** being $k$ dimensional measurement and measurement noise vectors, $k$ denoting the sequential number of measurement, and:

$$\mathbf{x} = \mathbf{U}\mathbf{a} \tag{5.54-b}$$

where **U**, **x** and **a** are the model input, output, and parameter vectors, respectively, as in Equation (5.10).

We assume that $k$ sets of measurement are thus available and that **n** has a Gaussian joint distribution such that:

$$p(\mathbf{n}) = f(\mathbf{N}, k) \cdot \exp(-\mathbf{n}^T \mathbf{N}^{-1} \mathbf{n}/2) \tag{5.55-a}$$

$$E(\mathbf{n}) = \mathbf{0} \tag{5.55-b}$$

$$E(\mathbf{n}\mathbf{n}^T) = \mathbf{N} \tag{5.55-c}$$

$E$ denoting expectation and $f$ being a scalar function of **N**, $k$. Consequently, *if the expectation* **N** *is a priori known*, we may derive a minimum variance linear estimate (Markov estimate) of the parameter vector **a** of Equation (5.59), as follows:[5]

Observing in equations (5.54-a), (5.54-b) that the estimate $\hat{\mathbf{a}}$ of the parameter **a** is related to $\hat{\mathbf{n}}$ by:

$$\hat{\mathbf{n}} = \mathbf{z} - \mathbf{U}\hat{\mathbf{a}} \tag{5.56}$$

we define a *likelihood function* $p(\hat{\mathbf{n}})$, such that:

$$p(\hat{\mathbf{n}}) = p(\mathbf{z} - \mathbf{U}\hat{\mathbf{a}}) \tag{5.57}$$

The estimate $\hat{\mathbf{a}}$ of **a** that maximizes $\ln[p(\hat{\mathbf{n}})]$ is thus given by:

$$\frac{\partial}{\partial \hat{\mathbf{a}}} [\ln[p(\mathbf{z} - \mathbf{U}\hat{\mathbf{a}})]] = 0 \tag{5.58}$$

$p(\cdots)$ denoting the probability of $(\cdots)$. Substituting for $p(\mathbf{n})$ from Equation (5.55), we obtain that:

$$\ln[p(\mathbf{z} - \mathbf{U}\hat{\mathbf{a}})] = \ln[f(\mathrm{N}, k)] - (\mathbf{z} - \mathbf{U}\hat{\mathbf{a}})^T\mathrm{N}^{-1}(\mathbf{z} - \mathbf{U}\hat{\mathbf{a}})/2 \tag{5.59}$$

such that Equation (5.58) becomes:

$$\frac{\partial}{\partial \hat{\mathbf{a}}}[(\mathbf{z} - \mathbf{U}\hat{\mathbf{a}})^T\mathbf{N}^{-1}(\mathbf{z} - \mathbf{U}\hat{\mathbf{a}})] = \mathbf{0} \tag{5.60}$$

Equation (5.60) thus yields:

$$\mathbf{U}^T\mathbf{N}^{-1}\mathbf{U}\mathbf{a}^* - \mathbf{U}^T\mathbf{N}^{-1}\mathbf{z} = \mathbf{0} \tag{5.61-a}$$

or, for nonsingular $(\mathbf{U}^T\mathbf{N}^{-1}\mathbf{U})$:

$$\mathbf{a}^* = (\mathbf{U}^T\mathbf{N}^{-1}\mathbf{U})^{-1}\mathbf{U}^T\mathbf{N}^{-1}\mathbf{z} \tag{5.61-b}$$

$\mathbf{a}^*$ being a minimum variance linear (Markov) estimate of $\mathbf{a}$ which is the (unconditional) maximum likelihood estimate[12] for a Gaussian $\mathbf{n}$, since it maximizes the likelihood function of Equation (5.57).

We note that the minimum variance estimate $\mathbf{z}^*$ of Equation (5.61-b) is in fact a weighted regression estimate, where a weighting matrix $\mathbf{N}^{-1}$ is introduced to the least-squares regression estimate of Equation (5.16), the latter being given by:

$$\mathbf{a}^* = (\mathbf{U}^T\mathbf{U})^{-1}\mathbf{U}^T\mathbf{z} \tag{5.62}$$

Obviously, if no prior knowledge of $\mathbf{N}$ is available (as is the general case), we could assume that $\mathbf{N} = \sigma^2\mathbf{I}$ ($\sigma$ being a scalar) such that Equations (5.61-b) and (5.62) become identical. However, if the covariance of the various components of $\mathbf{n}$ is known a priori, the estimate of $\mathbf{a}$ is as in Equation (5.61-b).

Since, for Gaussian $\mathbf{n}$, when $\mathbf{n}$ is independent, namely for $\mathbf{N} = \sigma^2\mathbf{I}$, the least-squares regression estimate is a maximum likelihood estimate, it follows that under the above conditions, the least-squares estimates have the same properties as maximum likelihood estimates. Consequently, they are unbiased (namely, for a sufficient number of measurements, $E[\mathbf{a}^*]$ equals $\mathbf{a}$) and consistent. They are also efficient (namely, assuming unbiasedness, for any sufficient number of measurements, they yield parameter estimates of minimum variance of the errors between actual and predicted measurements derived from any parameters that may be considered, for the given data).

We note that when least-squares identification of mixed autoregressive-moving-average Gaussian processes with moving-average noise terms is performed, any least-squares estimation of the autoregressive parameters alone is not efficient, since it disregards other parameters. The latter estimation is not of maximum likelihood since by transforming this mixed autoregressive-moving-average model, as in Section 2.5, a multi-dimensional noise vector $\mathbf{n}$ is obtained that is not independent, with $\mathbf{N} \neq \sigma^2\mathbf{I}$, as long as moving-average terms exist. The identification of processes with moving-average noise terms is considered in detail in Section 12.6 below.

## 5.6 REGRESSION-IDENTIFICATION OF NONLINEAR PROCESSES

Both static and dynamic processes may have nonlinear characteristics that cannot be ignored. When prior knowledge of the type of nonlinearity is available, the parameters of the "actual" nonlinear functions may be identified. An example for the latter cases occurs when a relationship between some variables in a certain process, such as that between velocity $W$ and pressure $P$, is known from theoretical considerations to be exponential, of the form of, say: $W = k_1 \cdot \exp(k_2 P) + k_3$, where $k_1$, $k_2$, and $k_3$ require identification. When the type of nonlinear function is unknown, an approximation to the actual nonlinearity is required, say, in terms of a polynomial fit. However, in all cases, identification may be performed *only* if a specific type of nonlinear approximation function is assumed, the parameters of which are to be identified. Hence, the identification problem is again that of estimating the parameters of an a priori given function. An attempt is made in the present section to approach both kinds of nonlinear identification problems (namely, when the type of nonlinear function is a priori known or when it is approximated) through employing nonlinear regression techniques, and to discuss the type of approximating functions that yield adequate approximation.

### 5.6.1 Polynomial Approximations

For describing the methods for identifying nonlinear processes by regression, we first consider a least-squares polynomial approximation of order three of a certain dynamic process having two state variables $x_1$, $x_2$ and one control variable $u$, as follows:

$$x_{i,k+1} = a_{i1}x_{1,k} + a_{i2}x_{1,k}^2 + a_{i3}x_{1,k}^3 + b_{i1}x_{2,k} + b_{i2}x_{2,k}^2 + b_{i3}x_{2,k}^3 + c_{i1}u + c_{i2}u^2 + c_{i3}u^3 \quad @ \quad i = 1, 2 \tag{5.63}$$

We note here that according to the Weierstrass theorem[14] continuous nonlinear functions of $x$ may be approximated by polynomials of $x$, such that the approximations converge to the original functions. Vectors $\mathbf{z}$, $\boldsymbol{\alpha}_i$ are subsequently defined to facilitate the application of the regression identification procedure for identifying the process of Equation (5.63), such that:

$$\mathbf{z} \triangleq [z_1 z_2 z_3 z_4 z_5 z_6 z_7 z_8 z_9]^T$$
$$\triangleq [x_{1k} x_{1k}^2 x_{1k}^3 x_{2k} x_{2k}^2 x_{2k}^3 u_k u_k^2 u_k^3]^T \qquad (5.64\text{-a})$$

and:

$$\boldsymbol{\alpha}_i \triangleq (\alpha_{i,1} \cdots \alpha_{i,9})^T = (a_{i1} a_{i2} a_{i3} b_{i1} b_{i2} b_{i3} c_{i1} c_{i2} c_{i3})^T \qquad (5.64\text{-b})$$

Consequently, Equation (5.63) becomes:

$$x_{i,k+1} = \mathbf{z}^T \cdot \boldsymbol{\alpha}_i \qquad (5.65)$$

which is fully analogous to equations (5.5) and (5.6) of Section 5.1, and is therefore of a linear-regression form. The elements of $\boldsymbol{\alpha}$ of the least-squares third-order polynomial expression employed for approximating the above process are now computed through following the derivation of equations (5.5) to (5.16). In the latter derivation, we replace $x$, $\mathbf{U}$, and $\mathbf{a}$ of equations (5.5) and (5.6) by $x_{1,k+1}$, $\mathbf{z}$, and $\boldsymbol{\alpha}$, respectively, of Equation (5.64). Consequently, $x$, $\mathbf{U}$ of equations (5.7) and (5.8) are derived in terms of $x_{i,k+1}$ and of the elements of $\mathbf{z}$, and $\boldsymbol{\alpha}_i$ is given by Equation (5.16).

If a polynomial approximation of a higher order than in Equation (5.63) is considered, exactly the same approach as in equations (5.63) to (5.65) is followed, though for a larger number of terms. The latter approach is obviously applicable also to static processes (i.e., when subscripts $k$, $k+1$ of Equation (5.63) are ignored). It may be adopted, in principle, to a higher number of variables than in Equation (5.63).

In certain cases we must identify the coefficients of a polynomial approximation, where powers of *functions of* the process-variables appear, and not powers of the process variables themselves, such as:

$$\begin{aligned} x_{i,k+1} &= a_{i1} f(x_{1k}) + a_{i1} f^2(x_{1k}) + a_{i3} f^3(x_{1k}) \\ &\quad + b_{i1} f(x_{2k}) + b_{i2} f^2(x_{2k}) + b_{i3} f^3(x_{2k}) \\ &\quad + c_{i1} f(u_k) + c_{i2} f^2(u_k) + c_{i3} f^3(u_k) \end{aligned} \qquad (5.66)$$

In this case, the elements of $\mathbf{z}$ are defined, as follows:

$$\mathbf{z} \triangleq [z_1 z_2 \cdots z_9]^T \triangleq [f(x_{1k}); f^2(x_{1k}); f^3(x_{1k}); \ldots f^3(u_k)]^T \qquad (5.67)$$

and the rest of the derivation is as in the case of Equation (5.63). In cases where terms with mixed variables appear in the polynomial to be identified, such as:

$$x_{i,k+1} = a_{i1} x_{1k} + a_{12} x_{1k} x_{2k} + a_{13} x_{1k}^2 + \cdots \qquad (5.68)$$

$\mathbf{z}$ is again redefined as:

$$\mathbf{z} \triangleq [z_1; z_2; z_3 \cdots]^T = [x_{1k}; x_{1k} \cdot x_{2k}; x_{1k}^2; \cdots]^T \qquad (5.69)$$

and the derivation continues as in the case of Equation (5.63). In full similarity to the cases of linear regression (sections 5.1, 5.2, and 5.3), we require that the number of sets of measurements $r \geq \omega + 1$ where $\omega$ is the dimension of $\mathbf{z}$ of equations (5.64) or (5.67), to facilitate the derivation of $\boldsymbol{\alpha}_i$ of Equation (5.65) while avoiding collocation of measurements with the approximation model.

A detailed derivation of a generalized model for dynamic systems with unknown nonlinearities based on Volterra series, is given in Section 7.3. The resulting lengthy formulation of this model implies that it be identified by sequential methods as in Chapters 6. 7.

**5.6.1-a Orthogonal polynomial expressions** Of the various polynomial expressions that are employed to approximate nonlinear processes, the orthogonal polynomial approximations deserve particular attention. These polynomials have certain properties that make them very attractive for smoothing of data whose characteristics are a priori unknown. Some of these properties[15] are discussed below, in the present section, and may be summarized as follows.

1. Due to the orthogonality property, the computation of the coefficients of the polynomial equation approximating a process is *faster* than with non-orthogonal polynomials. This property is most important in hand calculation, though it is merely a time-saving feature in machine computation.

2. The coefficients of the polynomial approximation equation are *independent of the highest power* in the polynomial equation that is considered. Hence, when a priori knowledge of the polynomial order is lacking, several orders may be checked, while all coefficients of the lower order remain valid for the higher one. This property is most important if the best order of a polynomial approximation is required.

3. A property that is related to Chebyshev polynomials, which are the most widely employed orthogonal polynomials for nonlinear approximations is their *almost equal-error property*. This property[15] implies that the approximation errors inside the range of measurements oscillates between two limits that are almost equal, as in Figure 5.3. The above property prevents very high errors in, say, the extremes of the data range to which approximation is applied, against small ones elsewhere, thus "damping" the approximation errors.

To further illustrate the identification of nonlinear processes by orthogonal polynomial approximations, we consider the following approximation equations relating $\hat{y}$ and $x$ for a one-dimensional system:

$$\hat{y}(x) = b_0 F_0(x) + b_1 F_1(x) + \cdots + b_m F_m(x) \tag{5.70}$$

$x$, $\hat{y}$ denoting input and (estimated) output variables to a nonlinear process

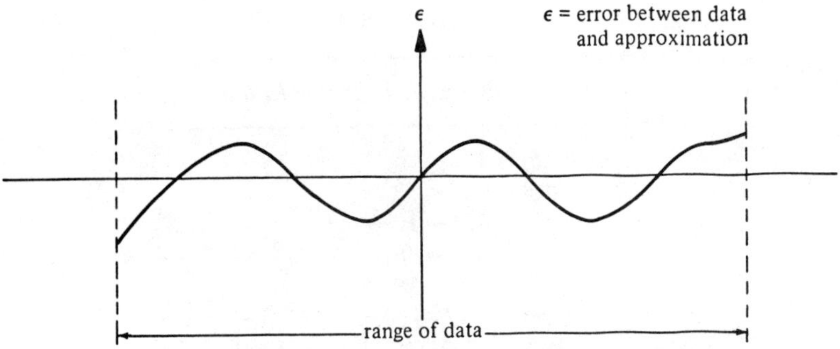


*Figure 5.3* Almost equal-error property of Chebyshev approximation.

(in problems of prediction or smoothing of time series, $x$ may represent time). In the present case $F_\nu(x)$ represents an orthogonal polynomial of order $\nu$ ($\nu = 1, \ldots m$) having the orthogonality property that:

$$\sum_{i=0}^{r} F_\mu(x_i)F_\nu(x_i) = 0 \qquad \forall \mu \neq \nu \tag{5.71-a}$$

or in a generalized form:

$$\int_a^b w(x)F_\mu(x)F_\nu(x)\,dx = 0 \qquad \forall \mu \neq \nu \tag{5.71-b}$$

$\mu$, $\nu$ being nonnegative integers and $r$ being the number of measurements.

For identifying $b_j$ of Equation (5.70) we again require that $r \geq m + 1$ since when $r = m$ the fitted polynomial would collocate with the measurements, and no smoothing of these measurements would take place.

As stated earlier in this section, Chebyshev polynomials are most attractive for orthogonal polynomial approximation (see also property (3) above). The Chebyshev polynomials are defined as:

$$F_\nu(\xi) = T_\nu(\xi) = \cos(\nu \cdot \arccos \xi); \qquad -1 \leq \xi \leq 1 \tag{5.72}$$

and have the following weighted orthogonality property:

$$\int_{-1}^{1} \frac{T_\mu(\xi)T_\nu(\xi)\,d\xi}{\sqrt{1-\xi^2}} = \left.\begin{matrix} 0 & @ & \mu \neq \nu \\ \pi/2 & @ & \mu = \nu \neq 0 \\ \pi & @ & \mu = \nu = 0 \end{matrix}\right\} \tag{5.73}$$

$\sqrt{1-\xi^2}$ being the weight $\omega(\xi)$ of Equation (5.71-b) above. Several Chebyshev polynomials of low order are given in Table 5.3.

TABLE 5.1

| *Chebyshev Polynomials $T_\nu(\xi)$ of order 0 to 6* |
|---|
| $T_0(\xi) = 1$ |
| $T_1(\xi) = \xi$ |
| $T_2(\xi) = 2\xi^2 - 1$ |
| $T_3(\xi) = 4\xi^3 - 3\xi$ |
| $T_4(\xi) = 8\xi^4 - 8\xi^2 + 1$ |
| $T_5(\xi) = 16\xi^5 - 20\xi^3 + 5\xi$ |
| $T_6(\xi) = 32\xi^6 - 48\xi^4 + 18\xi^2 - 1$ |
| $T_{\nu+1}(\xi) = 2\xi T_\nu(\xi) - T_{\nu-1}(\xi)$ |

The abscissa variable ($x$, in Equation (5.70) above) usually requires transformation to satisfy the range requirement on $\xi$ as in Equation (5.72). Once $T_\nu(\xi)$ is available, $T_{\nu+1}(\xi)$ may be obtained according to:

$$T_{\nu+1}(\xi) = 2\xi T_\nu(\xi) - T_{\nu-1}(\xi) \tag{5.74}$$

as results from the definition of $T_\nu(\xi)$ in Equation (5.72).

The least-squares Chebyshev polynomial approximation $\hat{y}$ of $y$ is subsequently computed to minimize $S$ where:

$$S = \int_{-1}^{1} w(\xi)\left[y(\xi) - \sum_{i=0}^{m} b_i T_i(\xi)\right]^2 d\xi \tag{5.75}$$

yielding:

$$b_k = \left[\int_{-1}^{1} w(\xi)y(\xi)T_k(\xi)\,d\xi\right] \Big/ \left[\int_{-1}^{1} w(\xi)T_k^2(\xi)\,d\xi\right]$$

$$= \begin{cases} \dfrac{1}{\pi}\displaystyle\int_{-1}^{1} \dfrac{y(\xi)}{\sqrt{1-\xi^2}}\,d\xi & @ \; k = 0 \\ \dfrac{2}{\pi}\displaystyle\int_{-1}^{1} \dfrac{y(\xi)T_k(\xi)}{\sqrt{1-\xi^2}}\,d\xi & @ \; k \neq 0 \end{cases} \tag{5.76}$$

such that:

$$\hat{y}(\xi) = \sum_{k=0}^{m} b_k T_k(\xi) \tag{5.77}$$

The relatively simple algorithms for $b_k$ result from the orthogonality property. We observe that $b_k$ of Equation (5.76) are *independent of the choice of m.*

Hence, a modification of $m$ requires no recomputation of $b_j$ $\forall j \leq m$, whereas in nonorthogonal approximations a recomputation is required, and is considerably time-consuming.

Another important property of the Chebyshev polynomials is that when:

$$\xi_i = \cos[(2i+1)\pi/2n]; \qquad i = 0, 1, \ldots n-1 \tag{5.78}$$

they may be easily shown to satisfy the following discrete orthogonality property for $\mu$, $\nu < n$ (see Ref. 15, p. 258):

$$\sum_{j=0}^{n} T_\mu(\xi_j) \cdot T_\nu(\xi_i) = \begin{cases} 0 & @ \quad \mu \neq \nu \\ \dfrac{n}{2} & @ \quad \mu = \nu \neq 0 \\ n & @ \quad \mu = \nu = 0 \end{cases} \tag{5.79}$$

We observe that in Equation (5.79) the weight $\omega(\xi)$ of Equation (5.71-b) is unity. Consequently, the weight to be considered in Equation (5.75) is also unity, and the coefficient $b_k$ of the Chebyshev approximation $\hat{y}$ of $y$ may be computed to minimize $S$, where:

$$S = \sum_{j=0}^{n-1} \left[ y(\xi_j) - \sum_{k=0}^{m} b_k T_k(\xi_j) \right]^2 \tag{5.80}$$

yielding:

$$b_0 = \frac{1}{n} \sum_{j=0}^{n-1} y(\xi_j) \tag{5.81-a}$$

$$b_k = \frac{2}{n} \sum_{j=0}^{n-1} y(\xi_j) T_k(\xi_j) \tag{5.81-b}$$

which are far simpler values to compute than those of Equation (5.76), though they require accessibility to $y(\xi_i)$ at $\xi_i$ as defined in Equation (5.78).

Computer programs for generating Chebyshev or other orthogonal polynomials are adequately discussed in the literature.[16] ALGOL subroutines for orthogonal polynomial curve-fitting of equally and unequally spaced data are given in Ref. 17, and similar subroutines in other compiler languages are readily available.

Example 5.1

To illustrate the applications of the Chebyshev approximations, we consider the fitting of a second order Chebyshev polynomial to $y(\xi) = \xi^4$ $\forall |\xi| < 1$ as follows: We determine the number of points to be considered as $n = 3$. Consequently, noting Equation (5.78), $\xi_0 = \cos \dfrac{\pi}{6} = \dfrac{\sqrt{3}}{2}$ and $\xi_1 = \cos \dfrac{3\pi}{6} = 0$;

$\xi_2 = \cos\frac{5\pi}{6} = -\frac{\sqrt{3}}{2}$ and, according to Equation (5.79):

$$b_0 = \frac{1}{3}\left[\left(\frac{\sqrt{3}}{2}\right)^4 + 0^4 + \left(-\frac{\sqrt{3}}{2}\right)^4\right] = \frac{3}{8}$$

$$b_1 = \frac{2}{3}\left[\left(\frac{\sqrt{3}}{4}\right)^5 + \left(-\frac{\sqrt{3}}{2}\right)^5\right] = 0$$

$$b_2 = \frac{2}{3}\left[2\left(\frac{\sqrt{3}}{2}\right)^6 - \left(\frac{\sqrt{3}}{2}\right)^4 + 2\left(-\frac{\sqrt{3}}{2}\right)^6 - \left(-\frac{\sqrt{3}}{2}\right)^4\right] = \frac{3}{8}$$

**5.6.1-b Multi-dimensional orthogonal polynomials** The application of orthogonal polynomials to *multi-dimensional problems* is less widely used than that for single-dimensional cases, because of the computational effort in generating these polynomials. Furthermore, the availability of fast computers and of sequential parameter estimators as in chapter 6 through 8 below, has reduced the attraction of the orthogonal polynomials for estimating parameters as in Equation (5.76). However, the multi-dimensional formulation of orthogonal polynomials satisfies, in full analogy to the single dimensional case:

$$\int\cdots\int w(x_1;\ldots x_n)F_{\mu,\nu,\ldots\Omega}(x_1;\ldots x_n)(F_{\mu',\nu'\ldots\Omega'}(x_1;\ldots x_n)\,dx_1\cdots\cdots dx_n$$
$$=0 \qquad \forall\mu;\nu;\ldots\Omega \neq \mu';\nu';\ldots\Omega' \quad (5.82)$$

$x_1$ to $x_n$ denoting the elements of the multi-dimensional $\mathbf{x}$, and is therefore similar to Section 5.6.1-a. A convenient form of generating $F_{\mu,\nu,\ldots\Omega}$ is through letting:

$$F_{\mu,\nu,\ldots\Omega}(x_1;\ldots x_n) = F_\mu(x_1)\cdot F_\nu(x_2)\cdots\cdot F_\Omega(x_n) \qquad (5.83)$$

where $F_\mu; F_\nu \cdots F_\Omega$ are all orthogonal polynomials in one dimension. Consequently, and because of the orthogonality of $F_\mu(x), \ldots F_\Omega(x_n)$, we obtain:

$$\int\cdots\int w(x_1\cdots x_n)F_{\mu;\nu,\ldots\Omega}F_{\mu';\nu';\ldots\Omega'}\,dx_1\cdots\cdots dx_n$$

$$= \int w_1F_\mu(x_1)F_{\mu'}(x_1)\,dx_1\cdot\int w_2F_\nu(x_2)F_{\nu'}(x_2)\,dx_2\cdots\int w_nF_\Omega(x_n)F_{\Omega'}(x_n)\,dx_n$$

$$= 0 \qquad \forall\mu;\nu;\ldots\Omega; \neq \mu';\nu';\ldots\Omega' \qquad (5.84)$$

such that Equation (5.82) is satisfied.

**5.6.1-c Determination of best order of the polynomial approximation** The best order $m^*$ of the polynomial approximation may be derived on the basis of the hypothesis[16] that the measurements $y_{(i)}$ (the bracketed subscript $(i)$ denoting the $i$'th measurement, $i = 1, 2, 3, \ldots r$) have an independent Gaussian distribution about some polynomial relation $\hat{y}$ of say, order $m^* + \mu$, where:

$$\hat{y}_{m^*+\mu}(x_i) = \sum_{j=0}^{m^*+\mu} b_j x_i^j \tag{5.85}$$

the variance $\sigma^2$ of this distribution of $y - \hat{y}$ being independent of $\mu$. Obviously, for very low $m$ ($m = 0, 1, 2, \ldots$), $\sigma_m^2$ decreases with increasing $m$. Since, under the hypothesis above, the variance $\sigma_m^2$ is independent of $m$, it follows that the best order $m^*$ is the lowest $m$ for which $\sigma_m \cong \sigma_{m+1}$.

The derivation of $m^*$ requires the computation of polynomial approximations of different orders. Since $b_j$ of Equation (5.85) may be dependent on the polynomial order $m$, the use of orthogonal polynomial approximations eliminates the need for recomputing all $b_j$ for every $m$, as has been shown in Section 5.6.1-a above.

### 5.6.2 Identification with respect to a priori given arbitrary nonlinear functions

In many cases, a nonlinear analytical model is available from theoretical considerations, and the identification of its parameters is required. In such cases, regression analysis may be employed as follows.

Consider a process given by the expression:

$$y = a_0 + a_1 x_1 x_2^3 + a_2 x_2 \exp\left(-a_3 \frac{x_1^2}{x_3}\right) + \frac{a_4 x_4}{\sqrt{1 - a_5 x_5^2}} \tag{5.86}$$

For identifying the latter process, we first define the following new variables.

$$\begin{aligned} &\zeta_1 \triangleq x_1 x_2^3;\ \zeta_3 \triangleq x_2;\ \zeta_5 \triangleq x_5 \\ &\zeta_2 \triangleq x_1^2/x_3;\ \zeta_4 \triangleq x_4 \end{aligned} \tag{5.87}$$

yielding:

$$y = a_0 + a_1 \zeta_1 + a_2 \zeta_2 \cdot \exp(-a_3 \zeta_2) + \frac{a_4 \zeta_4}{\sqrt{1 - a_5 \zeta_5^2}} \tag{5.88}$$

We now linearize Equation (5.88) by considering only small perturbations of its variables (see Appendix 1). Consequently, we obtain:

$$\Delta y = a_1\,\Delta\zeta_1 - a_2 a_3 \zeta_3 \exp(-a_3\zeta_2)\cdot\Delta\zeta_2 + a_2\exp(-a_3\zeta_2)\,\Delta\zeta_3 + \frac{a_4}{\sqrt{1-a_5\zeta_5^2}}\,\Delta\zeta_4 + \frac{a_4 a_5 \zeta_4 \zeta_5}{\sqrt{1-a_5\zeta_5^2}}\,\Delta\zeta_5 \tag{5.89}$$

We further define:

$$\begin{aligned} b_1 &\triangleq a_1 \\ b_2 &\triangleq -a_2 a_3 \zeta_3 \exp(-a_3\zeta_2) \\ b_3 &\triangleq a_2 \exp(-a_3\zeta_2) \\ b_4 &\triangleq \frac{a_4}{\sqrt{1-a_5\zeta_5^2}} \\ b_5 &\triangleq \frac{a_4 a_5 \zeta_4 \zeta_5}{\sqrt{1-a_5\zeta_5}} \end{aligned} \tag{5.90}$$

yielding:

$$\Delta y = b_1\,\Delta\zeta_1 + b_2\,\Delta\zeta_2 + b_3\,\Delta\zeta_3 + b_4\,\Delta\zeta_4 + b_5\,\Delta\zeta_5 = \sum_i b_i\,\Delta\zeta_i \tag{5.91}$$

Obviously, $b_1$ to $b_5$ may be identified by linear regression, as in Section 5.1. We subsequently observe that:

$$b_5 = b_4\cdot a_5\cdot\zeta_4\cdot\zeta_5 \tag{5.92}$$

to yield $a_5$ since $\zeta_4$, $\zeta_5$ are measurable. Substituting the latter result for $a_5$ in the expression for $b_4$ in Equation (5.90), we derive $a_4$. The term $a_1$ is directly given by $b_1$ according to Equation (5.90), while $a_2$, $a_3$ must be derived from the expressions for $b_2$, $b_3$ of that equation, as follows:

$$b_2 = -a_3\cdot\zeta_3\cdot b_3 \tag{5.93}$$

where $\zeta_3$ is measurable, thus yielding $a_3$. Finally, $a_2$ is derived by substituting the latter $a_3$ into the expression for $b_3$ in Equation (5.90).

Many other sets of nonlinear expressions may be identified in a similar manner as has been described for the process of Equation (5.86) above.

Processes given by exponential relations of the form:

$$y = a\cdot e^{bx} \tag{5.94}$$

may be identified by regression if $\log y$ is considered, giving:

$$\log y = \log a + b\cdot x \tag{5.95}$$

Defining: $\log y \triangleq Y$, $\log x \triangleq X$, $\log a \triangleq A$, we obtain that:

$$Y = A + b \cdot X \tag{5.96}$$

where $A$, $b$ are easily computable by linear regression.

Similarly, in cases of processes of the form:

$$y = a \cdot x^b \tag{5.97}$$

we may consider $\log y$, obtaining the relation:

$$\log y = \log a + b \cdot \log x \tag{5.98}$$

from which $a$, $b$ are derived as in the case of Equation (5.96). However, there are cases where the latter methods do not work, and at least some further information is required. An example for a system where the latter method is not valid is:

$$y = a_0 + a_1 \log(a_2 + x) \tag{5.99}$$

where $a_0$, $a_1$, $a_2$ require identification. Here small perturbations give:

$$\Delta y = \frac{a_1}{a_2 + x} \Delta x = b \, \Delta x \tag{5.100}$$

where $b$ may be identified by linear regression, yielding:

$$b = \frac{a_1}{a_2 + x} \tag{5.101}$$

which does not provide a solution for $a_0$, $a_1$, $a_2$. The employment of second and higher partial derivatives (or second and higher order perturbations) is, of course, possible, but may be useless in practical cases, since these derivatives are usually meaningless, especially if the measurements are noisy.

## REFERENCES

1. Cramer, H. *Mathematical Methods of Statistics*, Princeton University Press, Princeton, N.J., 1951.
2. Kalman, R. E. "Design of Self-Optimizing Control Systems," *Trans. A.S.M.E.*, Vol. 80, pp. 468–478, 1958.
3. Kerr, R. B., and Surber, W. H., Jr. "Precision of Impulse Response Identification Based on Short Normal Operating Records," *I.R.E. Trans.*, Vol. AC-6, pp. 173–182, 1961.
4. Elkind, J. I., Green, D. M., and Starr, E. A. "Application of Multiple Regression Analysis to Identification of Time-Varying Linear Dynamic Systems," *IEEE Trans.*, Vol. AC-8, pp. 163–166, 1963.

5. Eykhoff, P. "Process Parameter and State Estimation," Survey Paper, *Proc. I.F.A.C. 3rd Congress*, London, 1966.
6. Clarke, D. W. "Generalized Least Squares Estimation of the Parameters of a Dynamic Model," Paper 3.17, *Proc. I.F.A.C. Symp. on Identification*, Prague, 1967.
7. Graupe, D., Swanick, B. H., and Cassir, G. R. "Application of Regression Analysis to Reduction of Multivariable Control Problems and to Process Identification," *Proc. National Electronics Conf.*, Vol. 23, pp. 20–25, Chicago, 1967.
8. Kleinman, D. L. "Suboptimal Design of Linear Regulator Systems Subject to Storage Limitations," *Electronic Systems Lab. Rept. 297*, M.I.T., Cambridge, Mass., 1967.
9. Athans, M. "The Matrix Maximum Principle," *Inf. and Cont.*, Vol. 11, pp. 592–606, 1968.
10. Bobrovsky, B. Z. M.Sc. Thesis, Dept. of Mech. Eng., Technion, Israel Inst. of Technology, Haifa, 1970.
11. Wilts, C. H. *Principles of Feedback Control*, Addison-Wesley, Reading, Mass., 1960 (Chapter 11).
12. Box, G. E. P., and Jenkins, G. M. *Time Series Analysis, Forecasting and Control*, Holden Day, San Francisco, 1970.
13. Box, G. E. P., Jenkins, G. M., and Bacon, D. W. "Models for Forecasting Seasonal and Non-Seasonal Time Series," *Advanced Seminar on Spectral Analysis of Time Series* (edited by B. Harris), pp. 271–311, Wiley, New York, 1967.
14. Sokolnikoff, I. S., and Redheffer, R. M. *Mathematics of Physics and Engineering*, McGraw-Hill, New York, 1966 (Chapter 1).
15. Scheid, F. *Numerical Analysis*, Schaum, New York, 1968 (Chapter 21).
16. Forsythe, G. E. "Generation and Use of Orthogonal Polynomials for Data-Fitting with a Digital Computer," *Jour. Soc. Indst. Appl. Math.*, Vol. 5, No. 2, pp. 74–88, 1952.
17. Mackinney, J. G. "Algorithms 28/29," *Comm. A.C.M.*, Vol. 3, No. 11, 1960.


## PROBLEMS

**1.** Compute the coefficients $a_1$; $a_2$; $a_3$ of the linear regression equation $y = a_1 x_1 + a_2 x_2 + a_3 x_3$, given the following sets of measurements:

| | | | | | | | | | | | | |
|---|---|---|---|---|---|---|---|---|---|---|---|---|
| $x_1$ | 0.62 | 0.40 | 0.42 | 0.82 | 0.66 | 0.72 | 0.38 | 0.52 | 0.45 | 0.69 | 0.55 | 0.36 |
| $x_2$ | 12.0 | 14.2 | 14.6 | 12.1 | 10.8 | 8.2 | 13.0 | 10.5 | 8.8 | 17.0 | 14.4 | 12.8 |
| $x_3$ | 5.2 | 6.1 | .32 | 8.3 | 5.1 | 7.9 | 4.2 | 8.0 | 3.9 | 5.5 | 3.8 | 6.2 |
| $y$ | 51.6 | 49.9 | 48.5 | 50.6 | 49.7 | 48.8 | 42.6 | 45.9 | 37.8 | 64.8 | 53.4 | 45.3 |

**2.** Identify the discrete first order system $y(k+1) = ay(k) + bu(k)$ using linear regression, from the following input/output data:

| | | | | | | | | | | |
|---|---|---|---|---|---|---|---|---|---|---|
| 0, | 1, | 2, | 3, | 4, | 5, | 6, | 7, | 8, | 9, | 10 |
| 0, | 0, | 1, | 1, | 1, | 1, | 0, | 0, | 1, | 1, | 1 |
| −5, | −4, | −4, | −2, | −2, | −2, | 0, | 1, | 1, | 0, | 2 |

| | | | | | | | | | |
|---|---|---|---|---|---|---|---|---|---|
| 11, | 12, | 13, | 14, | 15, | 16, | 17, | 18, | 19, | 20 |
| 1, | 1, | 1, | 1, | 1, | 1, | 1, | 1, | 0, | 1 |
| 2, | 2, | 2, | 3, | 3, | 3, | 3, | 2, | 1, | 1 |

| | | | | | | | | | |
|---|---|---|---|---|---|---|---|---|---|
| 21, | 22, | 23, | 24, | 25, | 26, | 27, | 28, | 29, | 30 |
| 0, | 1, | 1, | 1, | 0, | 0, | 0, | 1, | 0, | 1 |
| 2, | 1, | 2, | 2, | 1, | 1, | 2, | 2, | 2, | 2 |

| | | | | | | | | | |
|---|---|---|---|---|---|---|---|---|---|
| 31, | 32, | 33, | 34, | 35, | 36, | 37, | 38, | 39, | 40 |
| 1, | 0, | 1, | 0, | 0, | 1, | 0, | 1, | 1, | 1 |
| 1, | 0, | 2, | 1, | 0, | 1, | 3, | 3, | 3, | 3 |

| | | | | | | | | | |
|---|---|---|---|---|---|---|---|---|---|
| 41, | 42, | 43, | 44, | 45, | 46, | 47, | 48, | 49, | 50 |
| 0, | 0, | 0, | 0, | 0, | 1, | 0, | 1, | 1, | 0 |
| 1, | 0, | 0, | −1, | −1, | −1, | −3, | −3, | −3, | −3 |

| | | | | | | | | | |
|---|---|---|---|---|---|---|---|---|---|
| 51, | 52, | 53, | 54, | 55, | 56, | 57, | 58, | 59, | 60 |
| 0, | 1, | 0, | 1, | 0, | 0, | 0, | 1, | 1, | 0 |
| −3, | −4, | - 4, | −5, | −6, | −7, | −6, | −4, | −4, | −5 |

| | | | | | | | | | |
|---|---|---|---|---|---|---|---|---|---|
| 61, | 62, | 63, | 64, | 65, | 66, | 67, | 68, | 69, | 70 |
| 1, | 0, | 0, | 0, | 0, | 1, | 1, | 1, | 1, | 1 |
| −5, | −5, | −5, | −4, | −4, | −2, | −2, | −1, | 0, | 0 |

| | | | | | | | | | |
|---|---|---|---|---|---|---|---|---|---|
| 71, | 72, | 73, | 74, | 75, | 76, | 77, | 78, | 79, | 80 |
| 0, | 1, | 1, | 0, | 1, | 0, | 0, | 0, | 0, | 1 |
| 0, | 2, | 2, | 2, | 1, | 2, | 2, | 2, | 3, | 2 |

| | | | | | | | | | |
|---|---|---|---|---|---|---|---|---|---|
| 81, | 82, | 83, | 84, | 85, | 86, | 87, | 88, | 89, | 90 |
| 1, | 1, | 1, | 0, | 1, | 1, | 0, | 1, | 0, | 0 |
| 3, | 3, | 2, | 2, | 1, | 2, | 2, | 2, | 0, | 0 |

| | | | | | | | | | |
|---|---|---|---|---|---|---|---|---|---|
| 91, | 92, | 93, | 94, | 95, | 96, | 97, | 98, | 99, | 100 |
| 1, | 0, | 1, | 0, | 0, | 0, | 0, | 1, | 0, | 1 |
| 2, | 2, | 2, | 3, | 3, | 3, | 4, | 4, | 4, | 2 |

| | | | | | |
|---|---|---|---|---|---|
| 101, | 102, | 103, | 104, | 105, | 106 |
| 1, | 1, | 1, | 1, | 0, | 1 |
| 2, | 1, | 1, | 1, | 0, | 1 |

Identify the parameter matrices $\mathbf{A} = \begin{bmatrix} a_{11} & a_{12} \\ a_{21} & a_{22} \end{bmatrix}$; $\mathbf{B} = \begin{bmatrix} b_1 \\ b_2 \end{bmatrix}$ of the system $\dot{\mathbf{x}} = \mathbf{A}\mathbf{x} + \mathbf{B}u$ by regression, from the following sets of measurements:

| | | | | | | | | | |
|---|---|---|---|---|---|---|---|---|---|
| 0 | 1 | 2 | 3 | 4 | 5 | 6 | 7 | 8 | 9 |
| 1. | .99 | .97 | .96 | .95 | .945 | .94 | .935 | .93 | .925 |
| 0 | −.1 | −.19 | −.23 | −.28 | −.25 | −.22 | −.18 | −.14 | −.07 |
| 1. | 1.25 | 1.5 | 1.75 | 2. | 2.25 | 2.5 | 2.75 | 3. | 3.25 |

| | | | | | | | | |
|---|---|---|---|---|---|---|---|---|
| 10 | 11 | 12 | 13 | 14 | 15 | 16 | 17 | 18 |
| .92 | .925 | .93 | .94 | .95 | .97 | .99 | 1.02 | 1.05 |
| 0 | .09 | .17 | .26 | .36 | .45 | .55 | .65 | .76 |
| 3.5 | 3.75 | 4. | 4.25 | 4.5 | 4.75 | 5. | 5.25 | 5.5 |

| | | | | | | | | |
|---|---|---|---|---|---|---|---|---|
| 19 | 20 | 21 | 22 | 23 | 24 | 25 | 26 | 27 |
| 1.1 | 1.15 | 1.22 | 1.28 | 1.32 | 1.36 | 1.44 | 1.52 | 1.58 |
| .86 | .96 | 1.05 | 1.13 | 1.21 | 1.3 | 1.38 | 1.45 | 1.51 |
| 5.75 | 6. | 6.25 | 6.5 | 6.75 | 7. | 7.25 | 7.5 | 7.75 |

| | | | | | | | | |
|---|---|---|---|---|---|---|---|---|
| 28 | 29 | 30 | 31 | 32 | 33 | 34 | 35 | 36 |
| 1.66 | 1.74 | 1.83 | 1.92 | 2.02 | 2.1 | 2.18 | 2.27 | 2.37 |
| 1.57 | 1.63 | 1.69 | 1.74 | 1.78 | 1.82 | 1.86 | 1.89 | 1.91 |
| 8. | 8.25 | 8.5 | 8.75 | 9. | 9.25 | 9.5 | 9.75 | 10. |

| | | | | | |
|---|---|---|---|---|---|
| 37 | 38 | 39 | 40 | 41 | 42 |
| 2.47 | 2.57 | 2.66 | 2.76 | 2.86 | 2.97 |
| 1.93 | 1.95 | 1.97 | 1.98 | 2.02 | 2.05 |
| 10.25 | 10.5 | 10.75 | 11. | 11.25 | 11.5 |

**4.** Generate:

$$y = 5 \sin x \qquad \forall 0 \le x \le \pi$$

and identify by nonlinear regression as in Section 5.6.1 the parameters $a_i$ of the polynomial approximation:

$$\hat{y} = \sum_{i=0}^{3} a_i x^i$$

to approximate $y$ over the given range.

**5.** Find the second order Chebyshev polynomial to approximate:

$$y = |x| \qquad \forall |x| < 1$$

using $n = 5$.

**6.** Prove that the Chebyshev polynomials satisfy the orthogonality property of Equation (5.73).

**7.** Employ Equation (5.74) to generate $T_\nu(\xi)$ for $\nu = 7, 8, 9, 10$.

**8.** Prove that $b_k$ of Equation (5.76) minimizes $S$ of Equation (5.75).

**9.** Prove the orthogonality property of Equation (5.79), noting Equation (5.78).

**10.** Assuming equations (5.78) and (5.79) prove that the least squares coefficients of the Chebyshev approximation are given by Equation (5.81).

**11.** Employ regression analysis to identify the parameters of a process $y = a \cdot e^{bx} + c$, from the following data:

| | | | | | | | | | | |
|---|---|---|---|---|---|---|---|---|---|---|
| $x$: | 1.84 | 1.92 | 2.0 | 2.08 | 2.16 | 2.24 | 2.32 | 2.4 | 2.48 | 2.56 |
| $y$: | 61.7 | 62.5 | 63.0 | 63.6 | 64.5 | 65.0 | 65.4 | 66.4 | 67.1 | 68.0 |
| $x$: | 2.64 | 2.72 | 2.8 | 2.88 | 2.96 | 3.04 | 3.12 | 3.2 | 3.28 | 3.36 |
| $y$: | 68.7 | 69.4 | 70.2 | 70.2 | 71.1 | 71.9 | 72.8 | 73.6 | 74.5 | 76.4 |
| $x$: | 3.44 | 3.52 | 3.6 | 3.68 | 3.76 | 3.84 | 3.92 | 4.0 | 4.08 | 4.16 |
| $y$: | 77.2 | 78.1 | 79.2 | 80.3 | 81.2 | 82.2 | 83.3 | 84.4 | 85.4 | 86.5 |
| $x$: | 4.24 | 4.32 | 4.4 | 4.48 | 4.56 | 4.64 | 4.72 | 4.8 | 4.88 | 4.96 |
| $y$: | 87.8 | 89.1 | 90.1 | 91.3 | 92.5 | 93.8 | 95.1 | 96.4 | 97.8 | 98.7 |

# 6

# SEQUENTIAL REGRESSION METHODS

Identification techniques based on sequential least squares are applicable to linear and nonlinear stationary systems, where they may substitute for the nonsequential regression techniques of Chapter 5. Their sequential feature makes them fast to implement and requires little computer storage. Computational *difficulties arising in matrix inversion are eliminated* in the sequential approach, thus overcoming a major obstacle in applying multivariate regression approaches, as in Chapter 5, to practical systems.

When applying the regression techniques of Chapter 5 to identifying slowly varying nonstationary processes, stationarity is assumed only over the regression interval during which data are gathered for regression identification, the regression interval consisting of $r$ sampling intervals. Identification is thus almost continuously updated when the end of the usually fixed regression interval is advanced with the advancement of time by one or several measurement intervals. Hence, for each such advancement, the whole parameters vector is reidentified, whereas the data not belonging to the present regression interval are completely ignored. In contrast to nonsequential regression, the interval over which data are collected for sequential regression is continuously increasing in length with the progress of time and no data become old enough to be completely ignored. Hence, sequential regression (and stochastic approximation discussed in Chapter 7) appears to be restricted to stationary processes. However, since sequential regression estimates converge to those of nonsequential regression after $m$ iterations ($m$ being the dimension of the parameter vector, as in Chapter 5), stationarity must be assumed over only $m$ intervals as in the nonsequential case (see Section 5.3).

In practice one may therefore apply sequential estimation of any kind to data collected over a finite interval, over which the system is assumed to be stationary, as follows: Consider an interval $T$, from $t - T$ to $t$, over which $n$ samples are taken at the instances $0, 1, \ldots k, \ldots n$. We may perform a sequential regression identification according to $k$ sets of samples, then over $k + 1$, $k + 2$, etc., up to the $n$'th set of samples, which gives the final identification estimate at time $t$. Now, at time $t + \Delta t$ ($\Delta t \triangleq T/n$) we repeat the whole regression estimation procedure such that the data at $t - T + \Delta t$ are the first sample, and so forth, until we have $n$ sets of samples at $t + \Delta t$, the latter giving the final identification estimate at $t + \Delta t$. The same procedure may be repeated for $t + 2\,\Delta t$, $t + 3\,\Delta t, \ldots, t + j\,\Delta t, \ldots$. The decision on restarting sequential regression identification may be based on the behavior of an identification performance index $S$ as in Equation (5.11) if no nonstationarity is suspected. The determination of the a priori unknown order of state vectors or of auto-regressive-moving-average models may also be performed (once for always) as in Section 5.4.1.

## 6.1 THE SCALAR CASE

We consider an unknown system as follows:

$$x_k = au_k + n_k \qquad \forall k = 0, 1, 2, \ldots \tag{6.1}$$

$u_k$ and $x_k$ being measurable input and output sequences, respectively, and $n_k$ being measurement noise at the $k$'th sampling interval. The identification problem is that of evaluating the system's unknown parameter $a$, and may be performed through employing least-squares linear regression. Consequently, an estimate $\hat{a}_r$ of $a$ is made, based on $r$ sets of measurement of $u_k$, $x_k$ $(k = 1 \ldots r)$ such that a cost index $J_r$ is minimized where:

$$J_r = \sum_{k=1}^{r} q_k(x_k - \hat{a}_r u_k)^2 \tag{6.2}$$

$q_k$ being an arbitrary weighting coefficient, say: $q_k = 1$. The inclusion of a nonunity $q_k$ in Equation (6.2) may serve to upweight more recent measurements. The least-squares regression estimate $\hat{a}_r$ of $a$ is given by:

$$\frac{\partial J_r}{\partial \hat{a}_r} = 0 = -2 \sum_{k=1}^{r} q_k u_k(x_k - \hat{a}_r u_k) \tag{6.3}$$

yielding:

$$\hat{a}_r = \frac{\sum_{k=1}^{r} q_k u_k x_k}{\sum_{k=1}^{r} q_k u_k^2} \tag{6.4}$$

The derivation of $\hat{a}_r$ may be formulated in a sequential manner to give a result identical to Equation (6.4) after $r$ sets of measurement, as follows: From Equation (6.3) we derive that:[1]

$$\hat{a}_1 = \frac{q_1 u_1 x_1}{q_1 u_1^2} \tag{6.5}$$

and:

$$\hat{a}_2 = \frac{q_1 u_1 x_1 + q_2 u_2 x_2}{q_1 u_1^2 + q_2 u_2^2} \tag{6.6}$$

However, Equation (6.6) can be rewritten as:

$$\begin{aligned} \hat{a}_2 &= \hat{a}_1 - \frac{\hat{a}_1 q_1 u_1^2 + \hat{a}_1 q_2 u_2^2}{q_1 u_1^2 + q_2 u_2^2} + \frac{q_1 u_1 x_1 + q_2 u_2 x_2}{q_1 u_1^2 + q_2 u_2^2} \\ &= \hat{a}_1 + \frac{q_1 u_1 (x_1 - \hat{a}_1 u_1) + q_2 u_2 (x_2 - \hat{a}_1 u_2)}{q_1 u_1^2 + q_2 u_2^2} \end{aligned} \tag{6.7}$$

Substituting from Equation (6.5) into the second term in the right-hand-side of Equation (6.7) yields:

$$\begin{aligned} \hat{a}_2 &= \hat{a}_1 + \frac{q_1 u_1 \left( x_1 - \frac{(q_1 u_1 x_1)}{q_1 u_1^2} u_1 \right) + q_2 u_2 \left( x_2 - \frac{q_1 u_1 x_1}{q_1 u_1^2} u_2 \right)}{q_1 u_1^2 + q_2 u_2^2} \\ &= \hat{a}_1 + \frac{0 + q_2 u_2 (x_2 - \hat{a}_1 u_2)}{q_1 u_1^2 + q_2 u_2^2} \\ &= \hat{a}_1 + \frac{q_2 u_2 (x_2 - \hat{a}_1 u_2)}{q_1 u_1^2 + q_2 u_2^2} \end{aligned} \tag{6.8}$$

and, in a similar manner we obtain:

$$\hat{a}_j = \hat{a}_{j-1} + p_j q_j u_j (x_j - \hat{a}_{j-1} u_j) \tag{6.9}$$

where:

$$\hat{a}_0 = 0 \tag{6.10}$$

Consequently:

$$\frac{1}{p_1} = q_1 u_1^2 \tag{6.11}$$

$$\frac{1}{p_2} = q_1 u_1^2 + q_2 u_2^2 = \frac{1}{p_1} + q_2 u_2^2 \tag{6.12}$$

and:

$$\frac{1}{p_j} = \sum_{k=1}^{j} q_k u_k^2 = \frac{1}{p_{j-1}} + q_j u_j^2 \qquad \forall j > 1 \tag{6.13}$$

We note that the sequentially derived result of equations (6.9) and (6.13) is identical to that of Equation (6.4) for all values of $r$.

## 6.2 THE MULTI-PARAMETER CASE

Consider a multi-parameter system given by:

$$x_k = a_1 u_{1,k} + a_2 u_{2,k} + \cdots a_m u_{m,k} + n_k \tag{6.14}$$

where $a_i (i = 1 \cdots m)$ are the unknown parameters that require identification, $x_k$ being the system's output at the $k$'th sampling interval, $u_{i,k}$ being the $i$'th input to the system at the $k$'th sampling interval, and $n_k$ being measurement noise. Equation (6.14) may be written in vector form as:

$$x_k = \mathbf{a}^T \mathbf{u}_k + n_k \tag{6.15}$$

where:

$$\mathbf{a}^T \triangleq [a_1 \cdots a_m] \tag{6.16}$$

$$\mathbf{u}_k \triangleq [u_{1,k} \cdots u_{m,k}]^T \tag{6.17}$$

The estimation of the parameters vector $\mathbf{a}$ is performed such that the estimated $\hat{\mathbf{a}}_r$ minimize the cost index $J_r$, $r$ denoting the number of sets of measurement, where, in analogy to Equation (6.2):

$$J_r = \sum_{k=1}^{r} q_k (x_k - \hat{\mathbf{a}}_r^T \mathbf{u}_k)^2 \tag{6.18}$$

Consequently, $\hat{\mathbf{a}}_r$ should satisfy:

$$\frac{\partial J_r}{\partial \hat{\mathbf{a}}_r} = 0 \tag{6.19}$$

such that:

$$\left(\sum_{k=1}^{r} q_k \mathbf{u}_k \mathbf{u}_k^T\right) \hat{\mathbf{a}}_r = \sum_{k=1}^{r} q_k x_k \mathbf{u}_k \tag{6.20}$$

Defining:

$$\mathbf{P}_r^{-1} \triangleq \sum_{k=1}^{r} q_k(\mathbf{u}_k\mathbf{u}_k^T) \tag{6.21}$$

$\mathbf{P}_r^{-1}$ being invertible only when $r \geq m$, $m$ being the dimension of $\mathbf{u}$ and $r$ being the number of sets of measurement considered, Equation (6.20) becomes:

$$\mathbf{P}_r^{-1}\hat{\mathbf{a}}_r = \sum_{k=1}^{r} q_k x_k \mathbf{u}_k \tag{6.22}$$

or:

$$\hat{\mathbf{a}}_r = \mathbf{P}_r \sum_{k=1}^{r} q_k x_k \mathbf{u}_k \tag{6.23}$$

the latter being the ordinary linear regression estimate of $\mathbf{a}$, which is identical to the regression estimate of Section 5.1. We observe that although $\mathbf{u}_k\mathbf{u}_k^T$ is singular, the matrix $\mathbf{P}_r^{-1}$ of Equation (6.21) is nonsingular due to the summation on $k$. Equation (6.22) may be further written as:

$$\mathbf{P}_r^{-1}\hat{\mathbf{a}}_r = \sum_{k=1}^{r-1} q_k x_k \mathbf{u}_k + q_r x_r \mathbf{u}_r \tag{6.24}$$

Noting from Equation (6.20) that:

$$\sum_{k=1}^{r-1} q_k x_k \mathbf{u}_k = \left(\sum_{k=1}^{r-1} q_k \mathbf{u}_k \mathbf{u}_k^T\right)\hat{\mathbf{a}}_{r-1} \tag{6.25}$$

we may substitute for $\sum_{k=1}^{r-1} q_k x_k \mathbf{u}_k$ from Equation (6.25) into (6.24), to yield:

$$\mathbf{P}_r^{-1}\hat{\mathbf{a}}_r = \left(\sum_{k=1}^{r-1} q_k \mathbf{u}_k \mathbf{u}_k^T\right)\hat{\mathbf{a}}_{r-1} + q_r x_r \mathbf{u}_r \tag{6.26}$$

Adding and subtracting $[q_r \mathbf{u}_r \mathbf{u}_r^T \hat{\mathbf{a}}_{r-1}]$ at the right-hand-side of Equation (6.26), we obtain that:

$$\begin{aligned}\mathbf{P}_r^{-1}\hat{\mathbf{a}}_r &= \left(\sum_{k=1}^{r-1} q_k \mathbf{u}_k \mathbf{u}_k^T\right)\hat{\mathbf{a}}_{r-1} + q_r \mathbf{u}_r(x_r - \mathbf{u}_r^T\hat{\mathbf{a}}_{r-1}) + q_r \mathbf{u}_r \mathbf{u}_r^T \hat{\mathbf{a}}_{r-1} \\ &= \left(\sum_{k=1}^{r} q_k \mathbf{u}_k \mathbf{u}_k^T\right)\hat{\mathbf{a}}_{r-1} + q_r \mathbf{u}_r(x_r - \mathbf{u}_r^T\hat{\mathbf{a}}_{r-1}) \end{aligned} \tag{6.27}$$

Considering the definition of $\mathbf{P}_r^{-1}$ of Equation (6.21), Equation (6.27) thus becomes:

$$\mathbf{P}_r^{-1}\hat{\mathbf{a}}_r = \mathbf{P}_r^{-1}\hat{\mathbf{a}}_{r-1} + q_r \mathbf{u}_r(x_r - \mathbf{u}_r^T\hat{\mathbf{a}}_{r-1}) \tag{6.28}$$

to yield:

$$\hat{\mathbf{a}}_r = \hat{\mathbf{a}}_{r-1} + \mathbf{P}_r q_r \mathbf{u}_r(x_r - \mathbf{u}_r^T\hat{\mathbf{a}}_{r-1}) \tag{6.29}$$

Hence, $\hat{\mathbf{a}}_r$ may be derived sequentially from the previous estimate $\hat{\mathbf{a}}_{r-1}$, and from the measurements and weights $x_r$, $\mathbf{u}_r$, $q_r$, provided that $\mathbf{P}_r$ may also be sequentially obtained. Furthermore, according to Equation (6.21):

$$\mathbf{P}_r^{-1} = \sum_{k=1}^{r-1} q_k(\mathbf{u}_k \mathbf{u}_k^T) + q_r \mathbf{u}_r \mathbf{u}_r^T = \mathbf{P}_{r-1}^{-1} + q_r \mathbf{u}_r \mathbf{u}_r^T \tag{6.30}$$

the latter equation being analogous to the scalar Equation (6.13).

The expression for $\mathbf{P}_r^{-1}$ as in Equation (6.30) appears to require the inversion of the matrix $\mathbf{P}_r$ and the availability of the initial matrix $\mathbf{P}_0$. However, instead of inverting the matrix $\mathbf{P}_r$, we now employ the *matrix inversion lemma*[2] to facilitate a recursive derivation of $\mathbf{P}_r$, as follows:
We first define:

$$\mathbf{H}_r \triangleq \sqrt{q_r}\,\mathbf{u}_r \tag{6.31-a}$$

such that:

$$\mathbf{H}_r \mathbf{H}_r^T = q_r \mathbf{u}_r \mathbf{u}_r^T \tag{6.31-b}$$

Multiplying both sides of Equation (6.30) by $\mathbf{P}_r$ at the left, yields:

$$\mathbf{I} = \mathbf{P}_r \mathbf{P}_{r-1}^{-1} + \mathbf{P}_r \mathbf{H}_r \mathbf{H}_r^T \tag{6.32}$$

Now, multiplying Equation (6.32) by $\mathbf{P}_{r-1}$ at the right results in:

$$\mathbf{P}_{r-1} = \mathbf{P}_r + \mathbf{P}_r \mathbf{H}_r \mathbf{H}_r^T \mathbf{P}_{r-1} \tag{6.33}$$

If we further multiply at the right by $\mathbf{H}_r$, we obtain:

$$\mathbf{P}_{r-1}\mathbf{H}_r = \mathbf{P}_r \mathbf{H}_r + \mathbf{P}_r \mathbf{H}_r \mathbf{H}_r^T \mathbf{P}_{r-1}\mathbf{H}_r = \mathbf{P}_r \mathbf{H}_r(1 + \mathbf{H}_r^T \mathbf{P}_{r-1}\mathbf{H}_r) \tag{6.34}$$

Multiplying Equation (6.34) by $[(1 + \mathbf{H}_r^T \mathbf{P}_{r-1}\mathbf{H}_r)^{-1}\mathbf{H}_r^T \mathbf{P}_{r-1}]$ at the right gives (noting that $[1 + \mathbf{H}_r^T \mathbf{P}_{r-1}\mathbf{H}_r]$ is a scalar):

$$\mathbf{P}_{r-1}\mathbf{H}_r(1 + \mathbf{H}_r^T \mathbf{P}_{r-1}\mathbf{H}_r)^{-1}\mathbf{H}_r^T \mathbf{P}_{r-1} = \mathbf{P}_r \mathbf{H}_r \mathbf{H}_r^T \mathbf{P}_{r-1} \tag{6.35}$$

Substituting for $[\mathbf{P}_r \mathbf{H}_r \mathbf{H}_r^T \mathbf{P}_{r-1}]$ from Equation (6.33) gives:

$$\mathbf{P}_{r-1}\mathbf{H}_r(1 + \mathbf{H}_r^T \mathbf{P}_{r-1}\mathbf{H}_r)^{-1}\mathbf{H}_r^T \mathbf{P}_{r-1} = \mathbf{P}_{r-1} - \mathbf{P}_r \tag{6.36}$$

to yield that:

$$\mathbf{P}_r = \mathbf{P}_{r-1} - \mathbf{P}_{r-1}\mathbf{H}_r(1 + \mathbf{H}_r^T \mathbf{P}_{r-1}\mathbf{H}_r)^{-1}\mathbf{H}_r^T \mathbf{P}_{r-1} \tag{6.37}$$

Since $(1 + \mathbf{H}_r^T \mathbf{P}_{r-1}\mathbf{H}_r)$ is a scalar, no matrix inversion is involved in deriving $\mathbf{P}_r$ by the recursive relation of Equation (6.37) above.

The initial estimate of $\mathbf{P}$ may be arbitrary.[3] However, for rapid convergence it may be advantageous to employ an initial estimate, due to Lee,[4] as follows:

Considering equations (6.21) and (6.30), we obtain:

$$\mathbf{P}_n^{-1} = \mathbf{P}_0^{-1} + \sum_{k=1}^{n} q_k(\mathbf{u}_k \mathbf{u}_k^T) \tag{6.38}$$

Noting the equivalence of equations (6.20) and (5.15), and since the regression procedure based on Equation (6.20) must lead to the same least-squares (and thus bounded) estimate of **a** as that based on Equation (5.15), we require that:

$$\mathbf{P}_0^{-1} = \mathbf{0} \tag{6.39}$$

Substituting from Equation (6.39) into (6.30), the estimated $\mathbf{a}_n$ derived from Equation (6.29), for $r = m$ ($m$ being the dimension of **a**), becomes identical to the least-squares estimate of Equation (5.16) for:

$$\hat{\mathbf{a}}_0 = \mathbf{0} \tag{6.40}$$

Consequently, the initial estimate:

$$\mathbf{P}_0 = \frac{1}{\varepsilon}\mathbf{I}; \qquad \varepsilon \to 0 \tag{6.41}$$

together with the initial parameter estimate of Equation (6.40) lead to a parameter estimate that converges in $n$ steps in a least-squares sense (namely, to the nonsequential regression estimate).

The term $1/\varepsilon$ may be chosen almost arbitrarily between 10 and the value corresponding to the highest number that can be stored in the computer that is employed. The solution to Problem 1 indicates that any such choice hardly affects $\hat{\mathbf{a}}_i$ or $\mathbf{P}_i$ for all $i$ but for $i = 1$. It should, however, be noted that $1/\varepsilon$ should not be larger than that value corresponding to the highest significant decimal place of the computer that is employed. Otherwise, $\varepsilon$ may be considered as zero and may lead to zero or at least to nonsensical matrices for $\mathbf{P}_i$, thus preventing the computation of $\hat{\mathbf{a}}_i$ of Equation (6.29), as is illustrated by the following example.

EXAMPLE 6.1

Consider a system $y = \mathbf{a}^T\mathbf{x}$, where **a** is the parameter vector to be identified and where:

$$x_1 = \begin{bmatrix} 4 \\ 3 \end{bmatrix}; \quad x_2 = \begin{bmatrix} 1 \\ 2 \end{bmatrix}, \quad y_1 = 11; \quad y_2 = 4$$

Let:

$$\mathbf{P}_0 = \frac{1}{\varepsilon}\mathbf{I} = 10^5\mathbf{I}; \qquad \varepsilon = 10^{-5}$$

Consequently, according to Equation (6.37):

$$\mathbf{P}_1 = \frac{1}{\varepsilon}\mathbf{I} - \frac{\frac{1}{\varepsilon}\begin{bmatrix}16 & 12\\ 12 & 9\end{bmatrix}}{\varepsilon + 25}$$

$$= 4\cdot 10^3\begin{bmatrix}9 + 1\cdot 10^{-5} & -12\\ -12 & 16 + 10^{-5}\end{bmatrix} = 4\cdot 10^3\begin{bmatrix}9+\varepsilon & -12\\ -12 & 16+\varepsilon\end{bmatrix}$$

$$\hat{\mathbf{a}}_1 = 4\cdot 10^3\begin{bmatrix}9+\varepsilon & -12\\ -12 & 16+\varepsilon\end{bmatrix}\begin{bmatrix}4\\ 3\end{bmatrix}11 = 4\cdot 10^3\begin{bmatrix}4\cdot\varepsilon\\ 3\cdot\varepsilon\end{bmatrix}\cdot 11 = \begin{bmatrix}1.76\\ 1.32\end{bmatrix}$$

$$\mathbf{P}_2 = 4\cdot 10^3\begin{bmatrix}9+\varepsilon & -12\\ -12 & 16+\varepsilon\end{bmatrix} - \frac{16\cdot 10^6\begin{bmatrix}9+\varepsilon & -12\\ -12 & 16+\varepsilon\end{bmatrix}\begin{bmatrix}1 & 2\\ 2 & 4\end{bmatrix}\begin{bmatrix}9+\varepsilon & -12\\ -12 & 16+\varepsilon\end{bmatrix}}{1 + 4\cdot 10^3[1;\ 2]\begin{bmatrix}9+\varepsilon & -12\\ -12 & 16+\varepsilon\end{bmatrix}\begin{bmatrix}1\\ 2\end{bmatrix}}$$

$$= 4\cdot 10^3\begin{bmatrix}9+\varepsilon & -12\\ -12 & 16+\varepsilon\end{bmatrix} - \frac{16\cdot 10^6\begin{bmatrix}(225 - 30\varepsilon + \varepsilon^2); (-300 - 10\varepsilon + 2\varepsilon^2)\\ (-300 - 10\varepsilon + 2\varepsilon^2); (400 + 80\varepsilon + 4\varepsilon^2)\end{bmatrix}}{1 + 4\cdot 10^3(25 + 5\varepsilon)}$$

$$= \frac{16\cdot 10^6\begin{bmatrix}(9+\varepsilon)25\cdot\varepsilon; -300\varepsilon\\ -300\varepsilon; (16+\varepsilon)\cdot 25\cdot\varepsilon\end{bmatrix} + \begin{bmatrix}(9+\varepsilon)(25+3\varepsilon); -12(25+3\varepsilon)\\ -12(25+3\cdot\varepsilon); (16+\varepsilon)(25+3\varepsilon)\end{bmatrix} - \begin{bmatrix}(225 - 30\varepsilon + \varepsilon^2); (-300 - 10\varepsilon + 2\varepsilon^2)\\ (-300 - 10\varepsilon + 2\varepsilon^2); (400 + 80\varepsilon + 4\varepsilon^2)\end{bmatrix}}{4\cdot 10^3(25 + 5\varepsilon)}$$

$$\cong \frac{4\cdot 10^3}{25}\begin{bmatrix}((9+\varepsilon)100\cdot\varepsilon + 92\cdot\varepsilon + 2\varepsilon^2); & (-300\cdot\varepsilon - 26\varepsilon - 2\varepsilon^2)\\ (-300\varepsilon - 26\varepsilon - 2\varepsilon^2); & ((16+\varepsilon)25\cdot\varepsilon - 7\varepsilon - \varepsilon^2)\end{bmatrix}$$

Neglecting terms of $\varepsilon^2$ we thus obtain:

$$\mathbf{P}_2 \cong \begin{bmatrix}0.507 & -0.522\\ -0.522 & +0.629\end{bmatrix}$$

and:

$$\hat{\mathbf{a}}_2 = \begin{bmatrix}1.913\\ 1.055\end{bmatrix}$$

while by nonsequential regression of the two sets of measurements above we obtain $\hat{\mathbf{a}}_2 = \begin{bmatrix} 2 \\ 1 \end{bmatrix}$, the latter being equal to the true **a** since the measurements above did not contain noise. We observe that had $\varepsilon$ been neglected at the denominator term $(\varepsilon + 25)$ of $\mathbf{P}_1$, then $\mathbf{P}_2$ would have been zero and no derivation of $\hat{\mathbf{a}}$ of Equation (6.29) would have been possible. Furthermore, the recursive computation of $\hat{\mathbf{a}}_i$ indicates that $\varepsilon$ may not be neglected since otherwise $\hat{\mathbf{a}}_1$ would also have been zero.

## 6.3 SEQUENTIAL NONLINEAR REGRESSION

We have already mentioned in Chapter 5 that according to the Weirstrass theorem,[5] every continuous nonlinear function $f[x(t)]$ of $x$ may be approximated by a polynomial of $x$ such that the latter polynomial converges to $f[x(t)]$. Furthermore, in Section 5.6 we showed how the parameters of a polynomial function of $x$ are identified in a least-squares sense, through reformulating the polynomial expression given by (for a two-input and third order case):

$$x(t) = a_1 f(u_1) + a_2 f^2(u_1) + a_3 f^3(u_1) + b_1 f(u_2) + b_2 f^2(u_2) + b_3 f^3(u_2) \tag{6.42}$$

to obtain:

$$\begin{aligned} x(t) &= \alpha_1 z_1 + \alpha_2 z_2 + \alpha_3 z_3 + \cdots \alpha_6 z_6 \\ &= \boldsymbol{\alpha}^T \mathbf{z} \end{aligned} \tag{6.43}$$

where:

$$\boldsymbol{\alpha} = \begin{bmatrix} \alpha_1 \\ \alpha_2 \\ \alpha_3 \\ \cdot \\ \cdot \\ \cdot \\ \cdot \\ \alpha_6 \end{bmatrix} \triangleq \begin{bmatrix} a_1 \\ a_2 \\ a_3 \\ b_1 \\ \cdot \\ \cdot \\ \cdot \\ b_3 \end{bmatrix} \tag{6.44-a}$$

and:

$$\mathbf{z} = \begin{bmatrix} z_1 \\ z_2 \\ z_3 \\ z_4 \\ z_5 \\ z_6 \end{bmatrix} \triangleq \begin{bmatrix} f(u_1) \\ f^2(u_1) \\ f^3(u_1) \\ f(u_2) \\ f^2(u_2) \\ f^3(u_2) \end{bmatrix} \tag{6.44-b}$$

The identification of $\alpha$ thus becomes a problem of identifying parameters of a linear regression Equation (6.43). The latter identification may be performed in a sequential manner through employing the procedure of Section 6.2, yielding sequential estimates of the parameters of nonlinear systems, which are based on least-squares error considerations. Sequential regression is similarly applicable to the generalized formulation of dynamic systems with unknown nonlinearities, which is given in Section 7.3 for reasons of convenience of the related analysis.

Since sequential nonlinear regression procedures avoid the inversion of matrices, they could be used whenever nonlinear regression identification is performed, and thus overcome ill-conditioning of matrices that arise in many nonlinear systems. We note that the matrices to be inverted are of higher dimensions than for the equivalent linear systems. For example, in the two-input processes of Equation (6.42), with a third order polynomial approximation, a six-dimensional input was considered. This case would have required the inversion of a $6 \times 6$ matrix instead of a $2 \times 2$ matrix in the linear case, if nonsequential regression were employed, thus illustrating the effectiveness of sequential regression even in low dimensional nonlinear systems.

## REFERENCES

1. Fu, K. S., Hass, V. B., Kashyap, R. L., Koivo, A. J., Saridis, G. N., and Wozny, M. J. *Modern Automatic Control*, Vol. 2, Text of short lecture course offered by the School of Electrical Engineering, Purdue University, (part of Summer School Lectures at Technion, Haifa, 1969).
2. Sage, A. P. *Optimum Systems Design*, Prentice Hall, Englewood Cliffs, N. J., 1968, p. 276.
3. Albert, A. E. and Gardner, L. A. *Stochastic Approximation and Nonlinear Regression*, M.I.T. Press, Cambridge, Mass., 1967.
4. Lee, R. C. K. *Optimal Estimation, Identification and Control*, M.I.T. Press, Cambridge, Mass., 1964 (Section 4.3.1.).
5. Sokolnikoff, I. S., and Redheffer, R. M. *Mathematics of Physics and Engineering*, McGraw-Hill, New York, 1966 (Chapter 1).

## PROBLEMS

**1.** Compute the parameter vector $\mathbf{a} = [a_1 \; ; \; a_2]^T$ of the system $y = \mathbf{a}^T\mathbf{x}$ by sequential regression, for three different values for $1/\varepsilon$, two of these being below the highest computer word length and one above that value (say $1/\varepsilon = 10^4$; $10^8$; $10^{20}$, for a computer maximum word length of 15 decimal bits). For identification, consider the following sets of measurements of $y$; $x_1$; $x_2$:

| $y$ | $x_1$ | $x_2$ |
|---|---|---|
| 3.78897E+00 | 3.35934E-01 | 1.33018E+00 |
| -4.67471E+00 | 3.78897E+00 | -8.00442E-01 |
| 9.17902E-02 | -4.67471E+00 | -9.04345E-01 |
| -5.12105E+00 | 9.17902E-02 | -1.68866E+00 |
| 3.81774E+00 | -5.12105E+00 | 2.48370E-01 |
| -9.24301E-02 | 3.81774E+00 | 7.32738E-01 |
| 2.79226E+00 | -9.24301E-02 | 9.12268E-01 |
| -2.68106E+00 | 2.79226E+00 | -3.35233E-01 |
| 6.97041E-01 | -2.68106E+00 | -3.03864E-01 |
| 5.71532E+00 | 6.97041E-01 | 2.04451E+00 |
| -4.32101E+00 | 5.71532E+00 | -2.97272E-01 |
| 5.00455E+00 | -4.32101E+00 | 8.03982E-01 |
| -7.16561E+00 | 5.00455E+00 | -1.38763E+00 |
| 2.02171E+00 | -7.16561E+00 | -7.59219E-01 |
| -7.22613E-01 | 2.02171E+00 | 1.63471E-01 |
| 2.27832E+00 | -7.22613E-01 | 6.14916E-01 |
| -6.38333E+00 | 2.27832E+00 | -1.67211E+00 |
| 5.44011E+00 | -6.38333E+00 | 5.36703E-01 |
| -3.17230E+00 | 5.44011E+00 | 3.05881E-02 |
| 1.63904E+00 | -3.17230E+00 | -8.61123E-02 |
| 1.84241E+00 | 1.63904E+00 | 9.41946E-01 |
| 6.30425E+00 | 1.84241E+00 | 2.46990E+00 |
| -5.93066E+00 | 6.30425E+00 | -7.16038E-01 |
| 8.13250E-01 | -5.93066E+00 | -9.15049E-01 |
| 5.99851E-01 | 8.13250E-01 | 3.62600E-01 |
| 3.25144E+00 | 5.99851E-01 | 1.20378E+00 |
| 4.09460E+00 | 3.25144E+00 | 2.01516E+00 |
| -1.16127E+00 | 4.09460E+00 | 4.31830E-01 |
| 5.52459E-01 | -1.16127E+00 | -4.81013E-02 |
| -2.40794E-01 | 5.52459E-01 | 3.02272E-02 |
| -3.04074E+00 | -2.40794E-01 | -1.06174E+00 |

$E+02$ indicating a multiplication by $10^{+2}$, etc.

**2.** Compute $\hat{\mathbf{a}}$ by sequential and by nonsequential regression for the following sets of measurements:

$$\mathbf{x}_1 = \begin{bmatrix} 1 \\ 2 \\ -2 \end{bmatrix}; \quad \mathbf{x}_2 = \begin{bmatrix} 2 \\ -1 \\ 1 \end{bmatrix}; \quad \mathbf{x}_3 = \begin{bmatrix} 1 \\ 1 \\ 2 \end{bmatrix}$$

$$\mathbf{x}_4 = \begin{bmatrix} -1 \\ -2 \\ 1 \end{bmatrix}; \quad y_1 = -1; \quad y_2 = 3; \quad y_3 = 9; \quad y_4 = -2$$

for $y = \mathbf{a}^T \mathbf{x}$.

**3.** Employ sequential regression to identify the parameters $a_i$ of the nonlinear system $y = \sum_{i=0}^{3} a_i x^i$, using the data of Problem 4 in Chapter 5.

# 7

# STOCHASTIC APPROXIMATION AND SEQUENTIAL LEARNING IDENTIFICATION

## 7.1 A STOCHASTIC APPROXIMATION APPROACH TO IDENTIFICATION

The stochastic approximation approach to the identification of linear and nonlinear stationary processes is essentially a sequential gradient-seeking approach. Its convergence is guaranteed if only very weak and general requirements are satisfied, which may be based on the Dvoretzky theorem.[1] Stochastic approximation identification procedures do not assume least-squares convergence at each estimation step past the first $m$ estimates as is the case in the sequential regression techniques of Chapter 6 ($m$ being the dimension of the parameter vector), and take therefore somewhat longer to converge. However, the convenient sequential structure of stochastic approximation techniques, which have been mentioned above, make them attractive and fast to implement and to compute. The gradient-seeking methods employed in the stochastic approximation identification algorithms may be considered to be extensions of Newton's classical root-seeking method. These have been successfully incorporated by Robbins and Munro[2] and by Kiefer and Wolfowitz[3] in a convergence philosophy that may be based on Dvoretzky's theorem. The applications of stochastic approximation to identification dates back to the work of Blum,[4] and has been discussed by several authors since.[5–8]

The techniques of the present chapter may be applied to predictor models as in Chapter 12, instead of sequential regression, but are usually slower to converge.

### 7.1.1 Outline of the Stochastic Approximation Identification Procedure

Consider a discrete stationary system given by:

$$x_k = \Phi(u_k\,; u_{k-1} \cdots \mathbf{p}) \tag{7.1}$$

which is a nonlinear generalization of Equation 5.47, and:

$$y_k = x_k + v_k \tag{7.2}$$

$x, u, y, v$ being message, input, output and measurement-noise terms, respectively, $\mathbf{p}$ denoting the parameter vector that requires identification, and $\Phi$ being a linear or a given nonlinear function of $x$, $\mathbf{u}$ and of the unknown $\mathbf{p}$, where:

$$\mathbf{u}_k = (u_k \cdots u_{k-r})^T \tag{7.3}$$

Substituting from equation (7.3) into (7.1), equation (7.1) becomes:

$$x_k = \Phi(\mathbf{u}_k\,; \mathbf{p}) \tag{7.4}$$

The estimate $\hat{\mathbf{p}}_n$ of $\mathbf{p}$ (at the $n$'th sequential stage) is derived from the stochastic approximation algorithm, as follows:

$$\hat{\mathbf{p}}_{n+1} = \hat{\mathbf{p}}_n - \rho_n \psi_n \qquad \forall n = 1, 2, 3, \ldots \tag{7.5}$$

$\psi_n$ being a function that can be readily evaluated from the measurements of $y$ and whose expected value is zero for the accurate $\mathbf{p}$, $\mathbf{u}$ of equations (7.1) and (7.3), and $\rho_n$ being a sequence of scalar correction coefficients.

For convergence, the sequence $\rho_n$ must satisfy the following conditions that are based on Dvoretzky's theorem[1, 6]

$$\lim_{n\to\infty} \rho_n = 0 \tag{7.6}$$

$$\lim_{n\to\infty} \sum_{k=1}^{n} \rho_k = \infty \tag{7.7}$$

$$\lim_{n\to\infty} \sum_{k=1}^{n} \rho_k^2 < \infty \tag{7.8}$$

Obviously, any function of the form $\rho_k = \rho_1/k$ satisfies the requirements of equations (7.6)–(7.8), as do many other functions of $k$.

The vector function $\boldsymbol{\psi}_k$ considered in Equation (7.5) was proposed by Kiefer and Wolfowitz[3] to represent a gradient function. Hence, $\boldsymbol{\psi}_k$ may be derived as follows:
Let $J_k(\hat{\mathbf{p}})$ be a scalar identification performance index, definable as:

$$J_k(\hat{\mathbf{p}}) \triangleq \tfrac{1}{2}(y_k - \Phi(\mathbf{u}_k; \hat{\mathbf{p}}_k))^2 \tag{7.9}$$

and:

$$\boldsymbol{\psi}_k \triangleq \frac{\partial J_k(\hat{\mathbf{p}})}{\partial \hat{\mathbf{p}}_k} = \begin{bmatrix} \dfrac{\partial J_k}{\partial \hat{p}_{1,k}} \\ \dfrac{\partial J_k}{\partial \hat{p}_{2,k}} \\ \vdots \\ \dfrac{\partial J_k}{\partial \hat{p}_{m,k}} \end{bmatrix} \tag{7.10}$$

$\hat{p}_{1,k}; \hat{p}_{2,k}; \ldots \hat{p}_{m,k}$ being the elements of $\hat{\mathbf{p}}_k$. Subsequently, in accordance with Appendix 2:

$$\begin{aligned} \boldsymbol{\psi}_k = \frac{\partial J_k(\hat{\mathbf{p}})}{\partial \hat{\mathbf{p}}_k} &= [\Phi(\mathbf{u}_k; \hat{\mathbf{p}}_k) - y_k] \cdot \frac{\partial \Phi(\mathbf{u}_k; \hat{\mathbf{p}}_k)}{\partial \hat{\mathbf{p}}_k} \\ &= [\Phi(\mathbf{u}_k; \hat{\mathbf{p}}_k) - y_k] \cdot \mathbf{g}_k(\mathbf{u}_k; \hat{\mathbf{p}}_k) \end{aligned} \tag{7.11}$$

where:

$$\frac{\partial \Phi(\mathbf{u}_k; \hat{\mathbf{p}}_k)}{\partial \hat{\mathbf{p}}_k} = \mathbf{g}_k(\mathbf{u}_k; \hat{\mathbf{p}}_k) \tag{7.12}$$

We note that $\boldsymbol{\psi}_k$ may be evaluated from measurements of $y_k$, $\mathbf{u}_k$ and from the previous estimates of $\hat{\mathbf{p}}$.
The identification procedure of Equation (7.5) thus depends on the initial estimates $\hat{\mathbf{p}}_1$ ($\mathbf{p}_1$ denoting the initial set $p_1 \ldots p_q$) and on the initial coefficient $\rho_1$, whereas the evaluation of $\boldsymbol{\psi}_k$ may be illustrated by considering the following example of a linear system, given by:

$$u_k = \mathbf{p}^T \mathbf{u}_k = \Phi(\mathbf{u}_k; \mathbf{p}) \tag{7.13}$$

Consequently, noting Appendix 2:

$$\mathbf{g}_k(\mathbf{u}_k; \hat{\mathbf{p}}_k) = \frac{\partial \Phi(\mathbf{u}_k; \hat{\mathbf{p}}_k)}{\partial \hat{\mathbf{p}}_k} \tag{7.14}$$

and:

$$\boldsymbol{\psi}_k = [\Phi(\mathbf{u}_k; \hat{\mathbf{p}}_k) - y_k] \cdot \mathbf{g}(\mathbf{u}_k; \hat{\mathbf{p}}_k) = (\hat{\mathbf{p}}_k \mathbf{u}_k - y_k)\mathbf{u}_k \tag{7.15}$$

If identification of state equations or of transfer functions is required, whose orders are unknown, the determination of the orders may be performed by the methods of Section 5.4.

### 7.1.2 Initial Estimates for the Identification Algorithm

For starting the identification procedure of Section 7.1.1, we may assume that $\hat{\mathbf{x}}_1 = \mathbf{y}_1$ ($\mathbf{y}_1$ denoting the first $m$ measurements), and that $\hat{\mathbf{p}}_1$ may be derived by an initial estimate as in the sequential learning procedure of Section 7.2 that is based on Equation (7.29) below, when:

$$\hat{\mathbf{p}}_1 = \mathbf{0} \tag{7.16}$$

Hence, if the system of Equation (7.1) is linear, the estimate $\hat{\mathbf{p}}_2$ becomes:

$$\Delta\hat{\mathbf{p}}_2 = \hat{\mathbf{p}}_2 - \hat{\mathbf{p}}_1 = \hat{\mathbf{p}}_2 = \frac{y_{m+1} - \hat{y}_{m+1}}{\hat{\boldsymbol{\mu}}_1^T \hat{\boldsymbol{\mu}}_1} \hat{\boldsymbol{\mu}}_1 \tag{7.17}$$

$\hat{y}_{m+1}$ being 0 in the absence of other prior information.

If, $\Phi$ of Equation (7.1) is a nonlinear function, a linear form of the latter equation can often be derived as may be illustrated by considering an example of a nonlinear system given by:

$$x_{k+1} = p_1 x_k^2 + 2p_2 u_k^3$$

where, defining:

$$\boldsymbol{\mu}_k \triangleq \begin{bmatrix} (x_k)^2 \\ (u_k)^3 \end{bmatrix}$$

we derive a linear system, which is to be considered for the subsequent derivation of the initial estimates.

Equation (7.17) fully satisfies Equation (7.5) if the initial coefficient $\rho_1$ is given by:[8]

$$\rho_1 = \frac{1}{\|\mathbf{g}_1(\hat{\boldsymbol{\mu}}_1; \mathbf{p}_1)\|} = \frac{1}{\mathbf{g}_1^T \mathbf{g}_1} \tag{7.18}$$

and adds no new algorithm to the procedure if the latter $\rho$ is adopted. We note that, because of the convergence features of the stochastic approximation techniques, other initial estimates are also possible.

EXAMPLE 7.1

Consider the identification of the parameter vector $\mathbf{p}$ of the system $\omega = \mathbf{p}^T\mathbf{u} + \mu$, $\mu$ being measurement noise and:

$$\omega_1 = 11.3; \qquad \omega_2 = 3.9; \qquad \omega_3 = 3.11;$$
$$\mathbf{u}_1 = [4; 3]^T; \qquad \mathbf{u}_2 = [1; 2]^T; \qquad \mathbf{u}_3 = [2; -1]^T$$

Consequently, and since $\boldsymbol{\psi}_k = (\hat{\mathbf{p}}_k^T\mathbf{u}_k - \omega_k)\mathbf{u}_k$, we obtain, according to Equation (7.7):

$$\begin{aligned}\hat{\mathbf{p}}_{k+1} &= \hat{\mathbf{p}}_k - \rho_k \boldsymbol{\psi}_k \\ &= \hat{\mathbf{p}}_k - \rho_k(\hat{\mathbf{p}}_k^T\mathbf{u}_k - \omega_k)\mathbf{u}_k\end{aligned}$$

Substituting:

$$\rho_1 = \frac{1}{\mathbf{g}_1^T\mathbf{g}_1}$$

and since:

$$\mathbf{u}_k = \mathbf{g}_k$$

we obtain that:

$$\rho_1 = \frac{1}{25}$$

Starting with $\hat{\mathbf{p}}_1 = 0$, and assuming that $\hat{\omega}_1 = 0$, we subsequently obtain that:

$$\hat{\mathbf{p}}_2 = \frac{\omega_1 - \hat{\omega}_1}{\mathbf{u}_1^T\mathbf{u}_1}\mathbf{u}_1 = \frac{11.3}{25}\cdot\begin{bmatrix}4\\3\end{bmatrix} = \begin{bmatrix}1.8\\1.35\end{bmatrix}$$

and:

$$\rho_i = \rho_1/i \qquad i = 2, 3, \ldots$$

$$\hat{\mathbf{p}}_3 = \hat{\mathbf{p}}_2 - \frac{\rho_1}{2}(\hat{\mathbf{p}}_2^T\mathbf{u}_2 - \omega_2^T)\mathbf{u}_2 =$$

$$\begin{bmatrix}1.8\\1.35\end{bmatrix} - \frac{1}{50}\left([1.8; 1.35]\begin{bmatrix}1\\2\end{bmatrix} - 3.9\right)\begin{bmatrix}1\\2\end{bmatrix} = \begin{bmatrix}1.8\\1.35\end{bmatrix} - \begin{bmatrix}0.012\\0.024\end{bmatrix} = \begin{bmatrix}1.788\\1.326\end{bmatrix}$$

$$\hat{\mathbf{p}}_4 = \hat{\mathbf{p}}_3 - \frac{\rho_1}{3}(\hat{\mathbf{p}}_3^T\mathbf{u}_3 - \omega_3)\mathbf{u}_3 = \begin{bmatrix}1.788\\1.326\end{bmatrix} - \frac{1}{75}(-0.85)\begin{bmatrix}2\\-1\end{bmatrix}$$

$$= \begin{bmatrix}1.788\\1.326\end{bmatrix} + \begin{bmatrix}0.026\\-0.013\end{bmatrix} = \begin{bmatrix}1.814\\1.313\end{bmatrix}$$

the true **p** being given by

$$\mathbf{p} = [1 \,; 2]^T$$

## 7.2 SEQUENTIAL LEARNING IDENTIFICATION

Nagumo and Noda[9,10] have proposed a method for sequential on-line identification of linear systems which is based on a simulated learning philosophy and where an impulse response model is derived. In similarity to stochastic approximation techniques, the sequential learning approach does not provide least-squares estimate of the parameters at the various sequential stages and is therefore somewhat slower in convergence than is sequential regression identification. It does, however, gradually converge to the true parameters (in the mean). Sequential learning differs from the stochastic approximation approach in the derivation of its convergence features and in its convenient applicability to processes having slowly-time-variant parameters. The main advantage of sequential learning in comparison to other sequential techniques lies in the simple formulation of the sequential identification algorithm.* The initial estimate of the sequential learning method may therefore be employed as an initial estimate to other sequential identification procedures, such as those based on stochastic approximation of Section 7.1 and on the quasilinearization approach of Chapter 8.

In nonstationary applications special identification noise may be required which is nondisturbing and therefore applicable on-line. We note that the present method is usually faster than stochastic approximation, and by far faster and simpler than the methods of Chapter 4.

In similarity to the regression and the stochastic approximation approaches, the sequential learning approach may employ a subroutine to determine the order of the state vector of transfer function, as is discussed in sections 5.3 and 5.4.

### 7.2.1 Identification of Stationary Processes

#### 7.2.1-a The fundamental identification algorithm

The sequential learning approach of Nagumo and Noda considers a system having a basically random input $u(t)$, an output $x(t)$, and an impulse response $g(t)$. These satisfy the convolution integral of Equation (4.2), which is restated below for zero initial conditions as:

$$x(t) = \int_0^t g(\tau)u(t-\tau)\, d\tau \tag{7.19}$$

*Sequential learning can be shown to converge[11] when identifying unstable systems, both deterministic and stochastic, stochastic systems being systems where input and/or output noises exist. No such convergence is possible via the method of Section 7.1, but it can be proven to exist for least squares regression algorithms[12].

$u$ being measurable and becomes, in discrete form:

$$x_j = \sum_{i=1}^{N} g_i u_{j-i} \tag{7.20}$$

which is similar to an infinite moving-average equation (for stochastic $u$). The derivation of $g_i$, which is the purpose of the identification, is accomplished through iteratively computing a set of values:

$$\hat{h}_1^{(j)}, \hat{h}_2^{(j)} \cdots \hat{h}_N^{(j)}; \qquad (\forall j = N+1, N+2, \ldots) \tag{7.21}$$

which should approach $g_1, g_2 \cdots g_N$ of Equation (7.20), $j$ denoting the iteration step. The estimated output $\hat{x}_j$ when employing $\hat{h}_i^{(j)}$ (at the $j$'th iteration), thus becomes, in analogy to Equation (7.20):

$$\hat{x}_j = \sum_{i=1}^{N} \hat{h}_i^{(j)} u_{j-i} \tag{7.22}$$

Defining:

$$\mathbf{g} \triangleq [g_1 \cdots g_N]^T \tag{7.23}$$

$$\hat{\mathbf{h}}_j \triangleq [\hat{h}_1^{(j)} \cdots \hat{h}_N^{(j)}]^T \tag{7.24}$$

and:

$$\mathbf{u}_j \triangleq [u_{j-1} \cdots u_{j-N}]^T \tag{7.25}$$

equations (7.20) and (7.22) become, respectively:

$$x_j = \mathbf{g}^T \mathbf{u}_j \tag{7.26}$$

and:

$$\hat{x}_j = \hat{\mathbf{h}}_j^T \mathbf{u}_j \tag{7.27}$$

We now consider a vector $\Delta\hat{\mathbf{h}}_j$ such that:

$$\Delta\hat{\mathbf{h}}_j \triangleq \hat{\mathbf{h}}_{j+1} - \hat{\mathbf{h}}_j \tag{7.28}$$

which serves to correct the next identification vector $\hat{\mathbf{h}}_{j+1}$, with respect to $\hat{\mathbf{h}}_j$, considering the $(x_j - \hat{x}_j)$ error in estimating $x_j$. Letting:[9, 13]

$$\Delta\hat{\mathbf{h}}_j = (x_j - \hat{x}_j) \frac{\mathbf{u}_j}{\mathbf{u}_j^T \mathbf{u}_j} \qquad @ \; j = 1, 2, 3, \ldots \tag{7.29}$$

we obtain that:

$$\mathbf{u}_j^T \Delta\hat{\mathbf{h}}_j = \frac{(x_j - \hat{x}_j)\mathbf{u}_j^T \mathbf{u}_j}{\mathbf{u}_j^T \mathbf{u}_j} = x_j - \hat{x}_j \tag{7.30}$$

which would satisfy equations (7.27) and (7.28) if $\hat{\mathbf{h}}_{j+1}$ were equal to $\mathbf{g}$. To start the estimation procedure of Equation (7.29) at $j = 1$, we may substitute $x_0$ for $\hat{x}_i$ in that equation.

### 7.2.1-b Convergence of Estimated Impulse Response to True Value

Noting equations (7.26) and (7.27), we observe that:

$$\mathbf{u}_j^T \Delta\hat{\mathbf{h}}_j \triangleq (\mathbf{g} - \hat{\mathbf{h}}_j)^T \mathbf{u}_j = \mathbf{u}_j^T(\mathbf{g} - \hat{\mathbf{h}}_j) \tag{7.31}$$

Hence, $\Delta\hat{\mathbf{h}}_j$ as defined in Equation (7.29) may represent a correction of $\hat{\mathbf{h}}_j$ towards $\mathbf{g}$, such that $\hat{\mathbf{h}}_{j+1}$ approach $\mathbf{g}$. The correction vector of Equation (7.29) thus yields $\hat{\mathbf{h}}_{j+1}$ according to Equation (7.28), on the basis of measurements of $x_j$, $\mathbf{u}_j$ and of the previous estimates $\hat{\mathbf{h}}_j$, $\hat{x}_j$. However, since $\mathbf{u}_j^T$ is a vector, it is not possible to conclude from Equation (7.31) that $\Delta\hat{\mathbf{h}}_j = \mathbf{g} - \hat{\mathbf{h}}_j$. It is therefore necessary to further examine the convergence of $\hat{\mathbf{h}}_j$ to $\mathbf{g}$.

A proof for the convergence of $\hat{\mathbf{h}}$ is presented in Ref. 9 and is based on a geometrical interpretation of equations (7.28) and (7.29) as in Figure 7.1.

For the geometrical interpretation of the convergence problem, we define an $(N-1)$-dimensional hyperplane $P_{j-1}$ in an $N$-dimensional space, such that $P_{j-1}$ describes the hyperplane which is *perpendicular* to $\mathbf{u}_{j-1}$. According to Equation (7.27), we have $\mathbf{u}_{j-1}^T\mathbf{g} = x_{j-1}$, whereas from Equation (7.30) we observe that $\mathbf{u}_{j-1}^T\mathbf{h}_j = \hat{x}_{j-1}$. Hence, and noting that a scalar is the inner product of two vectors such that the scalar is given by the product of their length times $\cos\theta$, $\theta$ being the angle between the vectors, the points $\mathbf{g}$ and $\mathbf{h}_j$ are on $P_{j-1}$. We similarly define a hyperplane $P_j$ that is perpendicular to $\mathbf{u}_j$. For the same reasoning as regarding $P_{j-1}$, the points $\mathbf{g}$, $\hat{\mathbf{h}}_{j+1}$ are on $P_j$. Equation (7.29) subsequently yields that $\mathbf{u}_j$ is parallel to $(\hat{\mathbf{h}}_{j+1} - \hat{\mathbf{h}}_j)$, and consequently that $(\mathbf{g} - \hat{\mathbf{h}}_{j+1})$ is perpendicular to $(\hat{\mathbf{h}}_{j+1} - \hat{\mathbf{h}}_j)$. Defining the angle between $\mathbf{u}_j$ and $(\mathbf{g} - \hat{\mathbf{h}}_j)$ as $\psi_j$, and denoting

$$\mathbf{e}_j \triangleq \mathbf{g} - \hat{\mathbf{h}}_j \tag{7.32}$$

we obtain that the angle between $\mathbf{u}_j$ and $\mathbf{e}_j$ is also $\psi_j$. Since, according to the definition of Equation (7.32):

$$\mathbf{e}_{j+1} = \Delta\hat{\mathbf{h}}_j \tag{7.33}$$

we further obtain that:

$$\frac{\|\mathbf{e}_{j+1}\|^2}{\|\mathbf{e}_j\|^2} = \sin^2\psi_j = 1 - \cos^2\psi_j \tag{7.34}$$

$\|\mathbf{e}_j{}^2\|$ denoting $\mathbf{e}_j^T\mathbf{e}_j$. Equation (7.34) yields that:

$$\|\mathbf{e}_{j+1}\|^2 = \|\mathbf{e}_{N+1}\|^2 \prod_{r=N+1}^{j} (1 - \cos^2\psi_r) \tag{7.35}$$

Finally, since $\cos\psi_r \leq 1\ \forall r$, Equation (7.35) indicates that:

$$\|\mathbf{e}_j\| \to 0 \qquad @\ j \to \infty \tag{7.36}$$

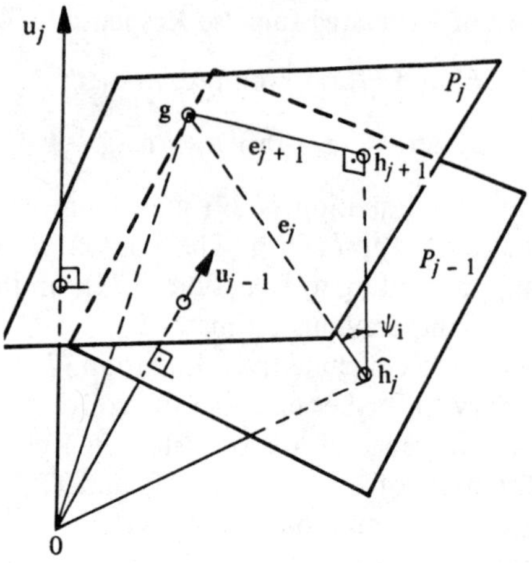


*Figure 7.1* Geometrical interpretation of convergence of $\hat{\mathbf{h}}$.

Noting that $\mathbf{e}_j$ represents the error in estimating $\mathbf{g}$ at the $j$'th iteration step (see Equation (7.32) and Figure 7.1), Equation (7.36) indicates that the estimate $\hat{\mathbf{h}}_j$ of $\mathbf{g}$ according to Equation (7.29) converges to $\mathbf{g}$, as is required.

Nagumo and Noda[9] further show that if an error- correcting coefficient $\alpha$ is considered in Equation (7.29), such that:

$$\hat{\mathbf{h}}_{j+1} = \hat{\mathbf{h}}_j + \alpha\,(x_j - \hat{x}_j)\,\mathbf{u}_j/\mathbf{u}_j^T\,\mathbf{u}_j \qquad @ \quad 0 < \alpha < 2 \tag{7.37}$$

convergence is still guaranteed.

### 7.2.1-c Determination of the Error-Correcting Coefficient

For determining the error-correcting coefficient $\alpha$ of Equation (7.37) we now consider a process given by:

$$x_j = \mathbf{u}_j^T\mathbf{g} + n_j \tag{7.38}$$

The latter equation is similar to Equation (7.20) but includes an added noise term $n_j$ where:

$$E[n_j] = 0 \tag{7.39}$$

$$E[n_j^2] < \infty \tag{7.40}$$

$E[\cdots]$ denoting expectation. The parameters of Equation (7.38) may be identified according to Equation (7.37) to yield the estimates $\hat{x}_j$ according to Equation (7.27). Defining a squared identification error $e_{j+1}^2$, such that:

$$e_{j+1}^2 \triangleq \|\hat{\mathbf{h}}_{j+1} - \mathbf{g}\|^2 \tag{7.41}$$

and noting from Equation (7.37) that:

$$\hat{\mathbf{h}}_{j+1} - \mathbf{g} = \left(\mathbf{I} - \alpha \frac{\mathbf{u}_j \mathbf{u}_j^T}{\|\mathbf{u}_j\|^2}\right)(\hat{\mathbf{h}}_j - \mathbf{g}) + \alpha \frac{n_j \mathbf{u}_j}{\|\mathbf{u}_j\|^2} \tag{7.42}$$

we obtain that the expected $e_{j+1}^2$ is given by:

$$\overline{e_{j+1}^2} = \overline{\left\|\left(\mathbf{I} - \alpha \frac{\mathbf{u}_j \mathbf{u}_j^T}{\|\mathbf{u}_j\|^2}\right) \overline{e_j^2}\right\|^2} + \left(\overline{\frac{\alpha^2 n_j^2}{\|\mathbf{u}_j\|^2}}\right) \tag{7.43}$$

where $\overline{(\cdots)}$ is employed to denote the expectation of $(\cdots)$ in alternative to $E$ in many-elements expressions for clarity reasons. Defining:

$$Z_j \triangleq \mathbf{I} - \frac{\alpha \mathbf{u}_j \mathbf{u}_j^T}{\|\mathbf{u}_j\|^2} \tag{7.44}$$

and noting that $\mathbf{u}_j^T \mathbf{u}_j = \|\mathbf{u}_j\|^2$, we obtain that:

$$\begin{aligned} Z_j^2 &= \mathbf{I} - 2\alpha \frac{\mathbf{u}_j \mathbf{u}_j^T}{\|\mathbf{u}_j\|^2} + \alpha^2 \frac{\mathbf{u}_j \mathbf{u}_j^T \mathbf{u}_j \mathbf{u}_j^T}{\|\mathbf{u}_j\|^4} \\ &= \mathbf{I} - \alpha(2 - \alpha) \frac{\mathbf{u}_j \mathbf{u}_j^T}{\|\mathbf{u}_j\|^2} \end{aligned} \tag{7.45}$$

Assuming at this point and onwards in Section 7.2 that all element of $\mathbf{u}_j$ are statistically independent and have the same symmetric distribution, we may write that:[9]

$$E\left[\frac{\mathbf{u}_j \mathbf{u}_j^T}{\|\mathbf{u}_j\|^2}\right] = \mathbf{I}N^{-1} \tag{7.46}$$

$N$ being the dimension of $\mathbf{u}$, which may be a special identification input. Consequently, equations (7.41) and (7.43) yield that:

$$\overline{e_{j+1}^2} = \left[1 - \left(\frac{\alpha(2 - \alpha)}{N}\right)\right] \overline{e_j^2} + \alpha^2 \left(\overline{\frac{n_j^2}{\|\mathbf{u}_j\|^2}}\right) \tag{7.47}$$

We now substitute into Equation (7.47) from:

$$\hat{n}_j^* \triangleq \frac{n_j}{\|\mathbf{u}_j\|} \tag{7.48}$$

Assuming that both the noise $n_j$ and the input $\mathbf{u}_j$ are stationary, $\overline{(n_j^*)^2}$ becomes independent of $j$. Hence:

$$\overline{e_{j+1}^2} = \left(1 - \frac{\alpha(2 - \alpha)}{N}\right)\overline{e_j^2} + \alpha^2 \overline{(n^*)^2} \tag{7.49}$$

and at the limit:

$$L \triangleq \lim_{j\to\infty} \overline{e_j^2} = \frac{\alpha N\overline{(n^*)^2}}{2-\alpha} > 0 \qquad @\, 0<\alpha<2 \tag{7.50}$$

Equation (7.50) yields that for $\alpha \to 2$ the identification error tends to infinity. Furthermore, Equation (7.50) indicates that for a low value of the steady state identification error we require that:

$$1 \gg \alpha > 0 \tag{7.51}$$

Reconstructing Equation (7.49), we further define:

$$\gamma_j \triangleq \left(\frac{\overline{e_{j+1}^2}}{\overline{e_j^2}}\right) = \left(1 - \frac{\alpha(2-\alpha)}{N}\right) + \alpha^2\left(\frac{\overline{(n^*)^2}}{\overline{e_j^2}}\right) \tag{7.52}$$

Consequently, the optimal correction coefficient $\alpha_j^*$ to minimize $\gamma_j$ of Equation (7.52) is that which satisfies:[10]

$$\frac{\partial \gamma_j}{\partial \alpha} = 0 = \frac{-2}{N} + \frac{2\alpha}{N} + 2\alpha\left(\frac{\overline{(n^*)^2}}{\overline{e_j^2}}\right) \tag{7.53}$$

such that:

$$\alpha_j^* = \frac{1}{1 + \left(\frac{\overline{(n^*)^2}}{\overline{e_j^2}}\right)N} = \frac{\overline{e_j^2}}{\overline{e_j^2} + N\overline{(n^*)^2}} \tag{7.54}$$

However, since $\overline{e_j^2}$ of Equation (7.54) is unknown, we only conclude[10] that $\alpha$ should be smaller than 1 for rapid convergence. We note that, according to Equation (7.51), $\alpha$ should be much smaller than 1 for guaranteeing small steady state error for independent inputs.*

### 7.2.2 Identification of Processes with Nonstationary Parameters

In contrast to the techniques of Section 7.1, which sequentially identify stationary processes only, the sequential approach of the present chapter is applicable also to nonstationary processes, provided that the nonstationarities are slow compared with the iteration step. Furthermore, the nonstationary parameters may be followed in a controlled rate. The identification algorithm for cases of slow nonstationarities is similar to that of Section 7.2.1. However, the vector of impulse responses **g** of Equation (7.26) is no more stationary, and is substituted for by $\mathbf{g}_j$ in the equations where **g** appears.

The limit accuracy of the identification can no longer be considered as a steady state accuracy, as it was in Section 7.2.1, and must be re-examined in terms of properties of $\mathbf{g}_j$ as follows,[10] assuming independent inputs:

*The present algorithm converges without any bias in the stable stochastic system case only if[11] $\alpha = \alpha_{0/k}$.

### 7.2.2-a Random Parameter Variations

We define:

$$\Delta \mathbf{g}_j \triangleq \mathbf{g}_{j+1} - \mathbf{g}_j \tag{7.55}$$

Consequently, Equation (7.37) leads to an expression analogous to (7.42), as follows:

$$\begin{aligned}\hat{\mathbf{h}}_{j+1} - \mathbf{g}_j &= \left(\mathbf{I} - \alpha \frac{\mathbf{u}_j \mathbf{u}_j^T}{\|\mathbf{u}_j\|^2}\right)(\hat{\mathbf{h}}_j - \mathbf{g}_j) + \alpha n_j \frac{\mathbf{u}_j}{\|\mathbf{u}_j\|^2} \\ &= \left(\mathbf{I} - \alpha \frac{\mathbf{u}_j \mathbf{u}^T}{\|\mathbf{u}_j\|^2}\right)(\hat{\mathbf{h}}_j - \mathbf{g}_{j-1}) - \left(\mathbf{I} - \alpha \frac{\mathbf{u}_j \mathbf{u}_j^T}{\|\mathbf{u}_j\|^2}\right) \Delta \mathbf{g}_{j-1} \\ &\quad + \alpha n_j \frac{\mathbf{u}_j}{\|\mathbf{u}_j\|^2}\end{aligned} \tag{7.56}$$

Squaring Equation (7.56), taking expectations, and noting Equation (7.48), yields[10], for independent inputs:

$$\begin{aligned}\overline{e_{j+1,j}^2} &= C\overline{e_{j,j-1}^2} + \alpha^2 \overline{(n_j^*)^2} + C\|\Delta \mathbf{g}_{j-1}\|^2 \\ &\quad - 2C\left\{D^{j-1}\Delta \mathbf{g}_{j-1}^T \cdot (\hat{\mathbf{h}}_1 - \mathbf{g}_0) - \sum_{i=0}^{j-1} D^i \Delta \mathbf{g}_{j-1}^T \Delta \mathbf{g}_{j-i-1}\right\}\end{aligned} \tag{7.57}$$

where:

$$C \triangleq 1 - \alpha(2-\alpha)/N \tag{7.58-a}$$

$$D \triangleq 1 - \alpha/N \tag{7.58-b}$$

Assuming that $\Delta \mathbf{g}_j$ are statistically independent over $j$, and that:

$$E[\Delta \mathbf{g}_j] = 0 \qquad \forall j \tag{7.59}$$

$$E[\|\Delta \mathbf{g}_j\|^2] = \sigma^2 \tag{7.60}$$

Equation (7.57) becomes:

$$\overline{e_{j+1,j}^2} = C(\overline{e_{j,j-1}^2} + \sigma^2) - \sigma^2 \overline{(n^*)^2} \tag{7.61}$$

or, in a more general form:

$$\begin{aligned}\overline{e_{j+1,j}^2} &= C^j \overline{e_{1,0}^2} + \sigma^2 \sum_{i=1}^{j} C^i + \alpha^2 \overline{(n^*)^2} \sum_{i=1}^{j-1} C^i \\ &= C^j(\overline{e_{1,0}^2} + \sigma^2) + (\sigma^2 + \alpha^2 \overline{(n^*)^2}) \sum_{i=1}^{j-1} C^i\end{aligned} \tag{7.62}$$

Consequently, the limit-accuracy $L_1 \triangleq \lim_{j\to\infty} \overline{e_{j+1,j}^2}$ becomes:

$$L_1 \triangleq \frac{\alpha N(n^*)^2}{2-\alpha} + \frac{CN\sigma^2}{\alpha(2-\alpha)} = L + \frac{CN\sigma^2}{\alpha(2-\alpha)} \tag{7.63}$$

$L$ being the limit-accuracy of the stationary case, as in Equation (7.50). For a sufficiently large $N$ and $0 < \alpha \ll 1$, Equation (7.63) is reduced to:

$$L_1 \cong \frac{\alpha N\overline{(n^*)^2}}{2} + \frac{N}{\alpha}\sigma^2 \tag{7.64}$$

Having derived the limit-accuracy $L$, for cases of nonstationary identification, we now attempt to derive the correction coefficient $\alpha'$ to minimize $L_1$. Consequently, for:

$$\frac{\partial L_1}{\partial \alpha} = 0 \tag{7.65}$$

Equation (7.64) yields that:

$$\frac{N\overline{(n^*)^2}}{2} - \frac{N\sigma^2}{(\alpha')^2} = 0 \tag{7.66}$$

and, for the assumptions above:

$$\alpha' \cong \sqrt{2\sigma^2/\overline{(n^*)^2}} \tag{7.67}$$

The corresponding best limit accuracy now becomes:

$$L_{1\min} \cong N\sqrt{2\sigma^2\overline{(n^*)^2}} \tag{7.68}$$

### 7.2.2-b Step Changes in Parameter

Nonrandom changes in the elements of the parameter vector $\mathbf{g}$ may be approximated by a staircase approximation, such that only step changes in $\mathbf{g}$ are considered. When the effect of such step changes on identification is analyzed, the transient behavior of the identification error must be considered. We therefore examine below this transient behavior and the number of iterations of the identification vector $\hat{\mathbf{h}}$ that are required to achieve a certain minimum accuracy in identification, as follows:[10]

We define the expected identification error:

$$\mathbf{e}_{j+\mu} \triangleq E[\hat{\mathbf{h}}_{j+\mu} - \mathbf{g}] \tag{7.69}$$

to derive, according to equations (7.42) and (7.46) that:

$$\mathbf{e}_{j+\mu+1} = \left(1 - \frac{\alpha}{N}\right)\mathbf{e}_{j+\mu} = \left(1 - \frac{\alpha}{N}\right)^j \mathbf{e}_\mu \tag{7.70}$$

such that the limit error becomes:

$$\mathbf{e} \triangleq \lim_{j\to\infty} \mathbf{e}_{j+\mu} = 0 \tag{7.71}$$

We further define $\beta_j$ to denote the normalized square expectation, such that:

$$\beta_{j+\mu+1} \triangleq \frac{\|\mathbf{e}_{j+\mu+1}\|^2}{\|\mathbf{e}_\mu\|^2} \tag{7.72}$$

Hence, according to Equation (7.70):

$$\beta_{j+\mu+1} = \left(1 - \frac{\alpha}{N}\right)^{2j} \tag{7.73}$$

Assuming that the iteration step $\lambda$ denotes the lowest value of the iteration step $j$ to satisfy:

$$\beta_{j+\mu+1} < \varepsilon_0; \qquad 0 < \varepsilon_0 \ll 1 \tag{7.74}$$

we derive from Equation (7.73) that:

$$\lambda = \frac{\ln(\varepsilon_0)}{2\ln\left(1 - \dfrac{\alpha}{N}\right)} + 1 \tag{7.75}$$

and for large $N$, assuming independent inputs:

$$\lambda \cong -\frac{N\ln(\varepsilon_0)}{2\alpha} \tag{7.76}$$

Equation (7.76) thus relates the rate at which step changes occur in $\mathbf{g}$ to $\alpha$ and $\varepsilon_0$. The property of the identification procedure to converge to $\varepsilon_0$ at a finite number of iterations $\lambda$ is that which makes the procedure applicable to nonstationary processes.

### 7.2.2-c Determination of Error Correcting Coefficient for Nonstationary Systems

The optimal value for the error coefficient $\alpha$ of Equation (7.37) may be derived for cases of nonstationary systems, in analogy to the derivation of Section 7.2.1, as follows: Noting the definition of the squared identification errors $e^2$ of Equation (7.41), we define the squared identification error in the non-stationary case, such that:

$$e^2_{j+1,j} \triangleq \|\hat{\mathbf{h}}_{j+1} - \mathbf{g}_j\|^2 \tag{7.77}$$

Consequently, we obtain from Equation (7.56) that:

$$\frac{\overline{e^2_{j+1,j}}}{\overline{e^2_{jj}}} = 1 - \frac{\alpha(2-\alpha)}{N} + \frac{\overline{\alpha^2 n_j^2}}{e^2_{jj}\|\mathbf{u}_j\|^2} \tag{7.78}$$

and:

$$\min_{\alpha}\left(\frac{\overline{e^2_{j+1,j}}}{\overline{e^2_{jj}}}\right) \to \alpha^* \tag{7.79}$$

to yield, for independent inputs:

$$\alpha^* = \frac{\overline{e_{jj}^2}}{\overline{e_{jj}^2} + N\left(\frac{\overline{n_j^2}}{\|\mathbf{u}_j\|^2}\right)} \tag{7.80}$$

The latter result is similar to the optimal $\alpha^*$ of the stationary case, as in Equation (7.54). However, in similarity to the case of Section 7.2.1, $e_{jj}^2$ are unknown, and may be only vaguely estimated, on the basis of the error in estimating $x_j$. Noda[10] proposes to estimate $\overline{e_{jj}^2}$ by $\hat{e}_{jj}^2$ where:

$$\hat{e}_{jj}^2 \triangleq N\left\{\frac{1}{m} \sum_{k=j-m+1}^{j} \frac{(x_k - \hat{x}_{jk})^2}{\|\mathbf{u}_k\|^2} - \overline{n_j^2}\right\} \tag{7.81}$$

and:

$$\hat{x}_{jk} \triangleq \mathbf{u}_k^T \hat{\mathbf{h}}_j \qquad @ \quad k \leq j \tag{7.82}$$

### 7.2.3 Extension to Multi-Input Processes

The output of a linear process $x_j$ at a discrete time interval $j$, may be described, for a multi-input case, in analogy to Equation (7.20), as follows:

$$x_j = \sum_{i=1}^{N} (g_{1,i} v_{1,j-i} + g_{2,i} v_{2,j-i} + \cdots g_{\mu,i} v_{\mu,j-i}) \tag{7.83}$$

$\mu$ being the number of inputs. Equation (7.83) may be rewritten as:

$$x_j = \mathbf{G}^T \mathbf{V}_j \tag{7.84}$$

where:

$$\mathbf{G} \triangleq [g_{1,1} \cdots ; g_{1,N} ; g_{2,1} \cdots ; g_{2,N} ; \cdots ; g_{\mu,1} \cdots g_{\mu,N}]^T \tag{7.85}$$

and:

$$\mathbf{V}_j \triangleq [v_{1,j-1} \cdots v_{1,j-N} ; v_{2,j-1} \cdots v_{2,j-N} ; \cdots v_{\mu,j-1} \cdots v_{\mu,j-N}]^T \tag{7.86}$$

We define an identification vector $\hat{\mathbf{H}}_j$ at the $j$'th iteration such that:

$$\hat{\mathbf{H}}_j = [\hat{h}_{11} \cdots \hat{h}_{1N} \cdots \hat{h}_{\mu_1} \cdots \hat{h}_{\mu N}]_j^T \tag{7.87}$$

Consequently, in analogy to equations (7.27) and (7.28), we define:

$$\hat{x}_j \triangleq \hat{\mathbf{H}}_j^T \mathbf{V}_j \tag{7.88}$$

and:

$$\Delta\hat{\mathbf{H}}_j \triangleq \hat{\mathbf{H}}_{j+1} - \hat{\mathbf{H}}_j \tag{7.89}$$

Again, in similarity to Equation (7.29), we let $\Delta\hat{\mathbf{H}}_j$ satisfy the relation:

$$\Delta\hat{\mathbf{H}}_j = (x_j - \hat{x}_j)\frac{\mathbf{V}_j}{\mathbf{V}_j^T\mathbf{V}_j} \tag{7.90}$$

to obtain that:

$$\mathbf{V}_j^T\,\Delta\hat{\mathbf{H}}_j = \frac{(x_j - \hat{x}_j)\mathbf{V}_j^T\mathbf{V}_j}{\mathbf{V}_j^T\mathbf{V}_j} \tag{7.91}$$

which satisfies equations (7.88) and (7.89). Again, as in the single input case of Equation (7.37), an error correcting coefficient $\alpha$ may be employed, $\alpha$ being between 0 and 2, and, for statisfactory performance, between 0 and 1. The convergence proof of Section 7.2.1-b is applicable to the multi-input case, even without assuming independent inputs.

EXAMPLE 7.2

To further illustrate the sequential learning identification procedure, we reconsider the system of Example 7.1, and identify it by sequential learning, as follows: Observing Equation (7.29), we obtain:

$$\hat{\mathbf{p}}_2 = \frac{\omega_1}{\mathbf{u}_1^T\mathbf{u}_1}\mathbf{u}_1 = \frac{11.3}{25}\begin{bmatrix}4\\3\end{bmatrix} = \begin{bmatrix}1.8\\1.35\end{bmatrix}$$

Consequently, Equation (7.27) yields:

$$\hat{\omega}_2 = \hat{\mathbf{p}}_2^T\mathbf{u}_2 = [1.8;\ 1.35]\begin{bmatrix}1\\2\end{bmatrix} = 4.5$$

and:

$$\hat{\mathbf{p}}_3 = \hat{\mathbf{p}}_2 + \frac{(3.9 - 4.5)}{5}\begin{bmatrix}1\\2\end{bmatrix} = \begin{bmatrix}1.8\\1.35\end{bmatrix} - \begin{bmatrix}0.12\\0.24\end{bmatrix} = \begin{bmatrix}1.68\\1.11\end{bmatrix}$$

$$\hat{\omega}_3 = \hat{\mathbf{p}}_3^T\mathbf{u}_3 = 2.25$$

$$\hat{\mathbf{p}}_4 = \hat{\mathbf{p}}_3 + \frac{(3.1 - 2.25)}{5}\begin{bmatrix}2\\-1\end{bmatrix} = \begin{bmatrix}1.68\\1.11\end{bmatrix} + \begin{bmatrix}0.32\\-0.17\end{bmatrix} = \begin{bmatrix}2.0\\0.94\end{bmatrix}$$

the true $\mathbf{p}$ being given by:

$$\mathbf{p} = \begin{bmatrix}2\\1\end{bmatrix}$$

which indicates a faster convergence rate than in the case of the stochastic approximation identification procedure, as in Example 7.1.

## 7.3 SEQUENTIAL PATTERN RECOGNITION PROCEDURE FOR IDENTIFYING NONLINEAR SYSTEMS

An extension of the sequential learning identification approach of Section 7.2 to nonlinear processes has been suggested by Roy and Sherman.[14] Their procedure employs a pattern recognition algorithm for classifying the type of nonlinearity which best describes the behavior of the system consisting of an a priori given set of nonlinear functions. The present approach employs sequential features which are analogous to those of Section 7.2.

For deriving the identification algorithms for nonlinear processes we first restate the convolution integral relation between input $x(t)$ and output $z(t)$ in a linear system as follows:

$$z(t) = \int_0^t g_1(\tau)x(t-\tau)\, d\tau \tag{7.92}$$

$g_1(t)$ denoting the impulse response of the linear system.

We subsequently consider a system with a parabolic nonlinearity as follows:

$$y(t) = z^2(t) \tag{7.93}$$

the output $y(t)$ of the latter nonlinear system may be considered as representing the product of the outputs $z_1$, $z_2$ of two linear systems, $g_1$, $g_2$, each of which obeys a relation as in Equation (7.92). We therefore describe $y(t)$ by:

$$\begin{aligned} y(t) &= \int_0^t g_1(\tau)x(t-\tau_1)\, d\tau_1 \int_0^t g_2(\tau_2)x(t-\tau_2)\, d\tau_2 \\ &= \int_0^t \int_0^t g_2(\tau_1)g_2(\tau_2)x(t-\tau_1)x(t-\tau_2)\, d\tau_1\, d\tau_2 \end{aligned} \tag{7.94}$$

Substituting:

$$\gamma_2(\tau_1;\tau_2) \triangleq g_1(\tau_1)g_2(\tau_2) \tag{7.95}$$

Equation (7.94) becomes:

$$y(t) = \int_0^t \int_0^t \gamma_2(\tau_1;\tau_2)x(t-\tau_1)x(t-\tau_2)\, d\tau_1\, d\tau_2 \tag{7.96}$$

We further consider a system that is described by:

$$y(t) = f[z(t)] \tag{7.97}$$

$f[z(t)]$ being an arbitrary continuous nonlinear function of $z(t)$. We already stated in Section 5.6 that, according to the Weierstrass theorem, any continuous $f[z(t)]$ may be approximated by a polynomial of $z(t)$ such that the latter polynomial converges to $y(t)$. We therefore approximate $y(t)$ by $y_m(t)$ where:

$$y(t) \cong y_m(t) \triangleq f_m[z(t)] \tag{7.98}$$

$f_m$ denoting a polynomial sequence of order $m$ of $x(t)$. We now define:

$$\gamma_1(\tau) \triangleq g_1(\tau) \tag{7.99-a}$$

$$\gamma_2(\tau_1;\tau_2) \triangleq g_1(\tau_1)g_2(\tau_2) \tag{7.99-b}$$

$$\vdots$$

$$\gamma_k(\tau_1 \cdots \tau_k) \triangleq \prod_{j=1}^{k} g_j(\tau_j) \tag{7.99-c}$$

to yield, in analogy to equations (7.94) and (7.96):

$$\begin{aligned} f_m[z(t)] &= a_1 \int_0^t \gamma_1(\tau_1)x(t-\tau_1)\,d\tau_1 \\ &\quad + a_2 \int_0^t \int_0^t \gamma_2(\tau_1\tau_2)x(t-\tau_1)x(t-\tau_2)\,d\tau_1\,d\tau_2 \\ &\quad + \cdots \\ &\quad \cdots \\ &\quad \cdots \\ &\quad + a_m \overbrace{\int_0^t \cdots \int_0^t}^{m \text{ integrals}} \gamma_m(\tau_1,\tau_2,\cdots\tau_m)x(t-\tau_1) \\ &\qquad\qquad \times x(t-\tau_2)\cdots x(t-\tau_m)\,d\tau_1\,d\tau_2\cdots d\tau_m \\ &= \sum_{k=1}^{m} a_k \overbrace{\int_0^t \cdots \int_0^t}^{k \text{ integrals}} \gamma_k(\tau_1,\tau_2,\ldots\tau_k)x(t-\tau_1) \\ &\qquad\qquad \times x(t-\tau_2)\cdots x(t-\tau_k)\,d\tau_1\,d\tau_2\cdots d\tau_k \end{aligned} \tag{7.100}$$

Equation (7.100) may be written in discrete form, as follows:

$$f_m[z(t)] \cong \sum_{k=1}^{m} \left( a_k \overbrace{\sum_{\mu_1=1}^{n} \cdots \sum_{\mu_k=1}^{n}}^{k \text{ sums}} \gamma_{\mu_1\mu_2\cdots\mu_k} \cdot x_{\mu_1} \cdot x_{\mu_2} \cdots x_{\mu_k} \right) \tag{7.101}$$

$x_{\mu_k}$ being given by:

$$x_{\mu_k} \triangleq x(t-\mu_k T) \tag{7.102}$$

where $T$ is the sampling interval. Obviously, if nonstationary systems are considered, then $\gamma_{\mu_1\mu_2\cdots\mu_k}$ becomes $\gamma_{\mu_1\mu_2\cdots\mu_k}(t)$. The expressions of equations (7.100) and (7.101) represent the $m$'th order Volterra series formulation of the nonlinear system that is considered.

### 7.3.1 The Sequential Learning Algorithm

Let:

$$\mathbf{x} \triangleq (x_1, x_2, \cdots x_n)^T \tag{7.103}$$

where $x_i$ are $x(t - iT)$. We define an $s$-dimensional vector $\boldsymbol{\Psi}_s(\mathbf{x})$ as follows:

$$\psi_s(\mathbf{x}) = [\phi_1(\mathbf{x}), \phi_2(\mathbf{x}) \cdots \phi_s(\mathbf{x})]^T \tag{7.104}$$

where:

$$\left.\begin{array}{l} \phi_1 \triangleq x_1; \phi_2 \triangleq x_2; \quad \cdots\cdots \quad \phi_n \triangleq x_n \\ \phi_{n+1} \triangleq x_1^2; \phi_{n+2} \triangleq x_1 x_2 \quad \cdots \quad \phi_{2n} \triangleq x_1 x_n \\ \phi_{2n+1} \triangleq x_2^2; \quad \cdots\cdots \quad \phi_{2n+n-1} \triangleq x_2 \cdot x_n \\ \vdots \end{array}\right\} \tag{7.105}$$

If the highest order terms to be considered in $\psi(\mathbf{x})$ are of $r$'th order, then the dimension of $\psi(\mathbf{x})$ is given by:

$$s = \binom{n+r}{r} - 1 = \frac{(n+r)!}{n!\,r!} - 1 \tag{7.106}$$

We subsequently define a function $\Phi(\mathbf{x})$, such that:

$$\Phi(\mathbf{x}) \triangleq \sum_{i=1}^{\mu} \omega_i \phi_i(\mathbf{x}) = \sum_{j=1}^{n} \omega_j x_j + \sum_{j=1}^{n} \sum_{h=1}^{n} \omega_{jh} x_j x_h$$

$$+ \cdots \underbrace{\sum_{j=1}^{n} \cdots \sum_{q=1}^{n}}_{r \text{ sums}} \underbrace{\omega_{j,h,\ldots q}}_{r \text{ subscripts}} \underbrace{x_j x_h \cdots x_q}_{r \text{ elements}} = \boldsymbol{\omega}^T \cdot \psi_s \tag{7.107}$$

$\omega_{j\ldots}$ being weighting coefficients, and $\boldsymbol{\omega}$ denoting a vector whose elements are $\omega_{j\ldots}$. Equation (7.107) indicates that $\Phi(\mathbf{x})$ represents a sum-weighted polynomial of $x_j$ of orders 1 to $r$, each having its equivalent in $\psi_s(\mathbf{x})$.

The sequential pattern recognition algorithm now assumes that the output $y(t)$ of Equation (7.94), denoting the output of the system that requires identification, be estimated in terms of $\hat{y}_m(t)$. Noting equations (7.98) and (7.101), the estimate $\hat{y}_m$ of $y$ is considered to be the output of a linear estimation model given by:

$$\hat{y}_m(t) = \Phi(\mathbf{x}) \tag{7.108}$$

$\Phi(\mathbf{x})$ being defined in Equation (7.107). The parameter vector $\boldsymbol{\omega}_{i+1}$ at the $i+1$ iteration of the estimator model is sequentially derived by an estimation algorithm that is analogous to that of Equation (7.37) of Section 7.2, as follows:

$$\omega_{i+1} = \omega_i + \frac{\alpha(y_i - \hat{y}_i)\psi_{s,i}(\mathbf{x})}{\psi_{s,i}^T \psi_{s,i}} \quad @ \quad 0 < \alpha < 2 \qquad (7.109)$$

such that $y_m(t)$ converge[12] to $\hat{y}_m(t)$, and hence to $y(t)$ of Equation (7.94).

The resulting procedure for sequential identification of nonlinear systems has similar properties to that for linear systems, as has been described in Section 7.2. Consequently, it converges also to parameters that vary slowly in comparison to the rate of iteration. However, as in the case of Section 7.2, the procedure is based on the rather arbitrary choice of error correcting algorithms (Equation (7.109)). Any optimization of the coefficient $\alpha$ would therefore yield an estimate that is best only with respect to the general form of Equation (7.108). A procedure that yields a most adequate identification of the same polynomial approximation of a nonlinear system may also be accomplished by employing sequential regression, as in Chapter 6., The sequential nonlinear regression procedure of Section 6.4, when applied to nonlinear systems is, however, somewhat more complex to compute than that of the present section, just as sequential linear regression is somewhat more complex to compute than the sequential linear learning procedures of Section 7.2.1.

## REFERENCES


1. Dvoretzky, A. "On Stochastic Approximation," *Proc. 3rd Berkeley Symp. on Mathematical Statistics and Probability*, Vol. 1, University of California Press, 1956.
2. Robbins, H., and Munro, S. "A Stochastic Approximation Method," *Annals of Math. Stat.*, Vol. 22, 1951.
3. Kiefer, J., and Wolfowitz, J. "Stochastic Estimation of the Maximum of Regression Problems," *Annals of Math. Stat.*, Vol. 23, 1952.
4. Blum, J. R. "Multidimensional Stochastic Approximation Methods," *Annals of Math. Stat.*, Vol. 25, 1954.
5. Kushner, J. J. "A Simple Iterative Procedure for the Identification of Unknown Parameters of a Linear Time Varying Discrete System," *Trans. A.S.M.E., Jour. Basic Eng.*, Vol. 85, 1963.
6. Kirvaitis, K., and Fu, K. S. "Identification of Nonlinear Systems by Stochastic Approximation," *Proc. Joint Automatic Control Conf.*, pp. 255–264, 1966.
7. Kashyap, R. L., Blaydon, C. C., and Fu, K. S. "Stochastic Approximation," in *Adaptive, Learning and Pattern Recognition Systems* (edited by J. M. Mendel and K. S. Fu), Academic Press, New York, 1970.

8. Blaydon, C. C., Kashyap, R. L., and Fu, K. S. "Applications of the Stochastic Approximation Methods," in *Adaptive, Learning and Pattern Recognition Systems*, (edited by J. M. Mendel and K. S. Fu) Academic Press, New York, 1970
9. Nagumo, J., and Noda, A. "A Learning Method for System Identification," *IEEE Trans.*, Vol. AC-12, pp. 282–287, 1967.
10. Noda, A. "Effects of Noise and Parameter-Variation on the Learning Identification Method," *Jour. of SICE of Japan*, Vol. 8, pp. 303–312, 1969.
11. Graupe, D. and Fogel, E., "A Unified Sequential Identification Structure based on Convergence Considerations." *Automatica*, Vol. 12, No. 1, Jan. 1976.
12. Graupe, D. and Fogel, E. "Convergence of Sequential Algorithms for Identifying Stable and Unstable Processes", *Proc. 6th Symp. on Nonlinear Estimation*, San Diego, Sept. 1975.
13. Albert, A. E., and Gardner, L. A. *Stochastic Approximation and Nonlinear Regression*, M.I.T. Press, Cambridge, Mass., 1967.
14. Roy, R., and Sherman, J. "Pattern Recognition in a Learning Automatic Control System," Paper 16, *Proc. I.F.A.C. Symp. on Identification*, Prague, 1967.

## PROBLEMS

1. Employ stochastic approximation to identify the parameters of Problem 1 in Chapter 6.
2. Study the effect of $\alpha$ of Equation (7.37) on the convergence rate in the identification of $\mathbf{a}$ from the data of Example 6.1. Consider $\alpha = 0.5$; 1.0; 1.5.
3. Identify the parameters of the nonlinear system of Problem 11 of Chapter 5 by sequential learning.
4. Identify the process $y = \mathbf{a}^T(t)\mathbf{x}$, $\mathbf{a}$ being a non-stationary parameter that varies by a step change, and where the following measurements are available:

| | | | | | | | | | |
|---|---|---|---|---|---|---|---|---|---|
| $y =$ | 2.05 | 3.65 | 1.55 | 0.8 | −2.05 | 5.9 | 3.95 | 2.0 | 0.8 |
| $x_1 =$ | 2 | 1.7 | 1.1 | 0.5 | 1.5 | 2.6 | 1.6 | 1.3 | 1.0 |
| $x_2 =$ | −0.5 | 0.1 | −0.3 | 0.1 | −1.0 | 0.3 | 0.4 | −0.3 | −0.6 |
| $y =$ | 1.25 | 2.85 | 4.45 | −0.75 | −0.3 | 2.35 | 4.9 | 2.25 | 5.35 |
| $x_1 =$ | 0.7 | 1.3 | 1.6 | 0.6 | 0.7 | 1.1 | 1.4 | 0.9 | 1.6 |
| $x_2 =$ | −0.1 | −0.5 | −0.2 | −1.1 | −0.9 | −0.5 | 0.2 | −0.3 | 0.3 |
| $y =$ | 5.45 | 1.55 | 1.55 | −0.1 | | | | | |
| $x_1 =$ | 2.1 | 1.0 | 0.6 | 0.1 | | | | | |
| $x_2 =$ | −0.4 | −0.7 | −0.1 | −0.2 | | | | | |

# 8

# QUASILINEARIZATION APPROACH TO IDENTIFICATION

The quasilinearization approach was first introduced by Bellman and Kalaba[1, 2] for solving boundary value problems arising in nonlinear differential equations. Its application to the identification of parameters of nonlinear systems is mainly due to Kumar and Shridar,[3] Sage and Eisenberg,[4, 5] and Detchmendy and Shridar.[6]

Quasilinearization is in essence a method for transforming a nonlinear multi-point boundary value problem which is basically stationary into a linear nonstationary such problem. It is applicable to continuous and to discrete processes. The parameters to be identified are assumed to be stationary, and, as in all other methods for identifying nonlinear systems, the type of nonlinearity must be given, at least in terms of an approximation. Nonstationarities in parameters may be considered if they are slow compared with the convergence rate of the identification procedure. The latter convergence is fairly fast if a close initial guess of the values of the parameters that are being identified is available. The approach is of iterative nature and requires no special identification inputs, thus being suitable for on-line application.

Since quasilinearization identification procedures converge to the true parameters only if the initial guess of the parameter values is within the convergence bounds, they require a certain prior knowledge of the parameter range of values, which is not required if the sequential approaches of chapters 6 and 7 are employed. However, the quasilinearization approach is of particular importance *if the various states of the system are not measurable simultaneously at all sampling instances.* In that case, the state space description of the system represents in itself a multi-point problem, for which the quasilinearization formulation is natural. The quasilinearization approach is, in principle, an identification approach based on a fixed number of measurements, rather than on a sequentially growing number of measurements as in chapters 6 and 7. When a sufficient number of measurements of certain states is available, but others are missing, the present approach may yield estimates of both the other states and the parameters simultaneously.

## 8.1 QUASILINEARIZATION IDENTIFICATION OF CONTINUOUS SYSTEMS

Consider a nonlinear system given by:

$$\dot{\mathbf{x}} = \mathbf{f}(\mathbf{x}, \mathbf{u}, \mathbf{p}) \tag{8.1}$$

**f** being a nonlinear function. The $j$'th row of Equation (8.1) may be written as:

$$\dot{x}_j = f_j(\mathbf{x}, \mathbf{u}, \mathbf{p}) \tag{8.2}$$

**x** being an $n$-dimensional state vector, **u** being an $m$-dimensional input vector and **p** being an $r$-dimensional parameter vector. The elements of **p** are unknown and require identification, whereas, **x**, **u** are measurable and the form of $f_j$ is known for all $j$. The system of Equation (8.1) is subject to $n + r$ boundary conditions given by $n + r$ measured (known) functions of $x_j(t_i)$, for several states $x_j$ at several instances $t_i$. An example for such a situation is the case of a system:

$$\dot{x} = a \cdot x^3 + b \cdot u(t) \tag{8.3}$$

where $a, b$ are the unknown parameters whose identification is required and $x$, $u$ are state and control variables, respectively. The elements of **p** are assumed to be *stationary*. Hence, we may add a state equation to (8.1), as follows:

$$\dot{\mathbf{p}} = \mathbf{0} \tag{8.4}$$

Combining equations (8.1) and (8.4), we obtain:

$$\dot{\mathbf{z}} = \psi(\mathbf{z}, \mathbf{u}) \tag{8.5}$$

where:

$$\mathbf{z} \triangleq [x_1 \cdots x_n, p_1 \cdots p_r]^T \tag{8.6}$$

Employing a first order Taylor series expansion, we derive the $(\mu + 1)$'th estimate of $\dot{\mathbf{z}}$ from the $\mu$'th estimate as follows:

$$\hat{\dot{\mathbf{z}}}_{\mu+1} = \hat{\boldsymbol{\psi}}_{\mu+1} = \hat{\boldsymbol{\psi}}_{\mu} + \frac{\partial \hat{\boldsymbol{\psi}}_{\mu}}{\partial \mathbf{z}} (\hat{\mathbf{z}}_{\mu+1} - \hat{\mathbf{z}}_{\mu}) \tag{8.7}$$

where:

$$\boldsymbol{\psi} \triangleq [\mathbf{f}^T, 0, \ldots 0]^T \tag{8.8}$$

$\mathbf{f}$ being as in Equation (8.2), the *number of zeros* being equal to $r$ of Equation (8.6) and:

$$\frac{\partial \hat{\boldsymbol{\psi}}_{\mu}}{\partial \mathbf{z}} \triangleq \left.\frac{\partial \hat{\boldsymbol{\psi}}}{\partial \mathbf{z}}\right|_{\mathbf{z}=\hat{\mathbf{z}}_{\mu}} \tag{8.9}$$

We note that Equation (8.7) is *linear* in $\hat{\mathbf{z}}_{\mu+1}$. It may therefore be expressed as:

$$\hat{\dot{\mathbf{z}}}_{\mu+1}(t) = \hat{\mathbf{A}}_{\mu} \cdot \hat{\mathbf{z}}_{\mu+1}(t) + \hat{\mathbf{V}}_{\mu} \tag{8.10}$$

where:

$$\hat{\mathbf{V}}_{\mu} \triangleq \hat{\boldsymbol{\psi}}_{\mu} - \frac{\partial \hat{\boldsymbol{\psi}}_{\mu}}{\partial \mathbf{z}} \hat{\mathbf{z}}_{\mu} = \hat{\boldsymbol{\psi}}_{\mu} - \hat{\mathbf{A}}\hat{\mathbf{z}}_{\mu} \tag{8.11-a}$$

$$\hat{\mathbf{A}} \triangleq \frac{\partial \hat{\boldsymbol{\psi}}_{\mu}}{\partial \mathbf{z}} \tag{8.11-b}$$

Equation (8.10) yields the general solution:

$$\hat{\mathbf{z}}_{\mu+1}(t) = \hat{\boldsymbol{\phi}}(t, t_0)\hat{\mathbf{z}}_{\mu+1}(t_0) + \hat{\mathbf{q}}_{\mu+1}(t) \tag{8.12}$$

where $\boldsymbol{\phi}$ is the fundamental solution of Equation (8.10), given by:

$$\hat{\dot{\boldsymbol{\phi}}}_{\mu+1}(t, t_0) = \frac{\partial \hat{\boldsymbol{\psi}}_{\mu}(t)}{\partial \mathbf{z}} \hat{\boldsymbol{\phi}}_{\mu+1}(t, t_0) \tag{8.13}$$

$$\hat{\boldsymbol{\phi}}_{\mu}(t_0, t_0) = \mathbf{I} \quad \forall \mu \tag{8.14}$$

and $\hat{\mathbf{q}}_{\mu+1}(t)$ is the particular solution of Equation (8.10), satisfying:

$$\hat{\dot{\mathbf{q}}}_{\mu+1}(t) = \hat{\boldsymbol{\psi}}_{\mu}(\hat{\mathbf{z}}, t) - \frac{\partial \hat{\boldsymbol{\psi}}_{\mu}(t)}{\partial \mathbf{z}} \mathbf{z}_{\mu}(t) + \frac{\partial \hat{\boldsymbol{\psi}}_{\mu}(t)}{\partial \mathbf{z}} \hat{\mathbf{q}}_{\mu+1}(t) \tag{8.15}$$

with:

$$\hat{\mathbf{q}}_{\mu+1}(t_0) = \mathbf{0} \tag{8.16}$$

The initial condition vector $\hat{\mathbf{z}}_{\mu+1}(t_0)\,\forall\mu$ for Equation (8.12) is derived such that it satisfies the multi-point boundary condition given by the $n + r$ values or functions of $x_j(t_i)$ which are accessible through measurement, and which are considered below to be $n + r$ measurements of states $x_j$ at time $t_i$. Consequently, Equation (8.12) yields that:

$$x_j(t_i) = \hat{\boldsymbol{\phi}}_{j,\mu+1}(t_i, t_0)\hat{\mathbf{z}}_{\mu+1}(t_0) + \hat{q}_{j,\mu+1}(t_i) \tag{8.17}$$

$\hat{\boldsymbol{\phi}}_{j,\mu+1}$ being the $j$'th row of $\hat{\boldsymbol{\phi}}_{\mu+1}$, and $x_j(t_i)$ denoting the $j$'th state variable at time $t = t_i$. Since the $n + r$ boundary value points yield $n + r$ equations of the form of (8.17) for the $n + r$ different $x_j(t_i)$, $n + r$ linear equations in $\hat{\mathbf{z}}_{\mu+1}(t_0)$ are available, to derive the $n + r$ elements of $\hat{\mathbf{z}}_{\mu+1}(t_0)$. In cases where the boundary values are suspected to be imbedded in noise, it may be advantageous to obtain more than $n + r$ boundary values. Consequently, the $n + r$ elements of $\hat{\mathbf{z}}_{\mu+1}(t_0)$ may be derived by applying linear regression to the parameters of Equation (8.17), to smooth the noise effects in the latter set of $v > n + r$ boundary values. The regression algorithm to be employed should be sequential to avoid matrix inversion. Equation (8.17) indicates that an initial estimate $\hat{\mathbf{x}}_0(t_0)$ must be assumed. The latter is employed together with the initially assumed $\hat{\mathbf{p}}$ to provide an initial estimate of the time solution of Equation (8.1) for $t = 0$ up to the highest $t_i$ of Equation (8.17). The latter time solution is subsequently substituted into Equation (8.12) to yield initial estimates of $\boldsymbol{\phi}$ and $\mathbf{q}$ for the initial evaluation of Equation (8.17). With further estimates ($\mu = 1, 2, \ldots$) of $\mathbf{x}(t_0)$; $\mathbf{p}$, the estimation of $\mathbf{x}$ from $t = 0$ to the highest $t_i$ above is repeated. The resulting computational effort in identification by quasilinearization is therefore considerable, and it limits the approach mainly to cases where only some states (not necessarily the same) are accessible at different times.

The procedure above for deriving the parameter vector $\mathbf{p}$ by quasilinearization may be further clarified by considering the following example.

EXAMPLE 8.1

We consider the process of Equation (8.3), which is restated as follows:

$$\dot{x} = ax^3 + bu(t)$$

where $u$ is measurable and where the parameters $a$, $b$ require identification. We formulate a vector $\mathbf{z}$ according to Equation (8.6), such that:

$$\mathbf{z} \triangleq [x, a, b]^T \tag{8.18}$$

The $(\mu + 1)$'th estimate of $\mathbf{z}$ of Equation (8.3) becomes, according to equations (8.7), (8.8):

$$\hat{\mathbf{z}}_{\mu+1} = \hat{\boldsymbol{\psi}}_\mu + \frac{\partial \hat{\boldsymbol{\psi}}_\mu}{\partial \mathbf{z}} (\hat{\mathbf{z}}_{\mu+1} - \hat{\mathbf{z}}_\mu)$$

$$= \begin{bmatrix} \hat{a}\hat{x}^3 + \hat{b}u \\ 0 \\ 0 \end{bmatrix}_\mu + \begin{bmatrix} 3\hat{a}\hat{x}^2; & \hat{x}^3; & u(t) \\ 0 & ; 0; & 0 \\ 0 & ; 0; & 0 \end{bmatrix}_\mu \begin{bmatrix} \hat{x}_{\mu+1} - \hat{x}_\mu \\ \hat{a}_{\mu+1} - \hat{a}_\mu \\ \hat{b}_{\mu+1} - \hat{b}_\mu \end{bmatrix}$$

Employing the notation of equations (8.1) and (8.10) we obtain that:

$$\dot{\hat{\mathbf{z}}}_{\mu+1}(t) = \hat{\mathbf{A}}_\mu \hat{\mathbf{z}}_{\mu+1}(t) + \hat{\mathbf{V}}_\mu$$

$$= \begin{bmatrix} 3\hat{a}\hat{x}^2; & \hat{x}^3; & u \\ 0 & ; 0 ; & 0 \\ 0 & ; 0 ; & 0 \end{bmatrix}_\mu \cdot \begin{bmatrix} \hat{x} \\ \hat{a} \\ \hat{b} \end{bmatrix}_{\mu+1} + \begin{bmatrix} \hat{a}\hat{x}^3 + \hat{b}u \\ 0 \\ 0 \end{bmatrix}_\mu - \begin{bmatrix} 3\hat{a}\hat{x}^2; & \hat{x}^3; & u \\ 0 & ; 0 ; & 0 \\ 0 & ; 0 ; & 0 \end{bmatrix}_\mu \cdot \begin{bmatrix} \hat{x} \\ \hat{a} \\ \hat{b}_\mu \end{bmatrix}_\mu$$

Subsequently, Equation (8.13) yields:

$$\dot{\hat{\boldsymbol{\Phi}}}_{\mu+1}(t_i, t_0) = \begin{bmatrix} 3\hat{a}\hat{x}^2(t); & \hat{x}^3(t); & u(t) \\ 0 & 0 & 0 \\ 0 & 0 & 0 \end{bmatrix}_\mu \cdot \hat{\boldsymbol{\Phi}}_{\mu+1}(t_i, t_0) \tag{8.19}$$

where:

$$\hat{\boldsymbol{\Phi}}_\mu(t_0, t_0) = \mathbf{I} \qquad \forall \mu$$

The initial condition vector $\hat{\mathbf{z}}(t_0)$ for Equation (8.12) is derivable from the a priori given boundary values $x(t_1)$, $x(t_2)$, $x(t_3)$, $x(t_4)$ by employing Equation (8.17), as follows (noting that the number of boundary values considered is larger than the minimum number of 3 that is required for a 3-dimensional vector $\mathbf{z}$):

$$x(t_1) = \hat{\Phi}_{11,\mu+1}(t_1, t_0) \cdot \hat{x}_{\mu+1}(t_0) + \hat{\Phi}_{12,\mu+1}(t_1, t_0)\hat{a}_{\mu+1} + \hat{\Phi}_{13,\mu+1}(t_1, t_0)\hat{b}_{\mu+1} + \hat{\mathbf{q}}_{1,\mu+1}(t_1)$$

$$x(t_2) = \hat{\Phi}_{11,\mu+1}(t_2, t_0) \cdot \hat{x}_{\mu+1}(t_0) + \cdot \quad \cdot \quad \cdot \quad \cdot \quad \cdot \quad + \hat{\mathbf{q}}_{1,\mu+1}(t_2)$$

$$\cdot$$
$$\cdot$$
$$\cdot$$

$$x(t_4) = \hat{\Phi}_{11,\mu+1}(t_4, t_0) \cdot \hat{x}_{\mu+1}(t_0) + \cdot \quad \cdot \quad \cdot \quad \cdot \quad \cdot \quad + \hat{\mathbf{q}}_{1,\mu+1}(t_2) \tag{8.20}$$

The parameters $\hat{\Phi}_{1j,\mu+1}(t, t_0)$ depend on $\left.\frac{\partial \hat{\psi}}{\partial \mathbf{z}}\right|_\mu$ according to equations (8.13) and (8.19), thus being independent of $\hat{x}_{\mu+1}(t_0)$. Similarly $\hat{\mathbf{q}}_{\mu+1}(t_i)$ is computable from Equation (8.15), on the basis of $\hat{\psi}_\mu$; $\left.\frac{\partial \hat{\psi}}{\partial \mathbf{z}}\right|_\mu$; $\hat{\mathbf{z}}_\mu$ and of Equation (8.16), and is therefore also independent of $x_{\mu+1}(t_0)$. Hence a derivation of $\hat{x}_{\mu+1}(t_0)$, $\hat{a}_{\mu+1}$; $\hat{b}_{\mu+1}$ by regression from equations (8.20) is facilitated assuming that initial guesses of $a$, $b$, $x(t_0)$ are available. A direct (nonregression) derivation of the latter three unknowns from equations (8.20) may be possible if only three boundary values of $x$ are considered, and if the measurements are noiseless. (See also Problem 1, this chapter.)

## 8.2 QUASILINEARIZATION IDENTIFICATION OF DISCRETE SYSTEMS

Procedures for identifying discrete systems by quasilinearization may be directly derived from the quasilinearization technique for continuous system identification of Section 8.1, as follows:
Consider a discrete system, given by:

$$\mathbf{x}(k+1) = \mathbf{g}[\mathbf{x}(k); \mathbf{u}(k); \mathbf{p}]; \qquad kT = t \tag{8.21}$$

where $k = 0, 1, 2, \ldots \nu$, and $\mathbf{x}, \mathbf{u}, \mathbf{p}$ are an $n$-dimensional state vector, an $m$-dimensional input vector, and an $r$-dimensional parameters vector, respectively, as in Equation (8.1). The system of Equation (8.21) is assumed to satisfy a set of $n + r$ boundary conditions which are $n + r$ scalar measurable functions $x_j(i)$, where $x_j(i)$ denotes the $j$'th elements of $\mathbf{x}$ at the $i$'th sampling interval. In similarity to the continuous case of Section 8.1, we define an $n + r$ dimensional vector $\mathbf{z}$, such that:

$$\mathbf{z} \triangleq \begin{bmatrix} \mathbf{x} \\ \mathbf{p} \end{bmatrix} \tag{8.22}$$

where:

$$\mathbf{p}(k+1) = \mathbf{p}(k) \tag{8.23}$$

Consequently, Equation (8.21) yields that:

$$\mathbf{z}(k+1) = \boldsymbol{\lambda}[\mathbf{z}(k), \mathbf{u}(k), k] \tag{8.24}$$

where, for stationary systems:

$$\boldsymbol{\lambda} \triangleq \begin{bmatrix} \mathbf{g}[\mathbf{x}(k), \mathbf{u}(k), \mathbf{p}; k] \\ \mathbf{p}[k] \end{bmatrix} \tag{8.25}$$

Again, in similarity to the continuous case, we apply a Taylor series expansion to Equation (8.24), to derive the following relation between the $(\mu + 1)$'th estimate $\hat{\mathbf{z}}_{\mu+1}$ of $\mathbf{z}$ and the $\mu$'th such estimate:

$$\hat{\mathbf{z}}_{\mu+1}(k+1) = \hat{\boldsymbol{\lambda}}_{\mu}[\hat{\mathbf{z}}_{\mu}(k), \mathbf{u}(k), k] + \left(\frac{\partial \hat{\boldsymbol{\lambda}}}{\partial \mathbf{z}}\right)_{\mu} [\hat{\mathbf{z}}_{\mu+1}(k) - \hat{\mathbf{z}}_{\mu}(k)] \tag{8.26}$$

Equation (8.25) may be rewritten in terms of a linear time-variant equation in $\mathbf{z}_{\mu+1}$, as follows:

$$\hat{\mathbf{z}}_{\mu+1}(k+1) = \hat{\mathbf{B}}(k)\hat{\mathbf{z}}_{\mu+1}(k) + \hat{\mathbf{w}}(k) \tag{8.27}$$

where:

$$\hat{\mathbf{B}}_{\mu}(k) \triangleq \left(\frac{\partial \hat{\boldsymbol{\lambda}}}{\partial \mathbf{z}}\right)_{\mu} \tag{8.28-a}$$

$$\hat{\mathbf{w}}(k) \triangleq \hat{\boldsymbol{\lambda}}[\hat{\mathbf{z}}_{\mu}(k), \mathbf{u}(k), \mathbf{u}(k), k] - \left(\frac{\partial \hat{\boldsymbol{\lambda}}}{\partial \mathbf{z}}\right)_{\mu} \hat{\mathbf{z}}_{\mu}(k) \tag{8.28-b}$$

The solution of Equation (8.26) thus becomes, in full analogy to Section 8.1:

$$\hat{\mathbf{z}}_{\mu+1}(k) = \hat{\boldsymbol{\Phi}}_{\mu+1}(k, h) \cdot \hat{\mathbf{z}}_{\mu+1}(h) + \hat{\mathbf{q}}_{\mu+1}(k) \tag{8.29}$$

where:

$$\hat{\boldsymbol{\Phi}}_{\mu+1}(k, h) = \hat{\mathbf{A}}_{\mu}(k)\hat{\boldsymbol{\Phi}}_{\mu+1}(k, h); \qquad k > h \tag{8.30}$$

$$\hat{\boldsymbol{\Phi}}(h, h) \triangleq \mathbf{I} \tag{8.31}$$

and $\hat{\mathbf{q}}(k)$ being the particular solution to Equation (8.26), as follows:

$$\hat{\mathbf{q}}_{\mu+1}(k + 1) = \hat{\mathbf{B}}_{\mu}(k)\hat{\mathbf{q}}_{\mu+1}(k) + \hat{\mathbf{w}}(k) \tag{8.32}$$

with the initial condition:

$$\hat{\mathbf{q}}_{\mu+1}(0) = \mathbf{0} \tag{8.33}$$

The $n + r$ elements of the initial vector $\hat{\mathbf{z}}_{\mu+1}(0)$ are obtained such that they satisfy the $n + r$ boundary conditions $x_j(i)$. To guarantee the uniqueness of the solution, in cases of noisy measurements, $v > n + r$ boundary conditions are required. Those yield a linear regression relation for deriving the $n + r$ elements of $\mathbf{z}_{\mu+1}(0)$ as in the continuous case of Section 8.1 above.

Initial estimates $\hat{\mathbf{p}}_0$ of $\mathbf{p}$ and $\hat{\mathbf{x}}_0(0)$ of $\mathbf{x}(0)$ are required to state the identification procedure. These should be as close as possible to the actual values since convergence is not always guaranteed and depends on that initial estimate. In similarity to the continuous case, when the number of measurements is sufficiently large, the initial estimate becomes less critical.

## REFERENCES


1. Bellman, R. *Dynamic Programming*, Princeton University Press, N.J., 1957.
2. Kalaba, R. "On Nonlinear Differential Equations, The Maximum Operation and Monotone Convergence," *Jour. Math. and Mechanics*, Vol. 8, pp. 519–574, 1959.
3. Kumar, K. S. P., and Shridar, R. "On the Identification of Control Systems by the Quasi-Linearization Method," *IEEE Trans.*, Vol. AC-9, pp. 151–154, 1964.
4. Sage, A. P., and Eisenberg, B. R. "Experiments in Nonlinear and Nonstationary System Identification via Quasilinearization and Differential Approximation," *Proc. Joint Automatic Control Conf.*, pp. 522–530, 1965.
5. Sage, A. P. *Optimum Systems Control*, Prentice-Hall, Englewood Cliffs, N.J., 1968.
6. Detchmendy, D. M., and Shridar, R. "On the Experimental Determination of the Dynamical Characteristics of Physical Systems," *Proc. National Electronics Conf.*, pp. 522–530, Chicago, 1965.

## PROBLEMS

**1.** Employ quasilinearization to identify a stationary process given by:

$$\dot{x}(t) = ax(t) + u(t)$$

where:

$$u(t) = \begin{cases} 1 & \forall t \geq 0 \\ 0 & \forall t < 0 \end{cases}$$

$$x(0) = 0; \qquad x(1) = 0.095 \qquad x(2) = 0.181$$

the initial estimate for $a$ being $\hat{a}_1 = -0.12$.

**2.** Identify the stationary discrete system given by:

$$x(k+1) = a \cdot x(k) + b \cdot u(k)$$

where:

$$x(0) = 0; \qquad x(1) = 0.095; \qquad x(2) = 0.181; \qquad x(3) = 0.259$$

and:

$$u(k) = \begin{cases} 1 & \forall k \geq 0 \\ 0 & \forall k < 0 \end{cases}$$

Choose a reasonable initial estimate according to the above data.

**3.** Identify the nonlinear system given by:

$$\dot{x} = ax^2$$

with $x(0) = 0.5$; $x(1) = 0.27$, and with the initial estimate $\hat{a}_1 = -4$. Repeat the solution with $\hat{a}_1 = -3$ and with $\hat{a}_1 = -10$.

# 9

# INVARIANT IMBEDDING IDENTIFICATION

Techniques where a two-point boundary value problem is imbedded into a single-point boundary value problem were first formulated by Bellman, Kalaba, and Wing,[1] and are termed as invariant imbedding techniques. Their application to system identification is due to Bellman, et al.,[2] Detchmendy and Shridar,[3] and Sage and Masters.[4]

Invariant imbedding techniques may be employed for parameter identification, and furthermore, for simultaneously identifying the parameters and estimating the state of linear and nonlinear observable systems in a sequential manner. In similarity to the techniques of the previous chapters, when invariant imbedding is employed to identify nonlinear systems, it requires prior knowledge of the form of the nonlinear function whose parameters are to be identified. Convergence of the invarient imbedding identification to the actual parameters may be guaranteed over a fairly wide range of initial estimates, though some a priori knowledge of the range, within which the parameter values lie, is required (this may be more vague than when employing boundary value techniques of quasilinearization, but it considerably affects the convergence rate of the identification). Furthermore, inadequate choice of the initial **Q** matrix that arises in the identification procedure (Equation (9.29) and onwards) may cause divergence or slow convergence of the identification, as is shown later in this chapter and in the solutions to the problems at the end of the chapter as given in Appendix 4.

Identification by invariant imbedding is based on integrating a set of nonlinear differential equations with respect to time, the solution of which is to converge to the required state and parameter estimates as time goes on. Since the measurements vs. time record provides the forcing function to these equations, the longer the measurements record, is the closer may the solution converge to the true values.

Invariant imbedding yields one of the most mathematically powerful techniques for identification, since it may provide sequential estimation of parameters and of all state variables simultaneously in an optimal manner for linear and nonlinear systems. The latter joint state and parameter estimation is also facilitated by some of the techniques of Chapter 12 below, and to a certain extent by quasilinearization, as in Chapter 8. However, most of the techniques of Chapter 12 are essentially applicable to linear systems and assume linearization in nonlinear cases, and quasilinearization requires close initial estimates for convergence. whereas invariant imbedding is less restricted in these respects. Despite its generality, invariant imbedding is of limited use for on-line identification, because of its computation complexity. It is therefore mainly applicable to cases where joint state and parameter estimation of nonlinear systems is required, or where a priori knowledge considerably reduces the estimation problem. We note that when the dimension of the state vector is unknown, iteration of orders is usually impractical due to the additional parameters involved and the respective increased computational effort.

## 9.1. FORMULATION OF THE INVARIANT IMBEDDING IDENTIFICATION PROBLEM

Consider a system given by:

$$\dot{\mathbf{x}} = \mathbf{f}[\mathbf{x}(t), \mathbf{p}, \mathbf{u}(t)] + \mathbf{n}(t) \tag{9.1}$$

and:

$$\mathbf{z}(t) = \boldsymbol{\phi}[\mathbf{x}(t), \mathbf{p}, \mathbf{u}(t)] + \mathbf{v}(t) \tag{9.2}$$

**f** being a nonlinear function; **x**, **u**, **n**, **z**, and **v** being state, measurable input, unmeasurable system noise, measurement, and measurement noise vectors, respectively; **p** being a vector of stationary parameters; and:

$$\dot{\mathbf{p}} = \mathbf{0} \tag{9.3}$$

The identification problem is formulated as one of minimizing a cost $J$, where:

$$J \triangleq \int_{t_0}^{t_f} \{[\mathbf{z} - \boldsymbol{\phi}(\hat{\mathbf{x}}, \mathbf{u})]^T \cdot \boldsymbol{\eta} \cdot [\mathbf{z} - \boldsymbol{\phi}(\hat{\mathbf{x}}, \mathbf{u})] + \hat{\mathbf{n}}^T \zeta \hat{\mathbf{n}}\}\, dt \tag{9.4}$$

$\hat{\mathbf{x}}$, $\hat{\mathbf{n}}$ being the estimates of $\mathbf{x}$, $\mathbf{n}$ of Equation (9.1), respectively, and $\boldsymbol{\eta}$, $\boldsymbol{\zeta}$ being positive diagonal weighting matrices, (note that in predictor models $\mathbf{u}$ is usually $\mathbf{0}$). We subsequently define a vector $\mathbf{y}$, as follows:

$$\mathbf{y} \triangleq \begin{bmatrix} \mathbf{x} \\ \mathbf{p} \end{bmatrix} \tag{9.5}$$

such that equations (9.1), (9.3) yield:

$$\dot{\mathbf{y}} = \boldsymbol{\psi} + \mathbf{V} \tag{9.6}$$

where:

$$\boldsymbol{\psi} \triangleq \begin{bmatrix} \mathbf{f} \\ 0 \end{bmatrix} \tag{9.7}$$

$$\mathbf{V} = \begin{bmatrix} \mathbf{n} \\ \mathbf{0} \end{bmatrix} \tag{9.8}$$

$\boldsymbol{\psi}$ of Equation (9.7) being nonlinear in $\mathbf{y}$ even when $\mathbf{f}$ is linear such as:

$$\dot{x} = px + u$$

where:

$$x \triangleq y_1$$
$$p \triangleq y_2$$
$$\mathbf{y}^T = [y_1, y_2]$$

and, according to Equation (9.6):

$$\left.\begin{aligned} \dot{y}_1 &= y_1 y_2 + u \\ \dot{y}_2 &= 0 \end{aligned}\right\} = \boldsymbol{\psi} + \mathbf{V}$$

such that:

$$\boldsymbol{\psi} = \begin{bmatrix} y_1 y_2 \\ 0 \end{bmatrix}$$

For minimizing $J$ with respect to estimates $\hat{\mathbf{y}}$ of $\mathbf{y}$, we consider the Hamiltonian $H$, where:

$$H \triangleq [\mathbf{z} - \boldsymbol{\phi}(\hat{\mathbf{y}}, \mathbf{u})]^T \boldsymbol{\eta} [\mathbf{z} - \boldsymbol{\phi}] + \hat{\mathbf{n}}^T \boldsymbol{\zeta} \hat{\mathbf{n}} + \boldsymbol{\lambda}^T \cdot \boldsymbol{\psi} \tag{9.9}$$

The minimization of $J$ with respect to $\hat{\mathbf{y}}$ yields the following set of equations:[5]

$$\frac{\partial H}{\partial \hat{\mathbf{y}}} = -\boldsymbol{\lambda} \tag{9.10}$$

$$\frac{\partial H}{\partial \boldsymbol{\lambda}} = \dot{\hat{\mathbf{y}}} \tag{9.11}$$

$$\frac{\partial H}{\partial \mathbf{u}} = \mathbf{0} \tag{9.12}$$

Furthermore, when $\hat{\mathbf{y}}(t_0)$, $\hat{\mathbf{y}}(t_f)$ are not given ($t_0$, $t_f$ denoting initial and final time), the transversality condition related to the minimization of $H$ yields:[5]

$$\boldsymbol{\lambda} = \mathbf{0}\Big|_{t=t_0}^{t=t_f} \tag{9.13}$$

Consequently, the following boundary conditions may be related to equations (9.10) and (9.11):

$$\boldsymbol{\lambda}(t_0) = \mathbf{0} \tag{9.14}$$

$$\boldsymbol{\lambda}(t_f) = \mathbf{0} \tag{9.15}$$

The estimation of $\hat{\mathbf{p}}$, $\hat{\mathbf{x}}$ thus becomes a problem of solving equations (9.10) and (9.11). It is based on the initial conditions for these equations, and this is where the application of invariant imbedding is required.

## 9.2 THE INVARIANT IMBEDDING SOLUTION TO THE CONTINUOUS SYSTEM IDENTIFICATION PROBLEM

The solution of the identification and state estimation problem over the interval $t_0$ to $t_f$ as formulated in equations (9.10) and (9.11) may be considered as generalized a two-point boundary value problem given by:

$$\dot{\mathbf{y}} = \mathbf{g}(\mathbf{y}, \boldsymbol{\lambda}, \mathbf{u}, t) \tag{9.16}$$

$$\dot{\boldsymbol{\lambda}} = \mathbf{h}(\mathbf{y}, \boldsymbol{\lambda}, \mathbf{u}, t) \tag{9.17}$$

where $\mathbf{g}$, $\mathbf{h}$ are functions of $\mathbf{y}$, $\boldsymbol{\lambda}$, $\mathbf{u}$, $t$, and where the boundary conditions may be expressed as:

$$\boldsymbol{\lambda}(t_0) = \mathbf{a} \tag{9.18}$$

$$\boldsymbol{\lambda}(t_f) = \mathbf{b} \tag{9.19}$$

The end conditions $\boldsymbol{\lambda}(t_f)$ may be further considered to be given by a more general function of $t_f$ when $t_f$ is a *running variable*, such that:

$$\boldsymbol{\lambda}(t_f) = \mathbf{C}(t_f) \tag{9.20}$$

yielding the following end conditions on $\mathbf{y}$:

$$\mathbf{y}(t_f) = \mathbf{F}(\mathbf{C}, t_f) \tag{9.21}$$

Hence, the missing end condition on $\mathbf{y}$ is substituted for by a function $\mathbf{F}$ of the corresponding end condition on $\boldsymbol{\lambda}$.

Applying a first order Taylor extrapolation to Equation (9.21), and noting Equation (9.16), we obtain that:

$$\mathbf{F}(\mathbf{C} + \Delta\mathbf{C}, t_f + \Delta t_f) = \mathbf{F}(\mathbf{C}, t_f) + \mathbf{g}(\mathbf{F}, \mathbf{C}, \mathbf{u}, t_f)\,\Delta t_f \tag{9.22}$$

A further approximation may be applied to $\mathbf{F}(\mathbf{C} + \Delta\mathbf{C}, t_f + \Delta t_f)$, to yield:

$$\mathbf{F}(\mathbf{C} + \Delta\mathbf{C}, t_f + \Delta t_f) = \mathbf{F}(\mathbf{C}, t_f) + \frac{\partial \mathbf{F}^T}{\partial \mathbf{C}} \Delta\mathbf{C} + \frac{\partial \mathbf{F}}{\partial t_f} \Delta t_f \tag{9.23}$$

where $\mathbf{C}$, $t_f$ are considered to be independent variables. From the definition of $\mathbf{C}$ and from Equation (9.17), we derive the first order Taylor approximation for $\Delta\mathbf{C}$, as follows:

$$\Delta\mathbf{C} = \mathbf{h}(\mathbf{F}, \mathbf{C}, \mathbf{u}, t_f)\, \Delta t_f \tag{9.24}$$

Substituting for $\Delta\mathbf{C}$ from Equation (9.24) into (9.23), and equating the right-hand sides of equations (9.22) and (9.23), yields the following invariant imbedding equation:

$$\left(\frac{\partial \mathbf{F}}{\partial \mathbf{C}}\right)^T \cdot \mathbf{h}(\mathbf{F}, \mathbf{C}, t_f) + \frac{\partial \mathbf{F}}{\partial t_f} = \mathbf{g}(\mathbf{F}, \mathbf{C}, \mathbf{u}, t_f) \tag{9.25}$$

However, comparing equations (9.10), (9.11) with (9.16), (9.17), we obtain that:

$$\mathbf{g}(\mathbf{F}, \mathbf{C}, t_f) = \left.\frac{\partial H}{\partial \boldsymbol{\lambda}}\right|_{\mathbf{F}, \mathbf{C}, t_f} = \left.\frac{\partial H}{\partial \mathbf{C}}\right|_{\mathbf{F}, \mathbf{C}, t_f} \tag{9.26}$$

and:

$$\mathbf{h}(\mathbf{F}, \mathbf{C}, t_f) = -\left.\frac{\partial H}{\partial \mathbf{y}}\right|_{\mathbf{F}, \mathbf{C}, t_f} = -\left.\frac{\partial H}{\partial \mathbf{F}}\right|_{\mathbf{F}, \mathbf{C}, t_f} \tag{9.27}$$

Hence, Equation (9.25) becomes:

$$\frac{\partial \mathbf{F}}{\partial t_f} - \left(\frac{\partial \mathbf{F}}{\partial \mathbf{C}}\right)^T \left.\frac{\partial H}{\partial \mathbf{F}}\right|_{\mathbf{F}, \mathbf{C}, t_f} = \left.\frac{\partial H}{\partial \mathbf{C}}\right|_{\mathbf{F}, \mathbf{C}, t_f} \tag{9.28}$$

According to the definition of $\mathbf{F}$ in Equation (9.21), we may guess a solution for $\mathbf{F}$ of Equation (9.28), as follows:

$$\mathbf{F}(\mathbf{C}, t_f) = \hat{\mathbf{y}}(t_f) - \mathbf{Q}(t_f)\mathbf{C}(t_f) \tag{9.29}$$

$\mathbf{Q}$ being a symmetrical matrix in analogy to the matrix $\mathbf{P}$ of Chapter 6. The latter guess is reasonable around $t_f$ since, for small $\mathbf{C}$, a linear relation between $\mathbf{F}(t_f)$ and its estimate may be assumed. Substituting for $\mathbf{F}$ from Equation (9.29) into (9.28), and noting the definition of $\mathbf{C}$, $\mathbf{F}$ as in equations (9.20), (9.21), we derive that:

$$\frac{\partial \mathbf{y}(t_f)}{\partial t_f} + \mathbf{Q}(t_f) \cdot \left.\frac{\partial H}{\partial \mathbf{F}}\right|_{\mathbf{F}, \mathbf{C}, t_f} = \left.\frac{\partial H}{\partial \mathbf{C}}\right|_{\mathbf{F}, \mathbf{C}, t_f} \tag{9.30}$$

From the derivation above it follows that Equation (9.30) satisfies the end conditions at $t_f$. Consequently, when generalizing equations (9.29) and (9.30) in terms of $t$ rather than the running variable $t_f$, but noting that $\mathbf{C}(t_f)$ cannot depend on $t$, we obtain a new set of equations that are bound to satisfy the end conditions $\mathbf{C}(t_f)$, as follows:

$$\mathbf{y}(\mathbf{C}, t) = \hat{\mathbf{y}}(t) - \mathbf{Q}(t)\mathbf{C} \tag{9.31}$$

and:

$$\frac{\partial \mathbf{y}(t)}{\partial t} - \mathbf{Q}(t)\mathbf{h}(\mathbf{y}, \mathbf{C}, \mathbf{u}, t) = \mathbf{g}(\mathbf{y}, \mathbf{C}, \mathbf{u}, t) \tag{9.32}$$

where $\mathbf{g}$, $\mathbf{h}$ are as in equations (9.26), (9.27) when substituting for $\mathbf{F}$, $t_f$ by $\mathbf{y}$, $t$. The latter equations may be combined into:

$$\dot{\hat{\mathbf{y}}} - \dot{\mathbf{Q}}(t)\mathbf{C} - \mathbf{Q}(t) \cdot \mathbf{h}(\mathbf{y}, \mathbf{C}, \mathbf{u}, t) = \mathbf{g}(\mathbf{y}, \mathbf{C}, \mathbf{u}, t) \tag{9.33}$$

or, substituting for $\mathbf{g}$, $\mathbf{h}$ from equations (9.26), (9.27), respectively, into Equation (9.33):

$$\dot{\hat{\mathbf{y}}} - \dot{\mathbf{Q}}\mathbf{C} + \mathbf{Q}\left.\frac{\partial H}{\partial \mathbf{y}}\right|_{\substack{\mathbf{y}=\hat{\mathbf{y}}-\mathbf{Q}\mathbf{C}\\ \boldsymbol{\lambda}=\mathbf{C};\ \partial H/\partial \mathbf{u}=\mathbf{0}}} = \left.\frac{\partial H}{\partial \boldsymbol{\lambda}}\right|_{\substack{\mathbf{y}=\hat{\mathbf{y}}-\mathbf{Q}\mathbf{C}\\ \boldsymbol{\lambda}=\mathbf{C};\ \partial H/\partial \mathbf{u}=\mathbf{0}}} \tag{9.34}$$

Equation (9.34) actually describes the behavior of the system near $t_f$ which has been considered to be a running variable, now denoted by $t$, thus yielding a sequential estimation for a running $t_f$ over the range of the variable $t$. Since, according to Equation (9.15), $\mathbf{C}$ must be close to $\mathbf{0}$, all terms of $C_i^2$, $C_i C_j$ ($C_i$, $C_j$ being elements of $\mathbf{C}$) may be omitted. Furthermore, since $\mathbf{C} \rightarrow \mathbf{0}$, Equation (9.34) yields two sets of equations, namely a set of equations resulting from equating $\mathbf{C}$ to $\mathbf{0}$ in Equation (9.34) and another set of equations obtained from equating all terms of Equation (9.34) that are multiplied by a certain element $C_i$ of $\mathbf{C}$ (see example below). In deriving the above equations, it is noted that $\mathbf{Q}$ is symmetrical. The resulting set of simultaneous first-order differential equations may be sequentially solved, given the initial conditions $\hat{\mathbf{y}}(t_0)$, $\mathbf{Q}(t_0)$. Because of the good convergence properties of the invariant imbedding technique, the values for $\hat{\mathbf{y}}(t_0)$, $\mathbf{Q}(t_0)$ may be almost arbitrarily chosen. However, the better the initial estimates of $\hat{\mathbf{y}}(t_0)$, the faster the convergence of the procedure. We note that for a system with $n$ states and $r$ unknown parameters, the number of simultaneous nonlinear differential equations that require solution in the above procedure is given by $\left[n + r + \dfrac{(n+r)\cdot(n+r+1)}{2}\right]$ where $n + r$ is the number of elements of $\mathbf{y}$ and $\dfrac{(n+r)\cdot(n+r+1)}{2}$ is the number of different elements in the symmetrical $\mathbf{Q}$ matrix. The latter large number of equations results in a severe computational effort, when identification by invariant imbedding is performed.

EXAMPLE 9.1

This example is presented to illustrate the invariant imbedding identification procedure: Consider a process given by:

$$\dot{x} = p_1 x + p_2 u$$
$$z = x + v$$

$p_1, p_2$ being the unknown but stationary parameters, and $x$, $u$, $v$, and $z$ denoting state, input, measurement noise, and output, respectively. We may write that:

$$\dot{p}_1 = \dot{p}_2 = 0$$

We define:

$$\mathbf{y} \triangleq \begin{bmatrix} x \\ p_1 \\ p_2 \end{bmatrix} = \begin{bmatrix} y_1 \\ y_2 \\ y_3 \end{bmatrix}$$

and:

$$J \triangleq \int_0^{t_f} (z - \hat{x})^2 \, dt$$

For minimizing $J$ with respect to $\hat{\mathbf{y}}$, we consider the Hamiltonian $H$, given by:

$$\begin{aligned} H \triangleq (z - x)^2 + \boldsymbol{\lambda}^T \mathbf{g} &= (z - \hat{x})^2 + \lambda_1(\hat{p}_1 \hat{x} + \hat{p}_2 u) + \lambda_2 \dot{p}_1 + \lambda_3 \dot{p}_2 \\ &= (z - \hat{y}_1)^2 + \lambda_1(\hat{y}_1 \hat{y}_2 + \hat{y}_3 u) + 0 + 0 \end{aligned}$$

We derive the following equations (see Ref. 5, p. 57):

$$\frac{\partial H}{\partial \lambda_1} = \dot{\hat{\mathbf{y}}}_1 = \hat{y}_1 \hat{y}_2 + \hat{y}_3 u$$

$u$ being measurable, and:

$$\frac{\partial H}{\partial \hat{y}_1} = -\dot{\lambda}_1 = -2z + 2\hat{y}_1 + \lambda_1 \hat{y}_2$$

$$\frac{\partial H}{\partial \hat{y}_2} = -\dot{\lambda}_2 = \lambda_1 \hat{y}_1$$

$$\frac{\partial H}{\partial \hat{y}_3} = -\dot{\lambda}_3 = \lambda_1 u$$

The boundary conditions for the latter equations are:

$$\boldsymbol{\lambda}(0) = \begin{bmatrix} \lambda_1(0) \\ \lambda_2(0) \\ \lambda_3(0) \end{bmatrix} = \mathbf{0}$$

$$\boldsymbol{\lambda}(t_f) = \mathbf{0}$$

The solution for the invariant imbedding equation (9.28) is assumed to be of the form of Equation (9.29), such that:

$$\mathbf{F}(\mathbf{C}, t_f) = \hat{\mathbf{y}}(t_f) - \mathbf{Q}(t_f)\mathbf{C}$$

Substituting the latter solution into Equation (9.28), yields according to Equation (9.34):

$$\begin{bmatrix} \dot{\hat{y}}_1 \\ \dot{\hat{y}}_2 \\ \dot{\hat{y}}_3 \end{bmatrix} - \begin{bmatrix} \dot{Q}_{11} & \dot{Q}_{12} & \dot{Q}_{13} \\ \dot{Q}_{12} & \dot{Q}_{22} & \dot{Q}_{23} \\ \dot{Q}_{13} & \dot{Q}_{23} & \dot{Q}_{33} \end{bmatrix} \cdot \begin{bmatrix} C_1 \\ C_2 \\ C_3 \end{bmatrix} - \begin{bmatrix} Q_{11} & Q_{12} & Q_{13} \\ Q_{12} & Q_{22} & Q_{23} \\ Q_{13} & Q_{23} & Q_{33} \end{bmatrix}$$

$$\begin{bmatrix} 2(z-\hat{y}_1+Q_{11}C_1+Q_{12}C_2+Q_{13}C_3)-C_1(\hat{y}_2-Q_{12}C_1-Q_{22}C_2-Q_{23}C_3) \\ -C_1(\hat{y}_1-Q_{11}C_1-Q_{12}C_2-Q_{13}C_3) \\ -C_1u \end{bmatrix}$$

$$= \begin{bmatrix} (\hat{y}_1-Q_{11}C_1-Q_{12}C_2-Q_{13}C_3)(\hat{y}_2-Q_{12}C_1-Q_{22}C_2-Q_{23}C_3) \\ \qquad + u(\hat{y}_3-Q_{13}C_1-Q_{23}C_2-Q_{33}C_3) \\ 0 \\ 0 \end{bmatrix}$$

The latter expression may be solved when expanded around $\mathbf{C} = \mathbf{0}$. Consequently, two sets of differential equations are derived, in $\hat{y}_i$ and in $\dot{Q}_j$, one set being obtained from substituting $\mathbf{C} = \mathbf{0}$ into the latter expression, and the second resulting from equating only terms multiplying the same $C_i \; \forall i$, while all other terms are omitted. Realistic initial conditions would be:

$x(t_0) = z(t_0)$.
$\hat{\mathbf{p}}(t_0)$ = anything reasonable. The closer $\hat{\mathbf{p}}(t_0)$ is to the true $\mathbf{p}$, the faster does the procedure converge.
$\mathbf{Q}(t_0) = k\mathbf{I}$; a too high value for $k$ may result in divergence, whereas a too low value may cause very slow convergence. The value of $k$ may thus be derived by trial and error, starting with a low value, since a stability analysis of the set on nonlinear differential equations that is involved may be too lengthy.

See also problems 9.1 to 9.5.

## 9.3 IDENTIFICATION OF DISCRETE SYSTEMS BY INVARIANT IMBEDDING

The identification of discrete systems by invariant imbedding techniques is analogous to the identification of continuous systems by these techniques. In the discrete case the equivalent two-point boundary value problem to equations (9.16), (9.17) becomes:

$$\mathbf{y}(k+1) = \mathbf{g}(\mathbf{y}, \boldsymbol{\lambda}, \mathbf{u}, k) \tag{9.35}$$

$$\boldsymbol{\lambda}(k+1) = \mathbf{h}(\mathbf{y}, \boldsymbol{\lambda}, \mathbf{u}, k) \tag{9.36}$$

where $kT = t$, with $k = 0 \cdots N$ and $T$ being a sampling interval. The boundary conditions are again defined as:

$$\boldsymbol{\lambda}(0) = \mathbf{a} \tag{9.37}$$

$$\boldsymbol{\lambda}(N) = \mathbf{b} \tag{9.38}$$

The more general end condition for a running $N$ is defined, as in Equation (9.20) such that:

$$\boldsymbol{\lambda}(N) = \mathbf{C}(N) \tag{9.39}$$

and therefore:

$$(N) = \mathbf{F}(\mathbf{C}, N) \tag{9.40}$$

The derivation thus continues in a similar manner as in the continuous case of Section 9.2, when noting that $t = kT$ and $t_f = NT$, to yield analogous estimation results.

## REFERENCES

1. Bellman, R., Kalaba, R., and Wing, G. "Invariant Imbedding and Mathematical Physics, I:—Particle Processes," *Jour. Math. Phys.*, Vol. 1, pp. 280–308, 1960.
2. Bellman, R., Kagiwada, H., Kalaba, R., and Shridar, R. "Invariant Imbedding and Nonlinear Filtering Theory," *Jour. Astro. Sci.*, Vol. 13, pp. 110–115, 1966.
3. Detchmendy, D. M., and Shridar, R. "Sequential Estimation of State and Paramters in Noisy Non-Linear Dynamical Systems," *Trans. A.S.M.E. Jour. Basic Eng.*, Vol. 88, pp. 362–366, 1966.
4. Sage, A. P., and Masters, G. W. "On-Line Estimation of States and Parameters of Discrete Non-Linear Dynamic Systems," *Proc. National Electronics Conf.*, Vol. 22, pp. 677–682, 1966.
5. Sage, A. P. *Optimum Systems Control*, Prentice-Hall, Englewood Cliffs, N.J., 1968.

## PROBLEMS

**1.** Employ invariant imbedding to identify the stationary parameters $a$, $b$ of the system $\dot{x} = ax + bu$, from measurements $z = x + v$, $v$ being zero-mean noise, and the values of $z$, (at intervals of 0.1), and $u$ being as follows:

$z(t) = 0.012$, .0134, .166, .169, .209, .065, .206, .348, .347, .402, .438, .437, .422, .517, .535, .534, .582, .59, .654, .565, .58, .512, .584, .58, .561, .471, .45, .545, .402, .437, .307, .323, .353, .358, .227, .325, .284, .265, .303, .365, .189, .218, .32, .395, .466, .414, .418, .451, .423, .414, .567, .573, .675, .674, .661, .598, .611, .682, .619, .802, .714, .623, .642, .659, .601, .608, .5, .443, .491, .498, .41, .383, .342, .429, .242, .362, .346, .309, .242, .341, .212, .296, .4, .388, .328, .39, .456, .443, .55, .594, .644, .533, .619, .598, .551, .605, .673, .768, .672, .666, .788, .733, .629, .651, .612, .585, .55, .545, .438. 409, .415, .439, .355, .356, .38, .391, .299, .281, .264, .295, .184, .324, .248, .411, .481, .411, .473, .352, .546, .525, .592, .592, .523, .591, .685, .625, .713, .682, .756, .788, .78, .727, .634, .58, .553, .514, .518, .467, .449, .527, .409, .459, .488, .477, .375, .275, .3, .282, .257, .371, .278

while $u(t)$ is a square-wave oscillating between 1 and 0 at intervals of 0.2, starting with 1 from $t = 0$ to $t = 0.2$. The initial conditions for the invariant imbedding solution are $\mathbf{Q} = \mathbf{I}$; $\hat{x}(0) = z(0)$; $-\hat{a}(0) = \hat{b}(0) = 1.0$.

2. Repeat Problem 1 for $-\hat{a}(0) = \hat{b}(0) = 1.5$ and for $\mathbf{Q}(0) = \mathbf{I}$.
3. Repeat Problem 1 for $-\hat{a}(0) = \hat{b}(0) = 1.0$ and for $\mathbf{Q}(0) = 0.2 \cdot \mathbf{I}; 5 \cdot \mathbf{I}; 10 \cdot \mathbf{I}$.
4. Repeat Problem 1 for $\hat{a}(0) = \hat{b}(0) = 0$ and for $\mathbf{Q}(0) = 5 \cdot \mathbf{I}; 10 \cdot \mathbf{I}$.
5. Identify the parameters of the stationary nonlinear system given by $\dot{x} = ax^2$; $z = x + v$, $v$ being zero average noise, for the initial conditions: $\hat{a}(0) = -1.0$; $\hat{x}(0) = 1.0$; $\mathbf{Q} = \mathbf{I}$ and for the following measured data (at intervals of 0.1):

$z(t) = 1.0$, .833, .714, .625, .555, .5, .455, .417, .385, .357, .333, .313, .294, .278, .263, .25, .238, .227, .217, .208, .2, .192, .185, .178, .172, .167, .161, .156, .152, .147, .143, .139, .135, .132, .128, .125, .122, .199, .116, .114, .111, .109, .106, .104, .102, .1, .098, .096, .0944, .0926, .091

# 10

# PREDICTIVE IDENTIFICATION AND PREDICTIVE GRADIENT TECHNIQUES

## 10.1 PREDICTIVE IDENTIFICATION AND CONTROL

Predictive identification is, in essence, an on-line pulse response technique, employing sampled input and output data.[1,2]. It leads, at each control interval, to a direct derivation of the next control vector, based on the last identification, the control vector elements being pulses of one-interval duration. Control is derived directly from the pulse response, without any translation of the latter to a transfer-function form or to a differential-equation formulation, thus facilitating relatively fast performance. The technique resembles, in a way, the identification performed by a human being. When driving a car, an unexperienced driver requires no differential equation model of the response of his steering wheel. However, he will predict the trajectory of the car, and decide on his next steering action from noting the deviation of the car's trajectory from the predicted one, due to his last steering action. The latter analogy indicates that the predictive identification has features of a learning technique.

The predictive identification approach that is described below is valid for linear and nonlinear systems, which are assumed to be stationary over a few control intervals. However, identification is continuously performed, at each control interval, and continuous updating of the identification functions is facilitated in case of parameter time-variations which are slow compared with the control interval.

The predictive gradient procedure that is subsequently discussed employs the predictive identification principles while considering the response of a performance function to control inputs and not the output responses to these inputs, as in the case of the predictive identification technique above.

### 10.1.1 Single-Input Processes

Consider a linear system as in Figure 10.1, where $u$ is the system's input and $\mathbf{y}$ is its $n$-dimensioned output vector (having elements $y_1$ to $y_n$). The input $u(t)$ is in the form of discrete steps $u(kT)$ with $k = 1, 2, \ldots$, and $T$ being the control interval. At any time $t = kT$ we may predict the output at $kT + \tau\ (\tau \leq t)$ from data from $t = kT - T$ up to $t = kT$, when assuming that the input $u$ remains unchanged after $t = kT - T$. The latter assumption is required since any new step-change of $u$ at $t = kT$ invalidates the data of $y$ from $kT - T$ to $kT$ for the purpose of prediction ahead of $t = kT$ such that the message contained in $\mathbf{y}(t)$ cannot be considered as stationary after $t = kT$ (see Figure 10.2). Hence, we define $y_{ipo}(kT + \tau)$ as the estimated value of $y_i$ that has been predicted at $t = kT$, according to measured data during the last control interval (from $kT - T$ to $kT$), when assuming that:

$$\Delta u(kT) = 0 \tag{10.1-a}$$

where:

$$\Delta u(kT) \triangleq u(kT) - u(kT - T) \tag{10.1-b}$$

If subsequently a nonzero $\Delta u(kT)$ is applied at $t = kT$, the corresponding measured output $y_i(t)\ \forall\ kT \leq t < kT + T$ yields the system's response $q_i(\tau)$ of the $i$'th output to the step $\Delta u(kT)$ as follows:[1]

$$q_i(\tau) = \frac{y_i(kT + \tau) - y_{ipo}(kT + \tau)}{\Delta u(kT)} \qquad \forall kT < \tau < kT + T \tag{10.2}$$

or in vector form:

$$\mathbf{q}(\tau) \triangleq \frac{1}{\Delta u(kT)} (\mathbf{y}(kT + \tau) - \mathbf{y}_{po}(kT + \tau)) \tag{10.3}$$

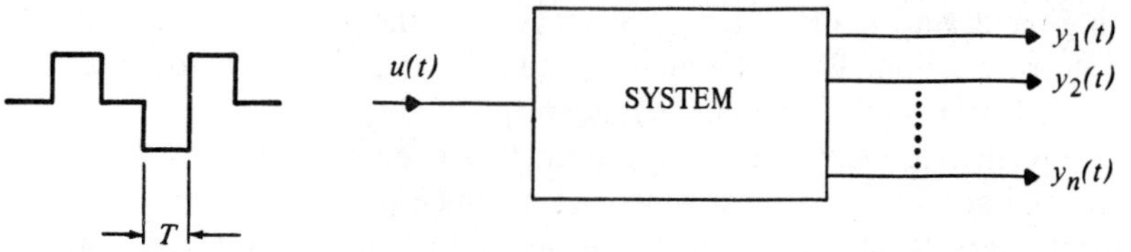


*Figure 10.1* Single input process.

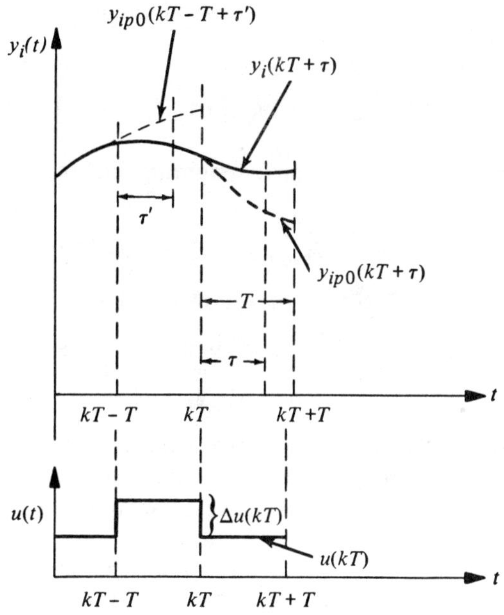


*Figure 10.2* Description of $y_{po}$.

$\mathbf{q}$ being the identification vector having elements $q_1 \cdots q_n$. The latter formulation assumes that the system is linear, or linearized (if variations in $u$ and $y_i$ are small during the $(k + 1)$'th interval from $kT$ to $kT + T$). Equation (10.3) indicates that the response of the $i$'th output of the system to a unit pulse of width $T$ is $q_i(\tau) \forall 0 < \tau < T$, this response being updated at every control interval. The latter $q_i(\tau)$ represents the step response of the latter, for $0 < \tau < T$, since during that period (up to $t = kT + T$) the pulse $\Delta u(kT)$ may be considered to be a step. Equation (10.3) thus provides identifications of the pulse response only. However, since the input at every control interval is in form of a pulse $\Delta u(kT)$, the response to a pulse input provides enough information for control purposes. Consequently, the step response information above may be directly employed for computing the next control input $\Delta u(kT + \tau)$, which is again a pulse, and no transformation of this response information to another formulation, such as to transfer function or differential equation models, is required. The fact that $\mathbf{q}(\tau)$ is computed for $\tau < T$ only is acceptable, since after each interval of duration $T$ a new control pulse $\Delta u(kT)$ is computed. Furthermore, the effect of the previous pulses is accounted for by predicting $\mathbf{y}_{po}$ such that Equation (10.3) yields the response to $\Delta u(kT)$ alone. Consequently, the change in the control input $\Delta u(kT)$ is computed at each control interval to bring the output $\mathbf{y}(kT + \tau)$ from its value as has been predicted for

$\Delta u(kT) = 0$ as close as possible to its desired value $\mathbf{y}_d(kT + \tau)$, to minimize $J_k$ where:

$$J_{k+1} = \int_0^T [(\mathbf{e}_p^T \mathbf{H} \mathbf{e}_p)_{kT+\tau} + \rho u_{kT}^2] \, d\tau \qquad \forall t = kT + \tau; \; \tau < T \quad (10.4)$$

$\mathbf{H}$ being a positive definite symmetric weighting matrix, $\rho$ being a weight on the control cost itself, and:

$$\hat{\mathbf{y}}(kT + \tau) \triangleq \mathbf{y}_{p0}(kT + \tau) + \Delta u(kT)\mathbf{q}(\tau) \quad (10.5\text{-a})$$

$$\mathbf{e}_p(kT + \tau) \triangleq \hat{\mathbf{y}}(kT + \tau) - \mathbf{y}_d(kT + \tau) \quad (10.5\text{-b})$$

$$\mathbf{e}_{p0}(kT + \tau) \triangleq \mathbf{y}_{p0}(kT + \tau) - \mathbf{y}_d(kT + \tau) \quad (10.5\text{-c})$$

$$\mathbf{e} \triangleq \mathbf{y} - \mathbf{y}_d \quad (10.5\text{-d})$$

The requirement that $\mathbf{H}$ be a positive definite symmetric matrix results from stability considerations[3] that are based on the Lyapunov stability theorem[4] and are out of the scope of the present text. The minimization of $J_{k+1}$ is accomplished when substituting $\mathbf{e}_p$ from Equation (10.5) into (10.4) and subsequently differentiating $J_{k+1}$ of (10.4) with respect to $\Delta u$. We note that $\mathbf{e}_{p0}(kT + \tau)$ is independent of $\Delta u(kT)$ since, by definition, it results from extrapolating $\mathbf{y}$ (or $\mathbf{e}$) for $\Delta u(kT) = 0$. Hence, $\Delta u(kT)$ should satisfy:

$$\frac{\partial J_{k+1}}{\partial \, \Delta u(kT)} = 0 \quad (10.6)$$

to yield, when substituting from Equation (10.5) for $\mathbf{e}_p$ of $J_k$ and $[u(kT - T) + \Delta u(kT)]$ for $u(kT)$:

$$\Delta u(kT) = -\frac{\int_0^T [\rho u(kT - T) + \mathbf{e}_{p0}^T(kT + \tau)\mathbf{H}\mathbf{q}(\tau)] \, d\tau}{\int_0^T [\rho + \mathbf{q}^T(\tau)\mathbf{H}\mathbf{q}(\tau)] \, d\tau} \quad (10.7)$$

$\mathbf{e}_{p0}$ (or $\mathbf{y}_{p0}$) being derived by prediction @ $\Delta u(kT) = 0$, and $\mathbf{q}$ being identified according to Equation (10.2) above at the $k - 1$ interval. Obviously, if $\mathbf{y}_{p0}$ is accurately predicted, and if $\mathbf{q}(\tau)$, as has been computed over the interval from $kT - T$ to $kT$, does also apply to the next interval, then the actual output $\mathbf{y}(kT + \tau)$ is very close to $\hat{\mathbf{y}}(kT + \tau)$. For adequate control we thus require both adequate prediction of $\mathbf{y}_{p0}$ and that $\mathbf{q}(\tau)$ changes very little from one control interval to the next, i.e., that the system's step response, and therefore, its characteristics change slowly inside the control interval $T$.

The *prediction procedures* to be employed for evaluating $\mathbf{y}_{p0}(kT + \tau)$ may be based on a least-squares orthogonal polynomial curve-fit of best order of $\mathbf{y}(t)$ from $kT - T$ to $kT$, the latter fit being extrapolated by a Taylor expansion into the next interval. The Taylor expansion should employ the analytical derivatives of the curve-fitted polynomial at $t = kT$, to avoid numerical differentiation in the prediction procedure.[1] The employment of Chebyshev polynomials for curve-fitting is advantageous due to the equal-error properties[5] as have been mentioned in Section 5.6 of this text, where the choice of best order is also discussed. More sophisticated prediction procedures, as outlined in Chapter 12 below may be alternatively employed for prediction, but their sophistication is usually outweighed by their length and slowness. It is noted that prediction is required up to a lead time $T$ (i.e., to $t + T$; $t$ being present time), where $T$ is equal to the period over which measurement data for prediction may be obtained, since new inputs are applied at $t = T, 2T, \ldots$, thus upsetting the stationarity of the output every $T$ seconds. (A further discussion of prediction problems is given in Chapter 12 below.)

The present predictive approach is applicable to a joint on-line identification and control procedure, since the same control input $u(kT)$ that has been computed to minimize $J_{k+1}$ of Equation (10.4) is also employed to identify $\mathbf{q}$ at the $k$'th interval, according to Equation (10.3). The latter $\mathbf{q}$ is subsequently employed at the next control interval for deriving $\Delta u(kT + T)$ that minimizes $J_{k+1} \ldots.$

EXAMPLE 10.1

Consider a scalar single-input/single-output system with inputs $u(kT)$ and outputs $y(kT)$ that is to follow a target trajectory of $y_d(t) = 2 + 0.5\,t$, where $t = kT$; $T$ being a control interval of 0.1. At time $t = 0.9$ the system is at $y(t) = 2.1$. Its behavior over the interval from $t = 0.9$ to 1.0 has been measured and follows a trajectory of $y(t) = 4.1 - 2\exp(0.9 - t)$; $0.9 \leq t < 1.0$, to reach 2.293 at $t = 1.0$, whereas the target is at $y_d = 2.5$ at that time. Assuming that the integral $J_{k+1}$ of Equation (10.4) is only a summation over two values during each interval $T$, such that:

$$J_{k+1} = \sum_{i=1}^{2} (e_{pi}^2 + 0.1\, u_{pi}^2)$$

we obtain, at the eleventh interval (from $t = 1.0$ to $t = 1.1$) that:

$$J_{11} = e_p^2(10.5) + u_p^2(10.5) + e_p^2(11) + u_p^2(11)$$

The measurements over the interval from 0.8 to 0.9 are also available and indicate a constant $y(t)$ of 2.2 over that interval, whereas the control disturbance at $t = 0.9$ has been $u(9) = \Delta u(9) = 0.2$.

An extrapolation of $y$ up to $t = 1.1$ would yield $y_{p0}(10.5) = 2.378$ and $y_{p0}(11) = 2.462$, whereas $y_d(10.5) = 2.525$ and $y_d(11) = 2.55$ yielding $e_{p0}(10.5) = -0.147$ and $e_{p0}(11) = -0.088$. Furthermore, the measurement of

$y$ over the intervals from 0.8 to 0.9 and from 0.9 to 1.0, and of $\Delta u(9)$ yield that:

$$q(0.5) = \frac{y(9.5) - y_{p0}(9.5)}{\Delta u(g)} = \frac{2.198 - 2.1}{0.2} = 0.49$$

and:

$$q(1) = \frac{y(10) - y_{p0}(10)}{\Delta\Delta u(g)} = \frac{2.293 - 2.1}{0.2} = 0.95$$

Consequently, $\Delta u(10)$ is obtained from Equation (10.7) to be equal to $+\frac{0.135}{1.34} = 0.1$ such that $u(10) = 0.3$ and $y(10.5) = 2.462$, $y(11) = 2.557$ as compared with $y_d(10.5) = 2.525$ and $y_d(11) = 2.550$. A similar calculation would yield further values of $q$ and $\Delta u$.

### 10.1.2 Multi-Input Systems

The computation of the elements $q_i$ of the identification vector in single input systems is accomplished by a division as in Equations (10.2), (10.3). In case of linear multi-input systems, equations (10.2), 10.3) can still be employed if identification is performed with respect to one input at a time. Hence, for an $m$-input system, all inputs but one are kept constant at a given interval and only one input $u_j$ is varied by $\Delta u_j$. This process is repeated at $m$ different intervals for $j = 1 \ldots m$, until identification with respect to all $m$ inputs is accomplished. In this manner, identification is valid only if the process is stationary over at least $m$ control intervals. Furthermore, in contrast to the single-input case, on-line identification is not possible in multi-input cases since it implies the application of one input only at each control interval, whereas adequate performance may require the employment of all inputs. For on-line identification we thus require that the process be identified *with respect to all control inputs simultaneously*, these inputs satisfying the normal control requirement at each control interval. A simultaneous identification subroutine to satisfy the latter requirements may be based on the employment of a linear multivariate regression approach[6] as in Chapter 5 above. The latter may be formulated in terms of sequential regression as described in Chapter 6, to avoid matrix inversions. Consequently, for an input vector $\mathbf{u}$ with element $u_1 \ldots u_m$, we define:

$$\Delta\mathbf{u}(kT) \triangleq \mathbf{u}(kT) - \mathbf{u}(kT - T) \tag{10.8}$$

In analogy to the single-input Equation (6.2) we may write, in the multi-input case that:

$$y_i(kT + \tau) - y_{i,p0}(kT + \tau) = q_{1i}(\tau)\,\Delta u_1\,(kT) + \cdots q_{mi}(\tau)\,\Delta u_m(kT) \tag{10.9}$$

where $q_{ji}(\tau)$ represents the response of the $i$'th output $y_i$ at time $\tau$ to a unit input pulse $u_j(0)$; $(j \in 1,m)$. The value of $y_{ipo}$ of Equation (10.9) is predicted as in the case of Section 10.1.1. Equation (10.9) may be subsequently expressed as:

$$y_i(kT+\tau) - y_{po,i}(kT+\tau) = \mathbf{q}_i^T(\tau)\,\Delta\mathbf{u}(kT) \tag{10.10}$$

where:

$$\mathbf{q}_i^T \triangleq [q_{i1} \cdots q_{im}] \tag{10.11}$$

Equation (10.10) represents the $i$'th row of the matrix equation:

$$\mathbf{y}(kT+\tau) - \mathbf{y}_{po}(kT+\tau) = \mathbf{Q}(\tau)\,\Delta\mathbf{u}(kT) \tag{10.12}$$

**Q** being given by:

$$\mathbf{Q} \triangleq \begin{bmatrix} q_{i1} & \cdots & q_{im} \\ \vdots & & \\ q_{n1} & \cdots & q_{nm} \end{bmatrix} = \begin{bmatrix} \mathbf{q}_i^T \\ \vdots \\ \mathbf{q}_n^T \end{bmatrix} \tag{10.13}$$

Equation (10.12) may be considered as a linear-regression equation that is analogous to Equation (5.18), when substituting for **x**, **A**, **u** of Equation (5.18) by $\mathbf{y} - \mathbf{y}_{po}$, **Q**, $\Delta\mathbf{u}$, respectively. The same analogy exists between Equations (10.10) and (5.26), when $x_i$, $\mathbf{a}_i$, **u** of Equation (5.26) are replaced by $y_i - y_{i,po}$; $\mathbf{q}_i$; $\Delta\mathbf{u}$ of Equation (10.10), respectively. Hence, the elements of **Q** Equation (10.12) are computable by least squares regression to yield, in analogy to Equation (5.26):

$$\mathbf{q}_i(\tau) = (\Delta\mathbf{U}_k^T \cdot \Delta\mathbf{U}_k)^{-1}\Delta\mathbf{U}_k^T[\mathbf{Y}_i(kT+\tau) - \mathbf{Y}_{i,po}(kT+\tau)] \tag{10.14}$$

where:

$$\Delta\mathbf{U} \triangleq \begin{bmatrix} \Delta u_1(kT-rT+T) & \cdots & u_m(kT-rT+T) \\ \vdots & & \vdots \\ \Delta u_1(kT-T) & \cdots & u_m(kT-T) \\ \Delta u_1(kT) & \cdots & u_m(kT) \end{bmatrix}; r > m \tag{10.15}$$

$$\mathbf{Y}_i(kT+\tau) \triangleq [y_i(kT-rT+T+\tau); \cdots y_i(kT+T+\tau); y_i(kT+\tau)]^T \tag{10.16-a}$$

$$\mathbf{Y}_{i,po}(kT+\tau) \triangleq [y_{i,po}(kT-rT+T+\tau); \cdots y_i(kT+\tau)]^T \tag{10.16-b}$$

The computation of **Q** according to the regression Equation (10.14) requires the storing of the last $r$ measurements of **y**, **u**. Consequently, the stationarity (or at least the quasistationarity) of the system over $r$ control intervals must be assumed. However, for slower nonstationarities of the system's parameters, continuous updating of the identification is possible. The elements of $\mathbf{Q}$ that have been identified according to Equation (10.14) may now serve to derive the control vector $\Delta\mathbf{u}(kT)$ to minimize a performance index $J_k$ that is given by:

$$J_{k+1} = \int_0^T [(\mathbf{e}_p^T \mathbf{H} \mathbf{e}_r)_{kT+\tau} + (\mathbf{u}^T \mathbf{R} \mathbf{u})_{kT}] \, d\tau$$

$$= \int_0^T tr[(\mathbf{H} \mathbf{e}_p \mathbf{e}_p^T)_{kT+\tau} + (\mathbf{R} \mathbf{u} \mathbf{u}^T)_{kT}] \, d\tau \qquad (10.17)$$

which is the multi-input form of $J_{k+1}$ of Equation (10.4), $\mathbf{H}$, $\mathbf{R}$ being positive definite symmetric matrices for stability consideration as in the case of Equation (10.4), and $\mathbf{e}_p$ being as in Equation (10.5). Hence, $\Delta\mathbf{u}(kT)$ should satisfy:

$$\frac{\partial J_{k+1}}{\partial \Delta\mathbf{u}(kT)} = 0 \qquad (10.18)$$

to yield, by matrix differentiation, as in Appendix 2, and when substituting for $\mathbf{y}$ of $J_{k+1}$ from Equation (10.12):

$$2 \int_0^T [\mathbf{Q}^T(\tau) \mathbf{H} \mathbf{e}_{p0}(kT + \tau) + \mathbf{R}\mathbf{u}(kT - T) + \mathbf{R}\Delta\mathbf{u}(kT) + \mathbf{Q}^T(\tau)\mathbf{H}\mathbf{Q}(\tau)\, \Delta\mathbf{u}(kT)] \, d\tau = 0 \qquad (10.19)$$

or, since $\Delta\mathbf{u}(kT)$ is independent of $\tau$:

$$\int_0^T [\mathbf{Q}^T(\tau)\mathbf{H}\mathbf{e}_{po}(kT + \tau) + \mathbf{R}\mathbf{u}(kT - T) \, d\tau = -\int_0^T [\mathbf{R} + \mathbf{Q}^T(\tau)\mathbf{H}\mathbf{Q}(\tau)] \, d\tau \cdot \Delta\mathbf{u}(kT) \qquad (10.20)$$

and, finally:

$$\Delta\mathbf{u} = -\left\{\int_0^T [\mathbf{R} + \mathbf{Q}^T(\tau)\mathbf{H}\mathbf{Q}(\tau)] \, d\tau\right\}^{-1} \left\{\int_0^T [\mathbf{Q}^T(\tau)\mathbf{H}\mathbf{e}_{po}(kT + \tau) + \mathbf{R}\mathbf{u}(kT)]\right\} \qquad (10.21)$$

### 10.1.3 Predictive Identification of Nonlinear Processes

In cases where process nonlinearities cannot be ignored, nonlinear regression relations as in Section 5.6 may be employed to express the response of the process to pulses of $\Delta u(kT)$. The response to $\Delta u(kT)$ thus becomes, for, say a third-order polynomial approximation of the nonlinearity:

$$
\begin{aligned}
y_i(kT+\tau) - y_{po,i}(kT+\tau) = {} & q'_{i1}\,\Delta u_1(kT) \\
& + q'_{i2}\,\Delta u_2(kT) \cdots q'_{im}\,\Delta u_m(kT) + q''_{i1}\,\Delta u_1^2(kT) \\
& + \cdots q''_{im}\,\Delta u_m^2(kT) + q'''_{i1}\,\Delta u_1^3(kT) \\
& + \cdots q'''_{im}\,\Delta u_m^3(kT)
\end{aligned}
\tag{10.22}
$$

$y_{po,i}$ being again derived by prediction as in case of Section 10.1.1; and, defining:

$$
\left.
\begin{aligned}
&\Delta u_1 \triangleq \Delta v_1; \;\cdots \Delta u_m \triangleq \Delta v_m \\
&\Delta u_1^2 \triangleq \Delta v_{m+1}; \;\cdots \Delta u_m^2 \triangleq \Delta v_{2m} \\
&\Delta u_1^3 \triangleq \Delta v_{2m+1}; \;\cdots \Delta u_m^3 \triangleq \Delta v_{3m}
\end{aligned}
\right\}
\tag{10.23}
$$

and:

$$
\left.
\begin{aligned}
&q'_{i1} \triangleq p_{i1}; \;\cdots q'_{im} \triangleq p_{im} \\
&q''_{i,1} \triangleq p_{i,m+1}; \;\cdots q''_{im} \triangleq p_{i,2m} \\
&q'''_{i,1} \triangleq p_{i,2m+1}; \;\cdots q''_{i,m} \triangleq p_{i,3m}
\end{aligned}
\right\}
\tag{10.24}
$$

Equation (10.22) may be considered as a linear regression equation that is again similar to Equation (10.10) or (5.26) ,as follows:

$$
y_i(kT+\tau) - y_{i,po}(kT+\tau) = \mathbf{p}_i^T(\tau)\,\Delta\mathbf{v}(kT)
\tag{10.25}
$$

where:

$$
\mathbf{p}_i^T \triangleq [p_1; p_2; \cdots p_{3m}]
\tag{10.26-a}
$$

$$
\Delta\mathbf{v} \triangleq [\Delta v_1; \cdots \Delta v_{3m}]
\tag{10.26-b}
$$

We observe that the identification of $p_i$ of Equation (10.26-a), even for a case of few inputs implies the storing of data over at least $3m + 1$ control intervals, thus requiring process stationarity over at least $3m + 1$ intervals. Furthermore, the computation of the control input $\Delta\mathbf{u}$ to minimize $J_k$ of Equation (10.17) can no longer be performed analytically. It is thus often preferable to employ predictive gradient control procedures for deriving $\Delta u$ as is described in Section 10.2 below, which are applicable to both linear and nonlinear processes, as far as control is concerned, and where the number of terms to be identified is considerably reduced.

## 10.2 PREDICTIVE GRADIENT IDENTIFICATION AND CONTROL

The predictive approach of Section 10.1 is concerned with the behavior of individual outputs or states and with identifying the parameters related to these, whereas the predictive gradient approach[7] deals with the behavior of one scalar performance index only. Consequently, the number of parameters to be identified by the predictive gradient procedure below is considerably reduced.

Consider a linear sampled data process, that is described by the discrete state equation having measurable states, as follows:

$$\mathbf{x}(k+1) = \mathbf{A}\mathbf{x}(k) + \mathbf{B}\mathbf{u}(k); \qquad k = 0, 1, 2, \ldots \tag{10.27}$$

where $\mathbf{x}$ and $\mathbf{u}$ are the state and the control vector, respectively, and $\mathbf{A}$, $\mathbf{B}$ are unknown and may be time-variant. Control is to be performed with respect to a performance index $J$, that is given by:

$$\begin{aligned} J(kT+T) &\triangleq \mathbf{e}^T(kT+T) \cdot \mathbf{H} \cdot \mathbf{e}(kT+T) + \mathbf{u}^T(kT) \cdot \mathbf{R} \cdot \mathbf{u}(kT) \\ &= tr[\mathbf{H} \cdot \mathbf{e} \cdot \mathbf{e}^T)_{kT+T} + (\mathbf{R} \cdot \mathbf{u} \cdot \mathbf{u}^T)_{kT}] \end{aligned} \tag{10.28}$$

$\mathbf{H}$, $\mathbf{R}$ being positive definite symmetric matrices, due to stability considerations, as in the case of Equation (10.4) above; and $\mathbf{e}$ being the difference between $\mathbf{x}$ and its respective desired values $\mathbf{x}_d$. We subsequently define a linearized predictive relationship that describes the predicted response of $J_{k+1}$ to small perturbations in the control vector $\Delta\mathbf{u}$ as follows:

$$\Delta J_p(kT+T) \triangleq \mathbf{S}^T(kT) \cdot \Delta\mathbf{u}(kT) = tr\,[\mathbf{S}(kT) \cdot \Delta\mathbf{u}^T(kT)] \tag{10.29}$$

where:

$$\Delta\mathbf{u}(kT) \triangleq \mathbf{u}(kT) - \mathbf{u}(kT-T) \tag{10.30}$$

$J_p(kT+T)$ being the predicted value of $J(kT+T)$ from data of measured $J$ up to $t = kT$, assuming that $\Delta\mathbf{u}(kT) = 0$. $\mathbf{S}$ of Equation (10.29) may be considered as the approximate predicted gradient $\nabla\mathbf{J}_p$ with respect to $\Delta\mathbf{u}$. Consequently, and noting the definition of $J$ in Equation (10.28), we may write that:

$$\mathbf{S}(kT) = \frac{\partial J(kT+T)}{\partial\mathbf{u}(kT)} = \frac{\partial\{tr[(\mathbf{H} \cdot \mathbf{e} \cdot \mathbf{e}^T)_{kT+T} + (\mathbf{R} \cdot \mathbf{u} \cdot \mathbf{u}^T)_{kT}]\}}{\partial\mathbf{u}(kT)} \tag{10.31}$$

Since, according to Equation (10.27):

$$\mathbf{e}(kT+T) = \mathbf{x}(kT+T) - \mathbf{x}_d(kT+T) = \mathbf{A} \cdot \mathbf{x}(kT) + \mathbf{B} \cdot \mathbf{u}(kT) - \mathbf{x}_d(kT+T) \tag{10.32}$$

Equation (10.31) becomes:

$$\begin{aligned} \mathbf{S}(kT) = \partial\{tr[\mathbf{H}(\mathbf{A}\mathbf{x}_{kT} + \mathbf{B}\mathbf{u}_{kT} - \mathbf{x}_{d,kT+T}) \cdot (\mathbf{A}\mathbf{x}_{kT} + \mathbf{B}\mathbf{u}_{kT} - \mathbf{x}_{d,kT+T})^T \\ + \mathbf{R}\mathbf{u}_{kT}\mathbf{u}_{kT}^T]\}/\partial\mathbf{u}_{kT} \end{aligned} \tag{10.33}$$

yielding, according to Appendix 2, that:

$$\mathbf{S}(kT) = 2\mathbf{B}^T\mathbf{H}(\mathbf{A}\mathbf{x}_{kT} - \mathbf{x}_{d,kT+T}) + 2(\mathbf{B}^T\mathbf{H}\mathbf{B} + \mathbf{R})\mathbf{u}_{kT} \tag{10.34}$$

Equation (10.34) indicates that $\mathbf{S}$ is nonstationary, even if $\mathbf{A}$, $\mathbf{B}$, $\mathbf{R}$, and $\mathbf{H}$ are stationary, since $\mathbf{u}$, $\mathbf{x}$, and $\mathbf{x}_d$ may vary from one control interval to the next.

Hence, **S** would usually vary with time at a faster rate than do **A** and **B**, if the latter are also nonstationary. Furthermore, **S** cannot be considered as stationary even for over short control intervals, over which **A** and **B** still hardly vary. We may, however, rewrite Equation (10.34) such that:

$$\mathbf{S}(kT) = \boldsymbol{\sigma}_x \mathbf{x}(kT) - \boldsymbol{\sigma}_{xd} \cdot \mathbf{x}_d(kT + T) + \boldsymbol{\sigma}_u \cdot \mathbf{u}(kT) \tag{10.35}$$

where $\boldsymbol{\sigma}_x$, $\boldsymbol{\sigma}_{xd}$, $\boldsymbol{\sigma}_u$ are stationary matrices for stationary or quasistationary processes, as follows:

$$\boldsymbol{\sigma}_x \triangleq 2\mathbf{B}^T\mathbf{H}\mathbf{A} \tag{10.36-a}$$

$$\boldsymbol{\sigma}_{xd} \triangleq 2\mathbf{B}^T\mathbf{H} \tag{10.36-b}$$

$$\boldsymbol{\sigma}_u \triangleq 2(\mathbf{B}^T\mathbf{H}\mathbf{B} + \mathbf{R}) \tag{10.36-c}$$

When substituting for **S** from Equation (10.35) into (10.29), we obtain that:

$$\begin{aligned}\Delta J_p(kT + T) &= \mathbf{x}^T(kT)\boldsymbol{\sigma}_x^T \Delta\mathbf{u}(kT) - \mathbf{x}_d^T(kT + T)\boldsymbol{\sigma}_{xd}^T \Delta\mathbf{u}(kT) + \mathbf{u}^T(kT)\boldsymbol{\sigma}_u{}^T \Delta\mathbf{u}(kT)\\ &= tr[\boldsymbol{\sigma}_x \mathbf{x}(kT)\,\Delta\mathbf{u}^T(kT) - \boldsymbol{\sigma}_{xd}\,\mathbf{x}_d(kT + T)\,\Delta\mathbf{u}^T(kT)\\ &\quad + \boldsymbol{\sigma}_u \mathbf{u}(kT)\,\Delta\mathbf{u}^T(kT)]\end{aligned} \tag{10.37}$$

When the state vector **x** is accessible (say, in terms of outputs and their derivatives), Equation (10.37) may be considered as a nonlinear regression equation whose coefficients are the elements of $\boldsymbol{\sigma}_x^T$, $\boldsymbol{\sigma}_{xd}^T$, $\boldsymbol{\sigma}_u$. If $n$ and $m$ are the dimensions of **x** and **u**, respectively, then $\boldsymbol{\sigma}_x$, $\boldsymbol{\sigma}_{xd}$ are both $m \cdot n$ matrices (having $m$ rows and $n$ columns), whereas $\boldsymbol{\sigma}_u$ is a symmetric $m^2$ matrix due to the symmetry of **H**. The total number of coefficients in Equation (10.37) is $N \cong 2n \cdot m + m^2/2$ (or $n \cdot m + m^2/2$ if $\mathbf{x}_d = 0$), while the total number of elements of **A**, **B** is $n^2 + m^2$. Consequently, the identification of **A**, **B** by regression according to Equation (10.27) requires process stationarity or quasistationarity over $n + m + 1$ control intervals only, whereas the identification of $\boldsymbol{\sigma}_x$, $\boldsymbol{\sigma}_{xd_2}$, $\boldsymbol{\sigma}_u$ from Equation (10.37) implies stationarity or quasistationarity over $2n \cdot m + m^2/2 + 1$ intervals (or $n \cdot m + m^2/2 + 1$ intervals @ $\mathbf{x}_d = \mathbf{0}$). In cases where $n \gg m$, the total number of elements in $\boldsymbol{\sigma}_x$, $\boldsymbol{\sigma}_{xd}$ and $\boldsymbol{\sigma}_u$ is smaller than in **A**, **B**. However, the identification of **A**, **B** is always faster since it may be performed such that all rows of Equation (10.27) are considered simultaneously, each row containing no more than $n + m$ elements of **A**, **B**. The matrix **S** may be identified by regression directly from the gradient Equation (10.29) only if the variations in **x**, $\mathbf{x}_d$, **u**, during $m + 1$ intervals are very small. It is therefore usually preferable to derive $\boldsymbol{\sigma}_x$, $\boldsymbol{\sigma}_{xd}$, $\boldsymbol{\sigma}_u$ from a regression identification of **A**, **B** according to Equation (10.27), according to Chapters 5, 6.

Following the derivation of $\boldsymbol{\sigma}_x$, $\boldsymbol{\sigma}_{xd}$, and $\boldsymbol{\sigma}_u$, a predictive gradient control procedure based on the static gradient optimization approach[8] may be employed. Consequently, a Lagrangian $L$ is defined, as follows:[7]

$$L_k \triangleq J_p(kT + T) - \gamma(|\Delta\mathbf{u}(kT)|^2 - r^2) \tag{10.38}$$

$\gamma$ being a Lagrange multiplier and $r$ being a constraint on $\mathbf{u}$, such that:

$$r^2 = |\mathbf{u}|^2 = \sum_{i=1}^{m} u_i^2; \quad (u_i = i\text{'th element of } \mathbf{u}) \tag{10.39}$$

The optimal gradient control $\Delta\mathbf{u}^o$ should satisfy the relation:

$$\partial L_k/\partial\mathbf{u} = \nabla\mathbf{L}_k = \nabla\mathbf{J}_p(kT+T) - 2\gamma\,\Delta\mathbf{u}^o(kT) = \mathbf{0} \tag{10.40}$$

Therefore and noting Equation (10.29):

$$\Delta\mathbf{u}^o(kT) = (2\gamma)^{-1}\nabla\mathbf{J}_p(kT) = (2\gamma)^{-1}\mathbf{S}(kT) \tag{10.41}$$

Substituting for $\mathbf{u}^o$ from Equation (10.41) into (10.39) yields that:

$$|\Delta\mathbf{u}^o(kT)|^2 = r^2 = (2\gamma)^{-2}|\Delta\mathbf{J}_p(kT)|^2 \tag{10.42}$$

and:

$$\gamma = (\underline{+})|\nabla\mathbf{J}_p(kT+T)|/2r = (\underline{+})|\mathbf{S}(kT)|/2r \tag{10.43}$$

Employing the latter expression for $\gamma$, Equation (10.41) becomes:

$$\Delta\mathbf{u}^o(kT) = (\underline{+})\mathbf{S}(kT)\cdot\frac{r}{|\mathbf{S}(kT)|} \tag{10.44}$$

Since the gradient approach implies that $\Delta J$ at each control interval should not exceed some $\Delta J_{\max}$, and substituting for $\Delta\mathbf{u}^o$ from Equation (10.44) into (10.29), we obtain that:

$$\Delta J_{\max}(kT+T) = (\underline{+})\frac{\mathbf{S}^T(kT)\cdot\mathbf{S}(kT)\cdot r}{|\mathbf{S}(kT)|} = (\underline{+})\frac{|\mathbf{S}(kT)|^2 r}{|\mathbf{S}(kT)|} \tag{10.45}$$

such that $r$ satisfies:

$$r = -\Delta J_{\max}/|\mathbf{S}| \tag{10.46}$$

to yield a sub-optimal control (since cost integrals over infinite time range are not available here):

$$\Delta\mathbf{u}^o(kT) = -\mathbf{S}(kT)\frac{\Delta J_{\max}}{\sum_{i=1}^{m} S_i^2} = -\mathbf{S}(kT)\frac{\Delta J_{\max}}{|\mathbf{S}|^2} \tag{10.47}$$

The sign in Equations (10.45), (10.46) results from the requirement that $\Delta J$ be negative at each control interval, regardless of $S_i$.

The performance index $J$ of Equation (10.28), on whose behavior the predective gradient approach is based, applies both to linear and to nonlinear systems, and is itself nonlinear in $\mathbf{x}$ and in $\mathbf{u}$. The approach is, however, restricted to small perturbations in $J$, of up to $\Delta J_{\max}$ per control interval, which result in constraining $\Delta\mathbf{u}$ according to Equation (10.45). Equation

(10.27) may therefore be considered as the linearized discrete state equation in case of nonlinear processes, such that the predictive gradient approach above may be applicable to nonlinear processes that are linearized for the above small perturbations. In nonlinear cases the matrix describing the gradient of the cost may be derived in terms of the stationary parameters of any nonlinearity that relates input and output.

EXAMPLE 10.2

A further insight into the present method may be obtained from the following example: Consider a system:

$$\mathbf{x}(k+1) = \mathbf{A}\mathbf{x}(k) + \mathbf{B}u(k)$$

$$kT = t; \qquad T = 0.01$$

which is to be identified and to be subsequently controlled to minimize $J$ of Equation (10.28) with $\mathbf{H} = \mathbf{I}$; $\mathbf{R} = 0.1$; $\mathbf{x}_d = \mathbf{0}$ through employing measurements of $\mathbf{x}$, $u$, as in Table 10.1. From the data of Table 10.1, the parameters $\boldsymbol{\sigma}_x$, $\boldsymbol{\sigma}_u$ of Equation (10.35) are subsequently derived by regression such that $\boldsymbol{\sigma}_x = [.04; 1.96]$, $\boldsymbol{\sigma}_u = 2.2$. The derivation of the latter parameters thus provides an identification of the stationary parameters of the nonlinear and nonstationary model of Equation (10.29), to facilitate the computation of the predictive gradient control policy of Equation (10.47) to minimize $\Delta J(k+1)$ at any $k$. We note again that $\boldsymbol{\sigma}_x$, $\boldsymbol{\sigma}_u$ may be derived from an identification of $\mathbf{A}$, $\mathbf{B}$, and that this indirect derivation of $\boldsymbol{\sigma}_x$, $\boldsymbol{\sigma}_u$ is usually (though not presently) faster and still permits predictive control according to prediction of $J$ alone.

TABLE 10.1

| $k$ | 0 | 1 | 2 | 3 | 4 | 5 | 6 | 7 | 8 | 9 | 10 |
|---|---|---|---|---|---|---|---|---|---|---|---|
| $x_1(k)$ | 0 | 0 | −.02 | −.02 | −.02 | 0 | .06 | .12 | .16 | .2 | .26 |
| $x_2(k)$ | 0 | −1 | .02 | .02 | 1.02 | 3 | 2.94 | 1.88 | 1.84 | 2.84 | 4.78 |
| $u(k)$ | −1 | 1 | 0 | 1 | 2 | 0 | −1 | 0 | 1 | 2 | 1 |

## REFERENCES

1. Graupe, D., and Cassir, G. R. "Adaptive Control by Predictive Identification and Optimization," *Proc. National Electronics Conf.*, Vol. 22, pp. 590–594, Chicago, 1966 (also: *Trans. IEEE* Vol. AC-12, pp. 191–194, 1967).

2. Powell, F. D. "Predictive Adaptive Control," *Trans. IEEE*, Vol. AC-14, pp. 550–552, 1969.
3. Tou, J. *Modern Control Theory*, McGraw-Hill, New York, 1964 (p. 343).
4. Koppel, L. B. *Introduction to Control Theory*, Prentice Hall, Englewood Cliffs, N.J., 1968.
5. Scheid, F. *Numerical Analysis*, Schaum-McGraw-Hill, New York, 1968.
6. Graupe, D., Swanick, B. H., and Cassir, G. R. "Reduction and Identification of Multivariable Processes," *Trans. IEEE*, Vol. AC-13, pp. 564–567, 1968.
7. Graupe, D., and Iddan, G. J. "A Learning Technique Based on Prediction and Reinforcement," *Proc. IEEE Systems Science and Cybernetics Conf.*, pp. 99–102, Philadelphia, 1968.
8. Wilde, D. J., and Beightler, C. S. *Foundations of Optimization*, Prentice Hall, Englewood Cliffs, N.J., 1967 (Chapter 7).

## PROBLEMS

**1.** Simulate the system $\dot{\mathbf{x}} = \mathbf{A}\mathbf{x} + \mathbf{B}u$, where:

$$\mathbf{A} = \left[\begin{array}{c|c} \begin{matrix} 0 \\ 0 \\ 0 \\ 0 \end{matrix} & \mathbf{I} \\ \hline \multicolumn{2}{c}{-333;\ -7000;\ -5080;\ -1540;\ -214} \end{array}\right]; \qquad \mathbf{B} = \begin{bmatrix} 0 \\ 0 \\ 0 \\ 0 \\ k \end{bmatrix}$$

and where $k = 3333$ up to $t = 9$ and $5000 \cdot [1 + 0.05(t - 9)]$ for $t > 9$. Employ the above data for generating $\mathbf{x}$ from $\mathbf{u}$ to predict future $\mathbf{x}$ and to identify $q_i$ of Equation (10.2). Subsequently, compute the performance of the system when tracking a target that follows the trajectory $s^2x_d + s \cdot x_d + x_d = \omega(t)$; $\omega(t)$ being 1 $\forall t \geq 0$ and 0 $\forall t < 0$, $s$ denoting the Laplace variable and $sx_d(0) = x_d(0) = 0$. In the computation assume that the control interval $T$ is 0.5, and that

$$H = \text{diag}(1, 2^{-1}, 2^{-2}, 2^{-3}, 2^{-4}); \rho = 0$$

**2.** Repeat Problem 1 for a nonlinear system given by

$$\dot{\mathbf{x}} = \mathbf{A}\mathbf{x} + \mathbf{B}u + \mathbf{C}u^2$$

where $\mathbf{A}$ is as in problem 1 and:

$$\mathbf{B} = [0; 0; 0; 0; 3333]^T; \qquad \mathbf{C} = [0, 0, 0, 0, 1667)^T$$

the target being given by:

$$s^2x_d + sx_d + x_d = \omega(t);\ sx_d(0) = x_d(0) = 0$$

$$\omega(t) = \begin{cases} 0 \ @\ t < 0 \\ 0.4 \ @\ 0 \leq t < 2.5 \\ 1.0 \ @\ t \geq 2.5 \end{cases}$$

**3.** Identify the stationary parameters $\boldsymbol{\sigma}_x$, $\boldsymbol{\sigma}_{xd}$, $\boldsymbol{\sigma}_u$ of the system $\mathbf{x}_{k+1} = \mathbf{A}\mathbf{x}_k + \mathbf{B}\mathbf{u}_k$ from the following data:

| $k$ | 0 | 1 | 2 | 3 | 4 | 5 | 6 | 7 |
|---|---|---|---|---|---|---|---|---|
| $x_1(k)$ | 0 | − .4 | − .86 | −1.52 | −2.3 | − .32 | −3.56 | −3.7 |
| $x_2(k)$ | 0 | 6 | .94 | 1.51 | −2.5 | −5.6 | −6.08 | 2.54 |
| $u_1(k)$ | − .1 | − .4 | − .4 | − .5 | − .5 | − .2 | − .1 | − .2 |
| $u_2(k)$ | −2 | −1 | −1 | 0 | 1 | −1 | −2 | −2 |

| $k$ | 8 | 9 | 10 | 11 | 12 | 13 | 14 |
|---|---|---|---|---|---|---|---|
| $x_1(k)$ | −3.6 | −3.83 | −3.81 | −3.90 | −3.78 | −2.95 | −1.98 |
| $x_2(k)$ | .19 | −3.49 | −7.49 | −9.54 | −3.05 | −6.62 | −7.5 |
| $u_1(k)$ | − .3 | − .1 | .2 | .1 | .3 | .5 | .2 |
| $u_2(k)$ | − .5 | 1 | 2 | 0 | .5 | 1.5 | 1.5 |

Assume that $\mathbf{H} = \mathbf{I}$; $\mathbf{R} = 0.1 \cdot \mathbf{I}$.

**4.** Apply the procedure of Section 10.2 to solve Problem 1.

# 11

# HEURISTIC IDENTIFICATION TECHNIQUES

Heuristic identification techniques are the most primitive approaches to process identification. They are not concerned with any analytical formulation and should be employed only when other identification techniques, such as those of chapters 3 to 10, fail, or when analytical formulations prove to be inadequate or impossible. This may happen in cases of systems that are of a highly nonlinear nature (in terms of input/state or input/output relations), especially where the nonlinearities are discontinuous with respect to the input or state variables, such that polynomial approximations are not acceptable. Heuristic techniques may also be applied to processes where complicated nonlinear functions of an a priori known form (say, known from theoretical considerations) are concerned, whose parameters require identification, and where no polynomial approximations are desired. As an example of the latter situations we may consider the following equation that arises in the modeling of a machine tool cutting process:

$$x = a_1 a_2^{u_1} u_2^{-u_1} + a_3 u_3 + a_4 \log (u_4 + a_5) \tag{11.1}$$

where $x$ is the process output, $u_i$ are constrained inputs and $a_j$ are the parameters requiring identification. Partial differentiation of $x$ with respect to $u_i$ (see Section 5.6) and linearization techniques may not always be practical for identifying $a_j$, especially when some inputs cannot be kept constant at will.

A heuristic identification may be performed though it could lead to non-unique results. However, if a knowledge of the range of values to which $a_j$ belongs is available, unique results may still be possible.

We shall discuss below two general types of heuristic identification approaches, namely, a random search approach and a direct search (gradient) approach that employs a merely heuristic mapping of the gradient. Although many variations of these approaches from their present versions do exist,[1] the outline below aims at illustrating the philosophy of heuristic identification such that it will enable the reader to develop or to adopt other heuristic versions. We note that heuristic identification requires the construction of models whose parameters are to be iterated. When identifying dynamic systems, the model output at a certain parameter iteration is affected by transients due to changing the parameters and which may take some time to die out. Consequently, when the general heuristic search techniques, as described in the vast literature in this field (see refs. 1 and 2) are applied to dynamic identification, care must be taken of the above transient effects, which do not exist in heuristic search of static parameters.

Due to their primitive nature, heuristic identification procedures may take long to converge to the true parameter values. They may often be speeded up when incorporated in a predictive control scheme similar to that of Chapter 10, as is further discussed in Section 11.3 of the present chapter. In that case, transient effects of past parameter iterations are adequately considered in the prediction, such that the time they take to die out may be disregarded. Differences between predicted and actual outputs thus depend on the last estimated parameters only, and parameter nonstationarities that are too fast for other heuristic methods may be followed. A careful resetting of initial conditions may also overcome the settling time problem but is impractical in many on-line applications.

Heuristic techniques based on random search and on direct search approaches may be conveniently combined. They may also serve as a highest identification hierarchy in a multi-hierarchical general purpose identifier structure, to initialize identification by faster procedures at lower levels, when these fail to work by themselves.

## 11.1 A RANDOM SEARCH PROCEDURE FOR IDENTIFYING DYNAMIC SYSTEMS

Consider a dynamic process given in discrete form by:

$$\mathbf{x}(k+1) = \mathbf{f}[\mathbf{P}; \mathbf{u}(k); \mathbf{x}(k); k] \tag{11.2}$$

where $k$ is an integer denoting the sampling interval, $\mathbf{x}$ being a state or output vector, $\mathbf{u}$ being an input vector and $\mathbf{P}$ being a vector of parameters. We further

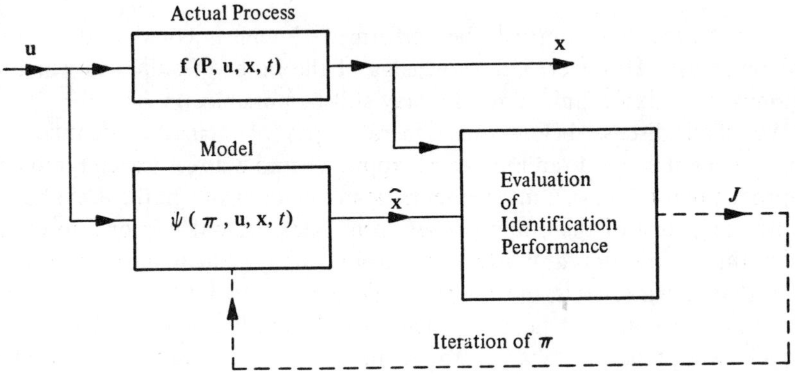


*Figure 11.1* General layout of the identifier.

consider a vector of estimated parameters $\boldsymbol{\pi}$ whose elements are to form a model of the system for identification purposes, as shown in Figure 11.1. The latter model is given by the following sampled data expression:

$$\hat{\mathbf{x}}(k+1) = \boldsymbol{\psi}[\boldsymbol{\pi}, \mathbf{u}(k), \mathbf{x}(k), k] \tag{11.3}$$

$\hat{\mathbf{x}}$ being the estimate of $\mathbf{x}$ when employing the model $\boldsymbol{\psi}$ with the estimated parameters $\boldsymbol{\pi}$. The form of $\boldsymbol{\psi}$ must be a priori assumed, though the elements of its parameters vector $\boldsymbol{\pi}$ are unknown. The function $\boldsymbol{\psi}$ need not be identical to the true but not-always-known function $\mathbf{f}$ that describes the actual system. Furthermore, $\boldsymbol{\pi}$ need not be of the same dimension as $\mathbf{P}$. It is however, assumed that $\boldsymbol{\pi}$ belongs to a bounded space $\boldsymbol{\Omega}$ such that:

$$\boldsymbol{\pi} \in \boldsymbol{\Omega} \tag{11.4}$$

the boundaries of $\boldsymbol{\Omega}$ being a priori given to define the space within which the search of $\boldsymbol{\pi}$ may take place.

For directing the search, an identification-performance index $J(v)$ must be formulated, such that $J(v)$ is a measurable scalar function of $\mathbf{x}$ and $\hat{\mathbf{x}}$, say:

$$J(v) \triangleq \sum_{k=1}^{m} [(\mathbf{x}(k) - \hat{\mathbf{x}}(k))^T(\mathbf{x}(k) - \hat{\mathbf{x}}(k))] \tag{11.5}$$

$v$ denoting the $v$'th iteration of $\boldsymbol{\pi}$.

Noting the definitions and the relationships of equations (11.2) to (11.5), the random search is performed as follows: First, $\mu$ models of the form of Equation (11.4) are simultaneously generated such that the elements of their respective parameter vectors $\boldsymbol{\pi}(1, m)$ @ $m = 1 \cdots \mu$ are randomly chosen to lie inside $\boldsymbol{\Omega}$, and the respective identification performance indices $J(1, m)$ are evaluated for each such model. We note that $\boldsymbol{\pi}(1, m)$, $J(1, m)$ relate to the $m$'th model of the first generation. If it is assumed that $\boldsymbol{\pi}$ may take only discrete positions in the space $\boldsymbol{\Omega}$, such that it may belong only to one of $r$ (say 1000) cells into which $\boldsymbol{\Omega}$ is divided, then a performance index $J$ is assigned to each cell, i.e., to each possible location of $\boldsymbol{\pi}$. The probability that a randomly chosen $\boldsymbol{\pi}$ vector would belong to a cell having one of the $r/100$ best performing cells is given by 0.01. Consequently, the probability that the latter $\boldsymbol{\pi}$ will not be in one of the $r/100$ best performing cells is given by $1 - 0.01 = 0.99$. However, when $\mu$ different $\boldsymbol{\pi}$ are selected by random, the probability that none of them be within the $r/100$ best performing cells is $(0.99)^{\mu}$. The probability of one of them being within the $r/100$ best performing cells is therefore given by $1 - 0.99^{\mu}\ \forall r \gg \mu$. (If $\mu = 228$, the probability of selecting one of the $r/100$ best performing $\mu$ among the randomly selected $\boldsymbol{\pi}$ is 90%.) For cases of $r \not\gg \mu$ see problem 3 of this chapter and its solution in Appendix 4.

The brief analysis above indicates that the number of simultaneous computations to be performed is very considerable if a fine grid division of $\boldsymbol{\Omega}$ is examined. It is, however, important to perform the computations of $\hat{\mathbf{x}}$ for the various $\boldsymbol{\pi}(h, m)$ @ $m = 1, 2, \ldots, \mu$; $h = 1, 2, \ldots$ simultaneously, since otherwise, it is necessary to readjust initial conditions too often or to wait between iterations of $\boldsymbol{\pi}$ in order that the transient effects on $\hat{\mathbf{x}}$ due to changing $\boldsymbol{\pi}$ die out. Once initial conditions are reset, another set of $\mu$ models may be examined (denoted by advancing $h$ by 1), say, around the best $\boldsymbol{\pi}$ of the previous generation. It should be noted that in this case, nonstationarities in $\mathbf{P}$ may avoid adequate identification.

The obvious slowness and the considerable computational effort involved in the identification of dynamic processes by random search limits the application of that approach mainly to processes where discontinuities in $\mathbf{f}$ of Equation (11.2) prevent the employment of gradient techniques or of analytical methods. In cases of multi-modality of the identification performance index (i.e., when $J$ has many minima in the $J$ vs. $\boldsymbol{\pi}$ space), random search may be incorporated in a direct search identification procedure, to locate the best minimum.

The need for many simultaneous computations of $\hat{\mathbf{x}}$ for different $\boldsymbol{\pi}$ and with the same input data may be overcome if random search identification is incorporated in a predictive control procedure, as is further discussed in Section 11.3 below. In that manner, $\boldsymbol{\pi}$ may be iterated sequentially, such that one iteration be made at each control interval. Several iterations may still be simultaneously applied at each control interval to increase the convergence rate if several models are simultaneously considered.

### 11.1.1 Convergence of the Random Search

The convergence of the random search may be proved when employing the following analysis due to Matyas:[3] Let $\boldsymbol{\pi}(k)$ be the random parameter vector chosen at the $k$'th interval and let $J(k)$ be its respective cost. Let also $\mathbf{v}(k)$

be a randomly chosen perturbation in $\pi(k)$, and let $\pi^*$ be the vector satisfying:

$$J(\pi^*) \leq J(\pi) \qquad \forall\, \pi \in \Omega \tag{11.6}$$

We define an auxiliary scalar $\xi(k)$ such that:

$$\xi(k) = \begin{cases} 1 & @ \quad J[\pi(k) + v(k)] < J[(\pi(k)] - \varepsilon; \\ 0 & @ \quad J[\pi(k) + v(k)] \geq J[\pi(k)] - \varepsilon; \end{cases} \qquad \varepsilon > 0 \tag{11.7}$$

and:

$$\pi(k+1) = \begin{cases} \pi(k) & @ \quad \xi = 0 \\ \pi(k) + v(k) & @ \quad \xi = 1 \end{cases} \tag{11.8}$$

Matyas proves that the sequence $\pi(1), \pi(2) \cdots$ derived above converges such that, for every $\delta > 0$, one may reach $N$ for which $\|\pi^* - \pi(N)\| \leq \delta$ by setting

$$J(\pi) = C \tag{11.9}$$

where the scalar $C$ determines a range $G(C)$ within which all $\pi$ satisfy:

$$J(\pi) < C \tag{11.10}$$

as shown in Figure 11.2.

For the latter proof we further define $\rho(\omega)$ as the probability density function of the random vector $\mathbf{v}$ of Equation (11.7). Hence the probability of selecting $\mathbf{v}$ to yield $\pi$ inside $G$ is given by (see Figure 11.2):

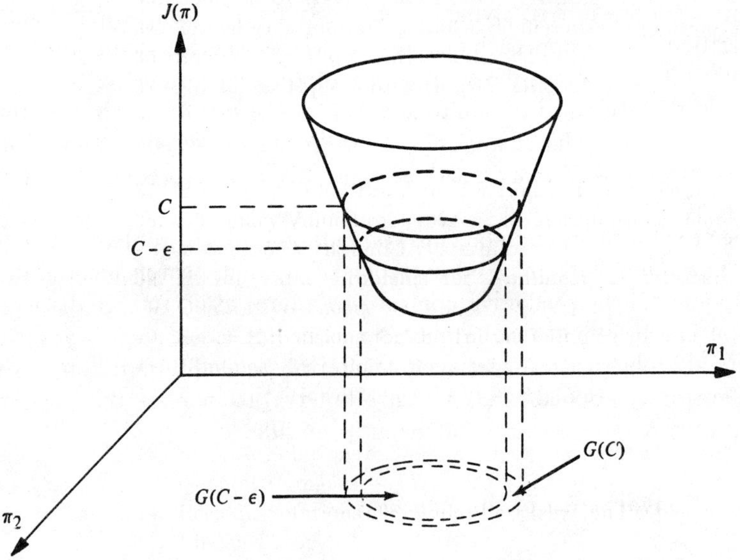


*Figure 11.2* Cost surface for random search.

$$\phi_{c-\varepsilon} = \int_{G(c-\varepsilon)} \rho(\pi + \mathbf{v})\, d\mathbf{v} \tag{11.11}$$

The probability that the $\pi(k)$ at the $k$'th trial is *not* within a distance of $\delta$ from $\pi^*$ is given by:

$$p\{\|\pi(k) - \pi^*\| > \delta\} = p\{\pi(k) \notin \delta(\pi^*)\} \tag{11.12}$$

where:

$$\delta(\pi^*) = \{\pi\colon \|\pi - \pi^*\| < \delta\} = \text{denoting that } \pi \text{ satisfies a location within a distance } \delta \text{ from } \pi^* \tag{11.13}$$

For convergence we require that:

$$\lim_{k \to \infty} p[\pi(k) \notin \delta(\pi^*)] \to 0 \tag{11.14}$$

However, we note that:

$$J(\pi) - \varepsilon > J(\pi^*) \quad @ \quad \pi \notin \delta(\pi^*) \tag{11.15-a}$$

$$J(\pi) - \varepsilon \leq J(\pi^*) \quad @ \quad \pi \in \delta(\pi^*) \tag{11.15-b}$$

If during search we obtain $m$ successful trials (within $\delta$), then from that stage onwards (according to Equation (11.8)) all $\pi \in \delta$. Hence, the probability of $\pi(k) \notin \delta(\pi^*)$ is smaller or equal to the probability that the number of successes is not larger than $m$, the first case being included in the second, i.e.:

$$p\{\pi(k) \notin \delta(\pi^*)\} \leq p\left\{\sum_{i=1}^{k} \xi(i) \leq m\right\} \tag{11.16}$$

Subsequently, if:

$$p(\pi \in \delta) \geqslant \alpha \tag{11.17}$$

then, by the binomial distribution expansion of $p(\sum \xi)$, we obtain:

$$p\left\{\sum_{i=1}^{k} \xi(i) \leq m\right\} \leq \sum_{i=0}^{m} \binom{k}{i} \alpha^i (1-\alpha)^{k-i} \tag{11.18}$$

Assuming (pessimistically) that: $k > 2m$ and $\alpha < 0.5$, we further have:

$$\sum_{i=0}^{m} \binom{k}{i} \alpha^i (1-\alpha)^{k-i} < (m+1) \binom{k}{m} (1-\alpha)^k \tag{11.19}$$

and:

$$(m+1)\binom{k}{m}(1-\alpha)^k = \frac{m+1}{m!}[k(k-1)\cdots(k-m+1)](1-\alpha)^k < \frac{m+1}{m!} k^m (1-\alpha)^k \tag{11.20}$$

Substituting from (11.20) into (11.16) yields:

$$p\{\pi(k) \notin \delta\} = p\{\|\pi(k) - \pi^*\| > \delta\} < \frac{m+1}{m!} k^m(1-\alpha)^k \tag{11.21}$$

Finally, at the limit:

$$\lim_{k\to\infty} k^m(1-\alpha)^k \to 0 \tag{11.22}$$

and, therefore:

$$\lim_{k\to\infty} p\{\|\pi(k) - \pi^*\| > \delta\} \to 0 \quad \text{Q.E.D.} \tag{11.23}$$

EXAMPLE 11.1

Consider a system $y = ax + bu$, where $a$ is known to be in the range of $-1$ to $-3$ and $b$ is known to be in the range of 0.5 to 2.5. Data for $u$, $x$, $y$ is available as follows:

| $k$ | 1 | 2 | 3 | 4 |
|---|---|---|---|---|
| $u$ | −0.5 | 1.2 | −0.8 | −4.3 |
| $x$ | 2.6 | 6.8 | 2.7 | 1.4 |
| $y$ | 4.7 | 14.8 | 4.6 | −1.5 |

We divide the ranges for $a$, $b$ into grids of $0.2 \times 0.2$, such that we have 100 cells in $\mathbf{\Omega}$. We subsequently choose three sets of random values for $\hat{a}$, $\hat{b}$ as follows:

$$\hat{a}_{11} = -2.8 \qquad \hat{b}_{11} = 1.7$$
$$\hat{a}_{12} = -1.6 \qquad \hat{b}_{12} = 1.5$$
$$\hat{a}_{13} = -2.6 \qquad \hat{b}_{13} = 2.1$$

and compute $\sum_{k=1}^{4} (y(k) - \hat{y}_i(k))^2$ where:

$$\hat{y}_j(k) = a_{ij}x(k) + b_{ij}u(k)$$

yielding:

$$J_1 = (4.7 - (-2.8 \cdot 2.6 - 1.7 \cdot 0.5))^2$$
$$+ (14.8 - (-2.8 \cdot 6.8 + 1.7 \cdot 1.2))^2 + (4.6 - (-2.8 \cdot 2.7 - 1.7 \cdot 0.8))^2$$
$$+ (-1.5 - (-2.8 \cdot 1.4 - 1.7 \cdot 4.3))^2$$

Continuing in that manner, we evaluate $J$ for all three sets of the first run, namely for $\hat{a}_{12}$, $\hat{b}_{12}$ and $\hat{a}_{13}$, $\hat{b}_{13}$ to yield $J_2$, $J_3$. Subsequently, we perform a second run where three sets of new random values are selected for $\hat{a}$, $\hat{b}$, and repeat this procedure to cover enough cells so that the required accuracy may be expected. The identification process is stopped when $J_v$ is better than a prespecified $J_{min}$. (See problem 11.1.)

## 11.2 A HEURISTIC DIRECT SEARCH IDENTIFICATION APPROACH

Procedures of direct search for identifying dynamic processes are based on gradient optimization techniques, known also as steepest-descent techniques. The direct search approach to be considered in this section implies the employment of a heuristic mapping of the region around any point of interest in the parameter space to derive the gradient of a scalar identification-performance index $J$ in that space in an experimental rather than an analytical manner. In principle the present approach employs the philosophy of the static direct search where the gradient of the performance-index $J$ with respect to the parameter vector $\pi$ is followed to reach the minimum $J$, as illustrated in Figure 11.3.

Many variations to the above static optimization approach are described in the literature (see Chapter 5 of Ref. 1), which are similar in principle and can usually be applied to dynamic identification. It is, however, important to note that the identification of parameters of dynamic systems requires some special consideration when any static gradient technique is adopted for this purpose. One application of the static gradient search has already been described, in Section 10.2, where a predictive gradient was employed to identify a functional approximate relation between the input and state vectors and the performance cost of the control. Since we are presently concerned with identifying the parameters of Equation (11.3) relating to an

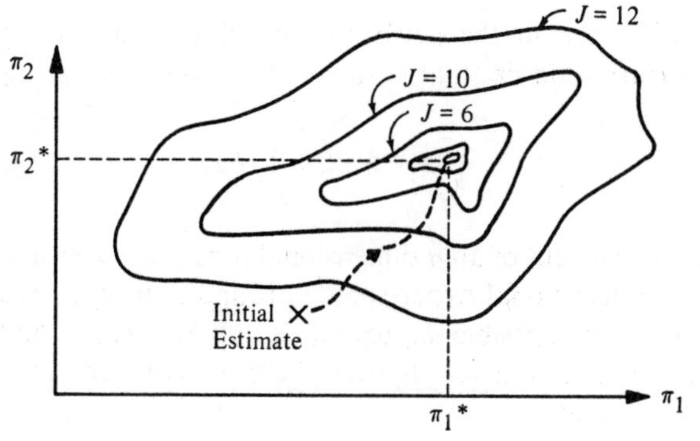


*Figure 11.3* Static direct search of best parameters $\pi_1$, $\pi_2$.

input/output model and *not* a control-performance/input model, the gradient technique below is somewhat different from that of Section 10.2. An incorporation of the present approach in a predictive controller is considered in Section 11.3 and is still concerned with the parameters of Equation (11.3) and not with control cost.

The gradient procedure for identifying the parameter vector $\pi$ of Equation (11.3) is based on the formulation of equations (11.2) to (11.4) of the previous section. It thus considers the identification-performance index $J$ of Equation (11.5) and the general identifier layout of Figure 11.1. When other prior information is lacking, the procedure starts by arbitrarily picking a parameter vector $\pi(1, 1)$ and simultaneously computing $J(1, 1)$ for $\pi(1, 1)$ and for several $\pi(1, m)$ which are randomly or systematically selected in the close neighborhood of $\pi(1, 1)$. The simultaneous computation of $J(1, m)$ for the above $\pi(1, m)$ near $\pi(1, 1)$ is necessary to avoid the transient effect of one set of parameters $\pi(1, i)$ on the other $\pi(1, m)\forall m$, or to avoid the need of repeating too often the readjustment of initial conditions. Once $J(1, m)$ have been evaluated for several $m$ around $\pi(1, 1)$ and with the same input data, the gradient may be established, and the next set of parameters vectors may be selected along the above gradient to establish a $\pi(2, 1)$ and new $\pi(2, m)$ around it. Consequently, $J(2, m)$ are recomputed for the new $\pi(2, m)$ and the gradients may be followed until, after examining several further $\pi(h, m)$ @ $h = 3, 4, \ldots$ along the gradient, the minimum of $J(h, m)$ may be approximately located. Obviously, the transient effect due to the step change from $\pi(h, m)$ to $\pi(h + 1, m)$ should die out before computing $J(h + 1, m)$.

The determination of the gradient as the optimal direction to be taken by the search procedure results from the following analysis:[2]
Let:

$$\Delta J = \nabla \mathbf{J}\, \partial\pi^T \tag{11.24}$$

$\Delta J$ being the change in the performance index as in Figure 11.3 due to parameter perturbation $\partial\pi$, that is subject to a constraint given by:

$$|\partial\pi|^2 = r^2 = \sum_{j=1}^{n} \partial\pi_j \tag{11.25}$$

$\pi_j$ being the $j$'th element of an $n$-dimensional parameter vector $\pi$ and $r$ being a radius of an $n$-dimensional hyper-sphere around a given $\pi$. We are required to find the maximum possible improvement in performance $\Delta J$ for parameter perturbations within a given hyper-sphere $r$. We consequently define a Lagrangian such that

$$L \triangleq \nabla \mathbf{J}\, \partial\pi^T - \lambda(|\partial\pi|^2 - r^2) \tag{11.26}$$

$\lambda$ being a Lagrange multiplier. The perturbation $\partial\pi^*$ to maximize $\Delta J$ above,[4] thus satisfies, in analogy to the analysis of equations (10.38) to (10.47):

$$\frac{\partial L}{\partial \pi} = 0 \tag{11.27}$$

yielding:

$$\nabla \mathbf{J} - 2\lambda\, \partial\pi^* = 0 \tag{11.28}$$

and, since $\lambda$ is a constant scalar:

$$\partial\pi^* = (2\lambda)^{-1}\nabla J \tag{11.29}$$

Substituting for $\partial\pi^*$ into Equation (11.25) yields

$$(2\lambda)^{-2}|\nabla \mathbf{J}|^2 = r^2 \tag{11.30}$$

and:

$$\lambda = (\pm)\frac{|\nabla \mathbf{J}|}{2r} \tag{11.31}$$

and further substituting the latter expression for $\lambda$ into Equation (11.29) gives:

$$\partial\pi^* = -\frac{r}{|\nabla \mathbf{J}|}\nabla \mathbf{J} \tag{11.32}$$

$\partial\pi^*$ thus being a vector in the direction opposing the gradient $\nabla \mathbf{J}$ as is obvious from Fig. 11.3.

Since every step of the search is preceded by a mapping of the performance index in the parameter space, the heuristic gradient procedure should converge to the neighborhood of the true minimum when a change in the sign of the gradient is observed (see Figure 11.3). At an iteration step where the above change in sign occurs, it may be appropriate to decrease the magnitude of the perturbations in $\pi$ to improve the mapping and hence to get closer to the true minimum.

### 11.2.1 Search in Cases of Multi-Modality

If many minima of $J$ in the space of $J$ vs. $\pi$ as in Figure 11.2 are suspected, the random search and the gradient (direct) search procedures may be combined. Hence, the random search subroutine will locate several of possible minima areas for subsequent detailed gradient search of the best $\pi$. Again, consideration must be made to transient effects of iterating $\pi$. This may lead to the necessity of evaluating the identification performance for the same input/output data all over the searched space, thus requiring enormous storage capacity, if any nonstationarity should be followed.

## 11.3 INCORPORATION OF HEURISTIC IDENTIFICATION IN PREDICTIVE STRUCTURES

A considerable speeding-up in heuristic identification may result if it is incorporated in a predictive control scheme, such as described in Chapter 10. In this case, a system is considered where control inputs are applied at discrete time instances 0; $T$; $2T$; ... $(k-1)T$; $kT$. The parameters of the control vector $\mathbf{u}$ are changed in a step-wise manner at each control interval as shown in Figure 11.4. The identification procedure requires that the behavior of $\hat{\mathbf{x}}$, $\mathbf{x}$ of equations (11.2), (11.3) over the interval from $kT$ to $kT+T$ be adequately predicted according to the data up to $k = kT$, assuming that, in analogy to Chapter 10:

$$\mathbf{u}(kT+\tau) = \mathbf{u}(kT); \qquad \forall\, 0 \leq \tau < T \tag{11.33}$$

Consequently, the transient effect of iterating $\pi$ before $t = kT - T$ should be accounted for in the prediction. The iteration of $\pi(jT-T)$ by $\Delta\pi(jT)$ at $t = jT$, such that:

$$\pi(jT) \triangleq \pi(jT-T) + \Delta\pi(jT) \tag{11.34}$$

subsequently yields a deviation of $\hat{x}(jT+\tau)$, $\forall\, 0 \leq \tau < T$, from its previously predicted value by $\Delta\hat{x}(jT+\tau)$. A direct search or a random search identification procedure thus modifies $\pi$ at each control interval according to the respective search principles. The random or direct search procedure requires the evaluation of an identification performance index $J_k$, where:

$$J_k = \int_{kT}^{kT+T} [(\Delta\mathbf{x}(\tau) - \Delta\hat{\mathbf{x}}(\tau))^T(\Delta\mathbf{x}(\tau) - \Delta\hat{\mathbf{x}}(\tau))]\, d\tau \tag{11.35}$$

at each control interval. It is noted that $\Delta\mathbf{x}(\tau)$ is measurable according to the difference between $\mathbf{x}(kT+\tau)$, $\forall\, 0 \leq \tau < T$, as has been predicted when assuming that $\Delta\mathbf{u}(kT) = \mathbf{0}$, and the actual $\mathbf{x}(kT+\tau)$. Similarly $\Delta\hat{\mathbf{x}}(kT+\tau)$ is given

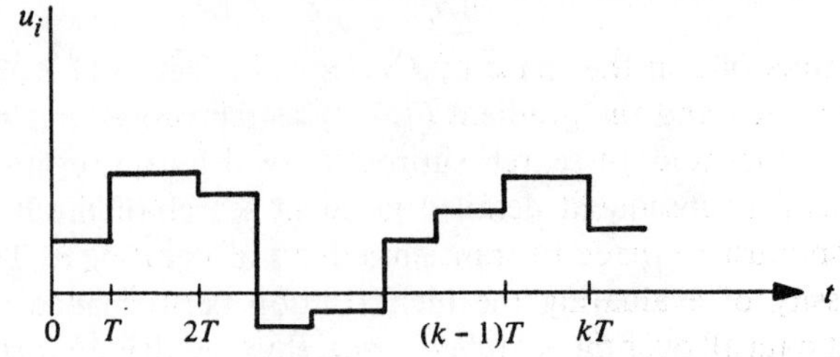


*Figure 11.4* Step-wise changes in control inputs.

by the difference between $\mathbf{x}_{po}(kT+\tau)$ as has been predicted assuming that $\Delta\mathbf{u}(kT)$ and $\Delta\pi(kT)$ are zero, and the actual output $\hat{\mathbf{x}}$ of the model of Equation (11.3), as shown in Figure 11.5. The latter model has an input vector of $\mathbf{0}$ prior to $t = kT$ and of $\Delta\mathbf{u}(kT)$ from $kT$ onwards, whereas its parameters are $\pi(kT)$, $\Delta\mathbf{u}(kT)$ and $\pi(kT)$ being updated at each interval.

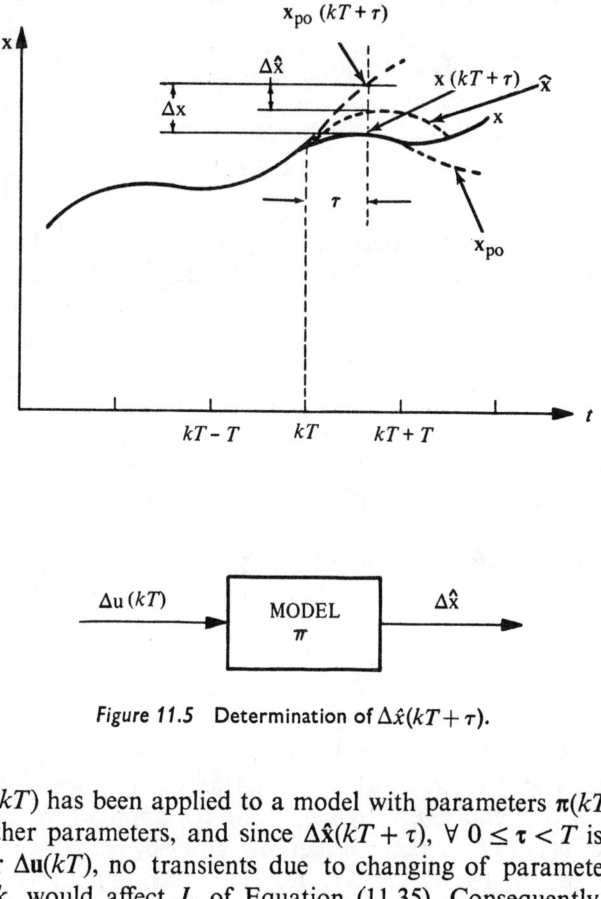


*Figure 11.5* Determination of $\Delta\hat{x}(kT+\tau)$.

Since $\Delta\mathbf{u}(kT)$ has been applied to a model with parameters $\pi(kT)$ and not with any other parameters, and since $\Delta\hat{\mathbf{x}}(kT+\tau)$, $\forall\ 0 \leq \tau < T$ is only due to the latter $\Delta\mathbf{u}(kT)$, no transients due to changing of parameters vectors $\pi(jT)\ \forall\ j < k$, would affect $J_k$ of Equation (11.35). Consequently, it is not necessary to wait until these transients die out or to readjust initial conditions before iterating $\pi$. Furthermore, if the values that yield the best $J_k$ are stored, a heuristic identification of $\pi$ of Equation (11.3) may be accomplished through relatively fast sequential iterations. The parameters $\pi$ of the model of Equation (11.3) are thus identified for any a priori given formulations of $\psi$, unlike the approach of Chapter 10, which is merely concerned with identifying a relation between the control cost and the state and control vectors.

## REFERENCES


1. Wilde, D. J. *Optimum Seeking Methods*, Prentice-Hall, Englewood Cliffs, N.J., 1964.
2. Wilde, D. J. and Beightler, C. S., *Foundations of Optimization*, Prentice-Hall, Englewood Cliffs, N.J., 1967.
3. Matyas, J. "Random Optimization," *Automation and Remote Control*, Vol. 26, No. 2, 1965.
4. Elgerd, O. I. *Control Systems Theory*, McGraw-Hill, New York, 1967 (Chapter 10).


## PROBLEMS

**1.** Calculate the number of cells that should be sampled if the best cell we expect (with a probability of 98%) to locate should be among the ten percent best performing cells, for a very large number of cells.

**2.** Employ random search to identify $a$ of $\dot{x} = ax^2$, from the data of Problem 5 in Chapter 9, when assuming that $a$ lies between $-0.4$ and $-2.4$ and when the latter range is divided into a grid of 0.01. You should reach one of the top ten cells with a probability of 0.97%.

**3.** When $\mu$ different simultaneous random trials are made on a grid of $r$ cells ($r \ggg \mu$), find the probability $p(\mu)$ to locate at least one of the $w$ best performing cells.

**4.** Identify the parameters of the process $y = ax^b + u$ by gradient search from the following data ($x(t)$ is given at intervals of $t = 0.1$ starting with $t = 0$):

$x(t)$ = 0.0, .099, .192, .276, .346, .404, .449, .483, .509, .528, .542, .552, .56, .565, .568, .571, .573, .5742, .5751, .5758, .5762, .5766, .5768, .577, .5771, .57715, .57721, .57725

$u(t)$ is 1.0 $\forall\ t \geq 0$ and 0 $\forall\ t < 0$. Start with $\hat{a}(0) = -2$; $\hat{b}(0) = 0.5$.

**5.** Simulate a system $x(k+1) = ax^2(k) + bx(k)$ with $a = -0.02$; $b = 1$, $x(0) = 1$ and identify $a$, $b$ by employing the approach of Section 11.3. Consider $u(k)$ to be a random sequence given by recycling the sequence: .01, .13, .69, .97, .09, .17, .21, .73, .49, .37, .81, .53, .89, .57, .41, .33, .29, .77.

# 12

# PREDICTOR PARAMETER IDENTIFICATION METHODS

Since the identification techniques of the present text are based on measured data, and since some of these techniques (as in Chapter 10) required prediction, problems of data smoothing and of prediction deserve careful attention. Furthermore, for adequate prediction, appropriate predictor parameters must be employed. Consequently, a problem of the identification of these parameters exists, and is to be treated in the present chapter.

When one is deriving predictor models, several types of message description may be considered; these are usually in terms of an input/output model, the message being the output, and, in the absence of any accessible or known input, some white noise sequence being the input. The predictor parameters to be identified may thus represent the auto- and cross-correlation functions of the message to be predicted and the input to the latter input/output model as in case of the Wiener filter approach.[1,2] They may alternatively be state equation parameters, as in case of the (finite dimensional) Kalman filter approach[3] or of a finite element transfer-function representation, as has been considered by Box and Jenkins.[4]

The prediction problems discussed in the present chapter are based on the two latter formulations, namely the discrete transfer function formulation, as in the work of Box and Jenkins[4] and the state space formulation, as in the Kalman filter.[3] As stated above, these and all other prediction methods require adequate predictor parameter identification. Although the original Kalman filter formulation assumes that the filter parameters are given, the Kalman filter may be modified such that it is applied to estimate its own parameters, as is shown in Section 12.4 below. This modification is further shown to be extendable to general process identification problems, and also to problems of joint state and parameter estimation. The resultant extended Kalman filter estimates of both state and parameters are competitive with the joint estimation procedures based on invariant imbedding as in Chapter 9 in linear Gaussian cases. They are usually faster than the invariant imbedding procedures when linear systems are considered. In cases of nonlinear systems, invariant imbedding is advantageous since it is directly applicable to such systems, whereas the extended Kalman filter requires linearization of the nonlinearities. However, the discrete transfer function formulation is usually the most efficient for predictor identification purposes. Furthermore, it is transformable into state space form, as in Section 2.5.

The techniques of the present Chapter, though dealing with predictor models, may be reformulated to apply to filter identification, when filtering inside a data range is required. They may be combined with a transformation procedure to yield optimal prediction of certain non Gaussian sequences.

## 12.1 SMOOTHING OF A PRIORI UNKNOWN SEQUENCES BY POLYNOMIAL CURVE-FITTING

It is not the purpose of the present text to survey smoothing techniques for a priori unknown sequences, since this would call for far more than one section or chapter. We shall therefore only briefly discuss the smoothing problem to facilitate some insight and to avoid a rigid restriction to a certain procedure. We shall subsequently describe in detail a smoothing procedure that is both satisfactory and numerically convenient for incorporation in on-line identification and control schemes.

Consider a measured time series $y(t)$ whose behavior is a priori unknown and which may contain noise whose parameters are also unknown, such that:

$$y(t) = s(t) + n(t) \tag{12.1}$$

The smoothing problem is that of deriving the message $s(t)$ from the measurement $y(t)$, or at least of obtaining a satisfactory estimate of $s(t)$. In case of the Wiener filter[1, 2] the optimal derivation of $s(t)$ is accomplished when the autocorrelation function of the message $\phi_{ss}(\tau)$, and the cross-correlation function of message and noise $\phi_{ns}(\tau)$ are known, where:

$$\left.\begin{aligned} \phi_{ss}(\tau) &= \lim_{T\to\infty} \int_0^T s(t)\, s(t-\tau)\, dt \qquad &(12.2\text{-a}) \\ \phi_{ns}(\tau) &= \lim \int_0^T n(t)\, s(t-\tau)\, dt \qquad &(12.2\text{-b}) \end{aligned}\right\} s(t<0)=0$$

$s(t)$ being Gaussian, namely, a joint Gaussian distribution, if the filter is to be optimal. In the Kalman filter approach,[3] a state vector $\mathbf{s}(t)$ of the message is considered, such that

$$\mathbf{s}(t+\tau) = \mathbf{A}(t)\mathbf{s}(t) + \mathbf{u}(t); \qquad @ \quad \tau \gtrless 0 \tag{12.3}$$

$\mathbf{u}$ being white noise, and the vector measurement equation (corresponding to Equation (12.1)) becomes:

$$\mathbf{y}(t) = \mathbf{M}(t)\mathbf{s}(t) + \mathbf{n}(t) \tag{12.4}$$

$\mathbf{M}$ denoting the measurement matrix and $\mathbf{n}$ being a white noise error vector. The optimal estimate according to Kalman's filter thus requires the knowledge of $\mathbf{A}(t)$, $\mathbf{M}(t)$, $\mathbf{N}(t)$, $\mathbf{W}(t)$, and $\mathbf{S}(t_0)$ where $\mathbf{A}(t)$ is the state transition matrix of Equation (12.3) and:

$$\mathbf{W}(t) \triangleq E[\mathbf{u}(t)\cdot\mathbf{u}^T(t)]; \;\; E[\mathbf{u}(t)] = 0 \tag{12.5-a}$$

$$\mathbf{N}(t) \triangleq E[\mathbf{n}(t)\cdot\mathbf{n}^T(t)]; \;\; E[\mathbf{n}(t)] = \mathbf{0}; E[\mathbf{n}(t)\mathbf{u}^T(\tau)] = \mathbf{0} \tag{12.5-b}$$

$$\mathbf{S}(t_0) \triangleq E[[\mathbf{s}(t_0) - \mathbf{s}^*(t_0)]\cdot[\mathbf{s}(t_0) - \mathbf{s}^*(t_0)]^T] \tag{12.5-c}$$

$E$ denoting an expected value, and $\mathbf{s}^*$ being the a priori mean estimate of $\mathbf{s}_0$, and $\mathbf{s}$, $\mathbf{n}$, $\mathbf{u}$ being Gaussian. If neither $\phi_{ss}$, $\phi_{ns}$ of equations (12.2) nor $\mathbf{A}(t)$, $\mathbf{N}(t)$, $\mathbf{W}(t)$, $\mathbf{S}(t_0)$ of equations (12.3) and (12.5) are a priori known, their identification would obviously be required for obtaining adequate estimates of $\mathbf{s}(t)$ above. A relatively fast smoothing procedure for cases where the (possibly nonstationary) averages of $\mathbf{s}$ are to be established, and where no a priori information is available, may be derived according to curve-fitting principles. The latter procedure provides a least-squares polynomial fit to these averages, which may be computed on-line. It requires only an assumption of the highest polynomial order to be considered, though this order may be derived according to error-variance considerations. When the latter fit is applied to randomly varying averages or to a set of noisy measurements, it may be reformulated in terms of equations (12.3), (12.4), to facilitate Kalman-type corrections, which are, however, not fully optimal since the Gaussian assumption does not hold in these cases. The details of the polynomial fit are thus discussed below.

### 12.1.1 Least-Squares Curve-Fit of Best Order Polynomials

Let $y_i$ denote a set of $N + 1$ measurements ($i = 0, 1, 2, \dots N$) having non-stationary averages, that is given over an interval $t - T$ to $t$, where:

$$y_i = s_i + n_i \tag{12.6}$$

$s_i$ being the message, $n_i$ being random noise with zero mean, and $y_N$ corresponding to $y(t)$, i.e., to the "present" time. In the absence of a priori information, we may assume that the message $s_i$ may be approximated by an orthogonal polynomial of order $m$, where $m \leq m'$ and that $n_i$ is of a nearly-stationary character during the interval $T$. These assumptions, although restricting the generality of the procedure, are reasonably valid for many practical smoothing and prediction problems that arise in control engineering, whereas the choice of orthogonal polynomials is based on the consideration of Section 5.6. Consequently, an orthogonal polynomial of best order $m \leq m'$ is fitted to the last $N + 1$ measurement of $y_i$, where $m$ is derived according to the algorithm described in Section 5.6.1-c. The value of $m'$ may be arbitrarily chosen unless some a priori knowledge of the message exists, though obviously $m' < N - 1$. In practice, the algorithm of Section 5.6.1-c converges fairly rapidly to the best order $m$ even without considering the constraint of $m'$. A restriction of $m'$ to 5 is, however, usually reasonable and subsequently yields adequate prediction, whereas higher order polynomials, if they arise, make prediction to a far lead time ahead fairly difficult.

Subsequent to the determination of the best polynomial order $m$, an orthogonal polynomial of that order is fitted to the measurements. Noting the discussion on orthogonal polynomials in Sections 5.6.1-a, a Chebyshev polynomial should preferably be selected because of its attractive curve-fitting features. An ALGOL algorithm for generating the Chebyshev polynomial by means of the Gram Schmidt method is described in Ref. 5. The orthogonal polynomial fit thus selected yields the smoothed output $z(t)$ as follows:

$$z(t) = a_0 p_0(t') + \cdots a_m p_m(t') \tag{12.7}$$

$z$ being the $m$'th order polynomial estimate of the average of $s$ of Equation (12.6), and $t'$ being a shifted time scale, starting from zero at the time of the first of the $N + 1$ samples to which the polynomial is fitted.

Defining:

$$\mathbf{Y}(t) \triangleq [y_0 \cdots y_N]^T; \qquad y_j = y(t - j\tau) \tag{12.8}$$

$\tau$ being the sampling interval, Equation (12.7) becomes, at the $N + 1$ sampling instances:

$$\mathbf{z} = \begin{bmatrix} z_0 \\ \cdot \\ \cdot \\ \cdot \\ z_N \end{bmatrix} = \begin{bmatrix} p_0(N) \cdots p_m(N) \\ \cdot \\ \cdot \\ \cdot \\ p_0(0) \cdots p_m(0) \end{bmatrix} \cdot \begin{bmatrix} a_0 \\ \cdot \\ \cdot \\ \cdot \\ a_m \end{bmatrix} \triangleq \mathbf{\Pi} \cdot \mathbf{a} \tag{12.9}$$

$z_j$ being $z(t - j\tau)$. The elements $a_v$ of $\mathbf{a}$ $\forall v \in (0, m)$, are chosen to minimize $J$, where:

$$J \triangleq \|\mathbf{Y} - \mathbf{z}\|^2 = \|\mathbf{Y} - \mathbf{\Pi} \cdot \mathbf{a}\|^2 \tag{12.10}$$

giving, for minimum $J$ (best fit), in similarity to Equation (5.27):

$$\mathbf{a} = [\mathbf{\Pi}^T\mathbf{\Pi}]^{-1}\mathbf{\Pi}^T\mathbf{Y} \tag{12.11}$$

and:

$$\mathbf{z}(t) = \mathbf{\Pi}[\mathbf{\Pi}^T\mathbf{\Pi}]^{-1}\mathbf{\Pi}^T\mathbf{Y} \tag{12.12}$$

Since $p_v(t')$ are orthogonal polynomials in $t'$, $z(t)$ may be expressed as:

$$z(t) = \sum_{j=0}^{m} \eta_j \cdot (t')^j; \qquad \eta_j = \text{coefficients of } (t')^j \tag{12.13}$$

## 12.2 TAYLOR SERIES EXTRAPOLATION OF CURVE-FITTED SIGNALS

Once the polynomial-like part $z$ of the measurements $y$ has been approximated, as in Equation (12.13), a Taylor series expansion is employed for extrapolating the polynomial $z(t)$ as follows:

$$\hat{z}(t + \theta) = z(t) + \theta \dot{z}(t) + \frac{\theta^2}{2!}\ddot{z}(t) + \cdots \frac{\theta^m}{m!}\overset{(m)}{z}(t); \quad \overset{(j)}{z} \triangleq d^jz/dt^j \tag{12.14}$$

We subsequently derive from Equation (12.7) that:

$$\overset{(k)}{z} = \sum_{j=k}^{m} a_j \overset{(k)}{p_j}(t) \tag{12.15}$$

Consequently:

$$\hat{z}(t + \theta) = \sum_{k=0}^{m} \frac{1}{k!}\theta^k \overset{(k)}{z}(t); \quad \forall \theta \in (0, T) \tag{12.16}$$

or according to Equation (12.15):

$$\hat{z}(t + \theta) = \sum_{k=0}^{m} \left\{ \frac{\theta^k}{k!} \sum_{j=k}^{m} \left[ a_j \overset{(k)}{p_j}(t') \right] \right\} \tag{12.17}$$

We now define:

$$\mathbf{F} \triangleq \begin{bmatrix} p_0 & 0 & 0 & \cdot & \cdot & \cdot & 0 \\ p_1 & \dot{p}_1 & 0 & \cdot & \cdot & \cdot & 0 \\ p_2 & \dot{p}_2 & \ddot{p}_2 & \cdot & \cdot & \cdot & 0 \\ \cdot & \cdot & \cdot & & & & \cdot \\ \cdot & \cdot & \cdot & & & & \cdot \\ \cdot & \cdot & \cdot & & & & 0 \\ p_m & \dot{p}_m & \ddot{p}_m & \cdot & \cdot & \cdot & p_m^{(n)} \end{bmatrix} \tag{12.18}$$

and:

$$\boldsymbol{\theta} \triangleq \left[1; \theta; \frac{\theta^2}{2!}; \cdots \frac{\theta^m}{m!}\right]^T = [\theta_1 \cdots \theta_{m+1}]^T \tag{12.19}$$

Consequently, and substituting for $a_j$ from Equation (12.11), we obtain that:

$$z(t + \theta) = (\mathbf{F} \cdot \boldsymbol{\theta})^T \mathbf{a} = [\mathbf{F}\boldsymbol{\theta}]^T \cdot (\boldsymbol{\Pi}^T \boldsymbol{\Pi})^{-1} \boldsymbol{\Pi}^T \mathbf{Y}(t) \tag{12.20}$$

Equation (12.20) describes the Taylor extrapolation of the least-squares orthogonal polynomial fit to measurements from $t = kT - T$ to $t = kT$, when expressed in matrix form. The latter matrix notation is adopted for convenience of computation. The extrapolation above does not incorporate a correction of the prediction through comparing measured and predicted data. This lack of correction may be justified in the particular case where fast prediction is required and where $\mathbf{s}(t)$ is assumed not to be noisy. However, the formulation of Equation (12.20) may serve as a message model to which a linear feedback sequential prediction approach may be applied, *in cases where the parameters of a state-equation model of the message* $z(t)$ *are not known a priori*, if the curve fit above is applied to a recent number of noise sequence elements or to randomly varying averages. In that case, the prediction is obviously not optimal, since the Gaussian assumptions regarding $\mathbf{s}$, $\mathbf{n}$, $\mathbf{u}$ do not hold.

### 12.1.2 State-Space Formulation of Taylor Extrapolation Algorithms

The prediction algorithm of Section 12.1.1 may be improved when a sequential correction as in Kalman's sequential predictor[3] is applied to the extrapolation model. Consequently, the extrapolation model of Equation (12.20) must be formulated in a state equation form to yield a state space extrapolation model, when the message parameters are a priori unknown. The parameters of this state-space model are derived from the formulation of equations (12.16) to (12.20), under the assumptions at the end of Section 12.1.1, as follows: We define:

$$z(t) \triangleq x_1(t) \tag{12.21}$$

$x(t)$ being as in Equation (12.17), and:

$$x_{i+1} \triangleq \overset{(i)}{x_i} \quad \forall i \in (1, m+1); \quad \overset{(i)}{x} = d^i x / dt^i \tag{12.22}$$

Equations (12.21) and (12.22) thus provide a description of the various states of the estimate $z(t)$. If we subsequently reformulate Equation (12.17) for deriving the predicted estimate $z(t + \theta)$, in terms of the notation of equations (12.21) and (12.22), while adding a prediction error term $u_1$ to the Taylor expansion, we obtain:

$$x_1(t + \theta) = \sum_{i=0}^{m} \theta_{i+1} \overset{(i)}{x_1}(t) + u_1(t) = \sum_{i=1}^{m+1} \theta_i x_i(t) + u_1(t) \tag{12.23}$$

$\theta_i$ being the elements of $\mathbf{\theta}$ of Equation (12.19). Consequently, we may express all $m + 1$ states of the predicted estimate by:

$$x_j(t + \theta) = \sum_{i=1}^{m+2-j} \theta_i x_{i+1-j}(t) + u_j(t) \qquad \forall j(1, m+1) \tag{12.24}$$

$u_j(t)$ being approximately given by:

$$u_j(t) = x_j(t + \theta) - x_{j,e}(t + \theta) \qquad \forall j(1, m+1) \tag{12.25-a}$$

where $x_{j,e}(t + \theta)$ denote $x_j$ as derived from extrapolating the polynomial that has been fitted to data from $t - T$ up to $t$, whereas $x_j(t + \theta)$ denote $x_j$ as actually fitted to data from $t - T + \theta$ to $t + \theta$ (see Figure 12.1). The above $u_j$

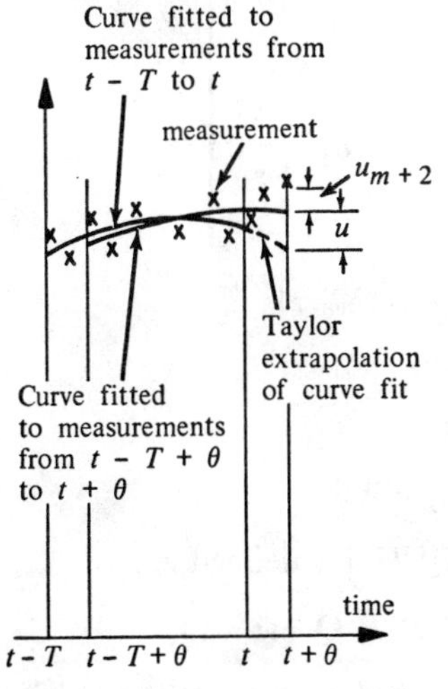


(a): Determination of $x_1$; $u_1$; $u_{m+2}$

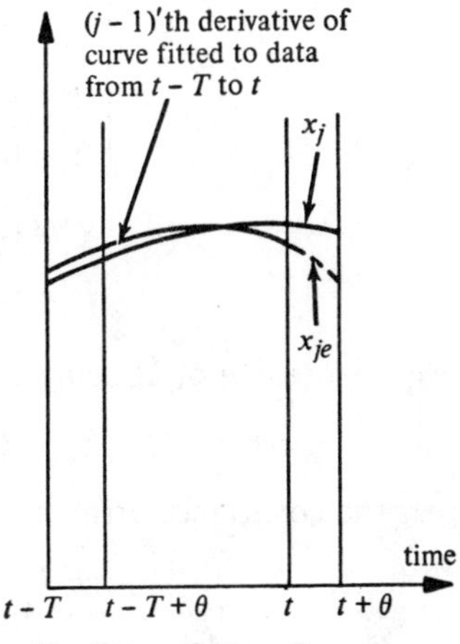


(b): Determination of $x_j$; $u_j$

*Figure 12.1*

may be assumed to satisfy:

$$E[u_j] = 0 \tag{12.25-b}$$

We may often further assume $u_j$ to be white noise of approximate Gaussian nature, so that $u_j$ may serve as inputs to be considered in Equation (12.24), as is required for a Kalman filter model.

We further define an additional state $x_{m+2}$ to describe the measurement error, such that:

$$x_{m+2}(t) \triangleq y(t-\theta) - x_1(t-\theta) \tag{12.26-a}$$

$y(t)$ being the measurement, as in Equation (12.6) above, yielding:

$$x_{m+2}(t+\theta) = u_{m+2}(t) \tag{12.26-b}$$

$$E[u_{m+2}(t)] = E[x_{m+2}(t)] = 0 \tag{12.26-c}$$

Equations (12.24) to (12.26) thus provide a state variable formulation of the predicted estimates, as follows:

$$\mathbf{X}(t+\theta) = \mathbf{\Phi X}(t) + \mathbf{U}(t) \tag{12.27}$$

where:

$$\mathbf{\Phi} \triangleq \begin{bmatrix} \theta_1 & \theta_2 & \cdots & & \theta_{m+1} & 0 \\ 0 & \theta_1 & \cdots & & \theta_m & 0 \\ 0 & 0 & \theta_1 & \cdots & \theta_{m-1} & 0 \\ \vdots & & & \ddots & \vdots & \vdots \\ 0 & 0 & \cdots & & \theta_1 & 0 \\ 0 & 0 & \cdots & & 0 & 0 \end{bmatrix} \tag{12.28}$$

$$\mathbf{X} \triangleq [x_1 \cdots x_{m+1} x_{m+2}]^T \tag{12.29}$$

$$\mathbf{U} \triangleq [u_1 \cdots u_{m+1} u_{m+2}]^T \tag{12.30}$$

the expected value of $\mathbf{U}$ being given by:

$$E[\mathbf{U}(t)] = \mathbf{0} \tag{12.31}$$

whereas the covariance error matrix $E[\mathbf{UU}^T]$ is defined as:

$$E[\mathbf{U}(t) \cdot \mathbf{U}^T(\tau)] \triangleq \mathbf{Q} \cdot \delta(t-\tau) \tag{12.32}$$

The prediction model is completed by employing Equation (12.26) to yield:

$$\mathbf{y}(t) = y(t) = x_1(t) + x_{m+2}(t) = \mathbf{M} \cdot \mathbf{X}(t) \tag{12.33}$$

where **M** is an $m + 2$ row-vector, as follows:

$$\mathbf{M} = [1, 0, 0 \cdots 0, 1] \tag{12.34}$$

and $\mathbf{y}(t)$ is one-dimensional. Consequently, a complete state-space model as employed in the Kalman filter formulation is obtained, but which is based on the assumption that the message is given by a polynomial curve fit to present measurements.

EXAMPLE 12.1

Consider a set of measurements given by:

| $t$ | .4 | .44 | .48 | .52 | .56 | .6 | .64 | .68 | .72 |
|---|---|---|---|---|---|---|---|---|---|
| $y(t)$ | .387 | .415 | .456 | .492 | .528 | .556 | .595 | .630 | .659 |

where $y(t) = s(t) + n(t)$, $s$ and $n$ denoting message and zero mean noise, respectively. When fitting the latter measurements with a polynomial $z(t) = a_0 + a_1 t + a_2 t^2$, where $a_0 = 0$, $a_1 = 1$, $a_2 = -0.118$, we obtain:

| $t$ | .4 | .44 | .48 | .52 | .56 | .6 | .64 | .68 | .72 |
|---|---|---|---|---|---|---|---|---|---|
| $z(t)$ | .381 | .417 | .453 | .488 | .524 | .558 | .592 | .636 | .659 |

to yield $\hat{z}(t + \theta) = 0.692$ for $t = 0.72$, $\theta = 0.04$, whereas $y(.76)$ is (later) measured to be 0.688. The state equation corresponding to Equation (12.27) thus becomes:

$$\begin{bmatrix} x_1(t+\theta) \\ x_2(t+\theta) \\ x_3(t+\theta) \\ x_4(t+\theta) \end{bmatrix} = \mathbf{\Phi}(t+\theta;\ t) \begin{bmatrix} x_1(t) \\ x_2(t) \\ x_3(t) \\ x_4(t) \end{bmatrix} + \begin{bmatrix} u_1(t) \\ u_2(t) \\ x_3(t) \\ u_4(t) \end{bmatrix}$$

where:

$$\mathbf{\Phi}(t+\theta; t) = \begin{bmatrix} 1 & \theta & \frac{\theta^2}{2} & 0 \\ 0 & 1 & \theta & 0 \\ 0 & 0 & 1 & 0 \\ 0 & 0 & 0 & 0 \end{bmatrix}$$

and: $x_1(t) = z(t)$; $x_2(t) = \dot{z}(t)$; $x_3(t) = \ddot{z}(t)$; $x_4(t) = y(t) - z(t)$. Assuming that the curve fit to $y(t)$ from $t = 0.44$ to $t = 0.76$, namely to the data that includes $y(0.76)$ yields $z(0.76) = 0.0690$ we obtain:

$$u_1(t) \cong 0.002 = z(0.76) - \hat{z}(0.76)$$

We similarly derive approximate values for $u_2(t)$, $u_3(t)$, whereas $u_4(t)$ is obtained from Equation (12.26-b).

## 12.3 APPLICATION OF SEQUENTIAL CORRECTIONS BASED ON KALMAN'S FILTERING APPROACH TO TAYLOR SERIES EXTRAPOLATIONS

We now employ the model of equations (12.27), (12.28), and (12.33) for sequentially deriving a feedback-corrected estimate $\mathbf{X}^*(t+\theta)$ of $\mathbf{X}(t+\theta)$, given measurements of $y$ up to $t$, as follows:

$$\mathbf{X}^*(t+\theta|t) = \mathbf{\Phi} \cdot \mathbf{X}^*(t|t-\theta) + \mathbf{D}\tilde{\mathbf{y}}(t|t-\theta) \tag{12.35}$$

$\mathbf{X}(t_\mu|t_\nu)$ denoting the value of $\mathbf{X}$ as estimated at $t_\mu$ on the basis of measurements up to $t_\nu$, $\mathbf{D}$ being a feedback matrix of the form:

$$\mathbf{D} \triangleq [d_1 \cdots d_{m+2}]^T \tag{12.36}$$

and $\tilde{\mathbf{y}}(t|t-\theta)$ being given by:

$$\tilde{\mathbf{y}}(t|t-\theta) = \mathbf{y}(t) - \mathbf{y}^*(t|t-\theta) \tag{12.37}$$

$$\mathbf{y}^*(t|t-\theta) \triangleq \mathbf{MX}^*(t|t-\theta) \tag{12.38}$$

Equations (12.37), (12.38) yield that:

$$\begin{aligned}\tilde{\mathbf{y}}(t|t-\theta) &= \mathbf{y}(t) - \mathbf{MX}^*(t|t-\theta)\\ &= y(t) - x_1^*(t|t-\theta) - x_{m+2}^*(t|t-\theta)\end{aligned} \tag{12.39}$$

Substituting for $\tilde{\mathbf{y}}$ from Equation (12.39) into (12.35), we obtain that:

$$\begin{aligned}\mathbf{X}^*(t+\theta|t) &= [\mathbf{\Phi} - \mathbf{DM}] \cdot \mathbf{X}^*(t|t-\theta) + \mathbf{Dy}(t)\\ &= \mathbf{\Phi}^*\mathbf{X}^*(t|t-\theta) + \mathbf{Dy}(t)\end{aligned} \tag{12.40}$$

where

$$\mathbf{\Phi}^* \triangleq \mathbf{\Phi} - \mathbf{DM} = \begin{bmatrix} [\theta_1 - d_1] & \theta_2 & \theta_3 & \cdots & \theta_{m+1} & -d_1 \\ -d_2 & \theta_1 & \cdots & \cdots & \theta_m & -d_2 \\ -d_3 & 0 & \theta_1 & \cdots & \theta_{m-1} & -d_3 \\ \vdots & \vdots & & \ddots & & \vdots \\ -d_{m+1} & 0 & \cdots & 0 & \theta_1 & -d_{m+1} \\ -d_{m+2} & 0 & \cdots & \cdots & 0 & -d_{m+2} \end{bmatrix} \tag{12.41}$$

The feedback matrix $\mathbf{D}$ is determined as follows:[3] Defining:

$$\tilde{\mathbf{X}}(t+\theta|t) \triangleq \mathbf{X}(t+\theta) - \mathbf{X}^*(t+\theta|t) \tag{12.42}$$

equations (12.35), (12.41), and (12.42) yield that:

$$\begin{aligned}\tilde{\mathbf{X}}(t+\theta\,|\,t) &= \mathbf{\Phi}\cdot\mathbf{X}(t)+\mathbf{U}(t)-\mathbf{\Phi}^{*}\mathbf{X}^{*}(t\,|\,t-\theta)-\mathbf{D}\cdot\mathbf{y}(t)\\ &= \mathbf{\Phi}^{*}\mathbf{X}(t)-\mathbf{\Phi}^{*}\mathbf{X}^{*}(t\,|\,t-\theta)+\mathbf{U}(t)\\ &= \mathbf{\Phi}^{*}\tilde{\mathbf{X}}(t\,|\,t-\theta)+\mathbf{U}(t)\end{aligned} \tag{12.43}$$

We further define[3] a covariance state-error matrix $\mathbf{P}$, such that:

$$\mathbf{P}(t+\theta) \triangleq E[\tilde{\mathbf{X}}(t+\theta\,|\,t)\cdot\tilde{\mathbf{X}}^{T}(t+\theta\,|\,t)] \tag{12.44}$$

Substituting for $\tilde{\mathbf{X}}(t+\theta\,|\,t)$ from Equation (12.43) and noting that $E[\mathbf{U}\mathbf{U}^{T}]=\mathbf{Q}$ according to Equation (12.32), we obtain that:

$$\begin{aligned}\mathbf{P}(t+\theta) &= \mathbf{\Phi}\mathbf{P}(t)\mathbf{\Phi}^{T}-\mathbf{D}(t)\mathbf{M}\cdot\mathbf{P}(t)\mathbf{\Phi}^{T}\\ &\quad-\mathbf{\Phi}\cdot\mathbf{P}(t)\mathbf{M}^{T}\mathbf{D}^{T}(t)+\mathbf{D}(t)\mathbf{M}\mathbf{P}(t)\mathbf{M}^{T}\mathbf{D}^{T}(t)+\mathbf{Q}(t)\end{aligned} \tag{12.45}$$

Since $\mathbf{M}$, $\mathbf{P}(t)$, $\mathbf{Q}(t)$ are independent of $\mathbf{D}(t)$, the trace of $\mathbf{P}$ denotes the sum of the squares of the state errors. Hence, the best feedback $\mathbf{D}(t)$ for the present formulation (and which is optimal in the Gaussian case) is this which minimizes $tr[\mathbf{P}(t+\theta)]$, to yield:

$$\frac{\partial \mathrm{tr}[\mathbf{P}(t+\theta)]}{\partial \mathbf{D}} = \mathbf{0} \tag{12.46}$$

Employing trace differentiation techniques as in Appendix 2, the optimum feedback matrix $\mathbf{D}$ for the present formulation becomes:

$$\mathbf{D}(t) = \mathbf{\Phi}\mathbf{P}(t)\mathbf{M}^{T}[\mathbf{M}\cdot\mathbf{P}(t)\cdot\mathbf{M}^{T}]^{-1} \tag{12.47}$$

Substituting the matrix $\mathbf{D}$ above into Equation (12.45), we derive that:

$$\mathbf{P}(t+\theta) = \mathbf{\Phi}^{*}\mathbf{P}(t)\phi^{T}+\mathbf{Q}(t) \tag{12.48}$$

The feedback predictor design thus implies the recursive solution of equations (12.47), (12.48) starting with $\mathbf{P}(t_0)$. The initial state-error covariance matrix $\mathbf{P}(t_0)$ may be derived from averaging $\tilde{\mathbf{X}}(t_{0i})\cdot\tilde{\mathbf{X}}(t_{0i})^{T}$ for several $t_{0i}$, where, if prediction is required for identification purposes as in Chapter 10, $t_{0i}$ denote the instances of applying the control vector. As long as no feedback estimate of $\mathbf{X}^{*}$ is available, $\mathbf{P}(t_0)$ may be given by (see Equation (12.44) and Figure 12.1):

$$\mathbf{P}(t_0) = \mathbf{Q}(t_0) \tag{12.49}$$

We note that $\mathbf{Q}(t)$ may be derived from $u(t)$ to $u_{m+1}(t)$ according to equations (12.25-a), (12.26), and (12.32).

The predictor formulation of this section is derived from a state-space formulation of a Taylor series extrapolator. The extrapolated values of the sequence considered are thus corrected in a least squares manner in terms of that formulation and of its initial estimates. The present predictor is advantageous to the Taylor extrapolation of the polynomial estimation $x_1(t)$ of the measurements $y(t)$ in the sense that it does not accept the a priori polynomial curve fit to be identical to the message. It considers the curve fit as the initial estimate which is subsequently corrected according to further data in a sequential manner. Consequently, once the assumption is made that the message and its derivatives represent the message state vector and when $\mathbf{u}$ is close enough to Gaussian white noise, the present derivation yields adequate feedback estimates (in the absence of other prior knowledge) for messages describable by analytical functions. Furthermore, in cases of complete ignorance, we may assume that $\mathbf{P}(t_0)$ is given by $a^2\mathbf{I}$ where $a \to \infty$ (in similarity of $\mathbf{P}$ of Chapter 6). In fact any reasonably high enough $a$ is usually adequate, this $a$ indicating a pessimistic guess of the initial estimation error. We re-emphasize that the present approach is only valid when the assumptions above are reasonable. Hence, though no optimal prediction is achieved, as by Kalman filtering, extrapolation is improved when proper Kalman filtering cannot be employed.

## 12.4 DERIVATION OF PREDICTOR PARAMETERS BY REFORMULATING THE STATES IN KALMAN'S FILTER

In Ref. 6 Mayne has presented a technique by which the Kalman filter of Ref. 3 is employed for estimating the parameters of the state equations of a Kalman-type predictor. Mayne's estimator is essentially a Kalman filter where a parameter rather than a state vector is to be estimated. It therefore requires that the state vector be directly accessible. In cases where this is not possible it may be assumed that the measurement represents the state vector of the message. If, however, only a scalar measurement sequence is available, and no a priori information of the state-vector structure of the message is known, the approach of Section 12.3 could be adopted, where the smoothed measurements and their derivatives are assumed to represent the message state vector. Alternatively, techniques as in Section 12.6 may be employed, where no such assumptions are required.

For deriving Mayne's estimator we consider the following state equation:

$$\mathbf{X}(k+1) = \mathbf{\Phi}\mathbf{X}(k) + \mathbf{V}(k); \quad k = 0, 1, 2, \ldots \tag{12.50}$$

where:

$\mathbf{X} = n \times 1$ state vector

$\mathbf{\Phi} = n \times n$ state-transition matrix (parameter matrix) which may be time-varying

$\mathbf{V}$ = white noise error vector with zero average

We subsequently define:

$$E[\mathbf{V}(k)\mathbf{V}^T(k)] \triangleq \mathbf{Q}(k) \tag{12.51}$$

$$\mathbf{Z}(k) \triangleq \mathbf{X}(k+1) \tag{12.52}$$

$E[\cdots]$ denoting the unconditional expectation of $[\cdots]$.

Equation (12.50) may be reformulated as:

$$\mathbf{Z}(k) = \mathbf{M}(k)\mathbf{a}(k) + \mathbf{V}(k) \tag{12.53}$$

where:

$$\mathbf{M}(k) = \begin{bmatrix} \mathbf{X}^T(k) & 0 & \cdots & \cdots & \cdots \\ 0 & \mathbf{X}^T(k) & 0 & \cdots & \cdots \\ 0 & 0 & \mathbf{X}^T(k) & 0 & \cdots \\ 0 & 0 & 0 & \mathbf{X}^T(k) & 0 \cdots \\ \cdots & \cdots & \cdots & \cdots & \cdots \\ \cdots & \cdots & \cdots & \cdots & \cdots \\ 0 & 0 & 0 & 0 \cdots & \mathbf{X}^T(k) \end{bmatrix} = n \times n^2 \text{ matrix} \tag{12.54}$$

and:

$$\mathbf{a}(k) = [\mathbf{\Phi}_1(k); \mathbf{\Phi}_2(k) \cdots \mathbf{\Phi}_n(k)]^T = n^2 \times 1 \text{ vector} \tag{12.55}$$

$\mathbf{\Phi}_i(k)$ being the $i$'th row of $\mathbf{\Phi}$.

Assuming that $\mathbf{\Phi}$ is constant, we obtain that:

$$\mathbf{a}(k+1) = \mathbf{a}(k) \tag{12.56}$$

Consequently, equations (12.53) and (12.56) represent the reformulated measurements and state equations, respectively, in analogy to equations (12.27) and (12.33) of Section 12.2 above.

We further define:

$$\tilde{\mathbf{a}}(k) \triangleq \mathbf{a}(k) - \mathbf{a}^*(k) \tag{12.57}$$

$$\mathbf{P}(k) \triangleq E[\tilde{\mathbf{a}}(k)\tilde{\mathbf{a}}^T(k)] \tag{12.58}$$

$\mathbf{a}^*(k)$ being the optimal estimate of $\mathbf{a}(k)$.

Mayne's estimation problem thus becomes that of obtaining least-squares estimates of $\mathbf{a}(k)$, that minimize the trace of the parameter error density matrix $\mathbf{P}(k)$, in analogy to Kalman's original problem[3] of estimating $\mathbf{X}(k)$ to minimize the trace of the state error density matrix $E[\tilde{\mathbf{X}}(k)\tilde{\mathbf{X}}^T(k)]$. Equations (12.53) and (12.56) provide Mayne's estimation model, which is analogous to Kalman's estimation equations where **a** and **X** interchange roles. Therefore, in full similarity to Kalman's results of Ref. 3, the estimation requires the employment of a feedback matrix given by:

$$\mathbf{D}(k) = \mathbf{P}(k)\mathbf{M}^T(k)[\mathbf{M}(k)\mathbf{P}(k)\mathbf{M}^T(k) + \mathbf{Q}(k)]^{-1} \tag{12.59}$$

yielding the optimal estimate of $\mathbf{a}(k+1)$ and hence only (and given the other parameters,) of $\mathbf{\Phi}$ of Equation (12.50), as follows:

$$\mathbf{a}^*(k+1) = \mathbf{a}^*(k) + \mathbf{D}(k)\tilde{\mathbf{Z}}(k) \tag{12.60}$$

$$\tilde{\mathbf{Z}}(k) = \mathbf{Z}(k) - \hat{\mathbf{Z}}(k) \tag{12.61}$$

$$\hat{\mathbf{Z}}(k) = \mathbf{M}(k)\mathbf{a}^*(k) \tag{12.62}$$

Mayne's filter requires the recursive evaluation of $\mathbf{P}(k+1)$ according to the following expression, which is again, equivalent to Kalman's expression for $E[\tilde{\mathbf{X}}(k+1)\tilde{\mathbf{X}}^T(k+1)]$:

$$\mathbf{P}(k+1) = \mathbf{P}(k) - \mathbf{P}(k)\mathbf{M}^T(k)[\mathbf{M}(k)\mathbf{P}(k)\mathbf{M}^T(k) + \mathbf{Q}(k)]^{-1} \cdot [\mathbf{P}(k)\mathbf{M}^T(k)]^T \tag{12.63}$$

The parameter estimates above thus require the computing of equations (12.59) to (12.63) for $k = 0, 1, 2, \ldots$. The full derivation of equations (12.59) and (12.63) is omitted here, since it is adequately given in Refs. 3 and 6, and since a very similar derivation, noting the different placing of the noise terms in the state and measurement equations, is presented in Section 12.3.

For identification, a knowledge of $\mathbf{P}(0)$, $\mathbf{Q}(k)$ is required. In the absence of other information on $\mathbf{a}$, the initial estimates of $\mathbf{P}(0)$ may be derived through computing the coefficients $\psi_{ij}$ of the following regression equation:

$$X_i(\mu+1\,|\,\mu+1) = \sum_{j=1}^{n} \psi_{ij}(\mu)X_j(\mu\,|\,\mu) \tag{12.64}$$

$X_i(\mu+1\,|\,\mu+1)$ denoting the values $x_i(\mu+1)$ obtained at the $(\mu+1)$'th sampling interval (when assumptions on state accessibility are incorrect, derivatives of curve-fitted values may be employed). We subsequently assume that the initial estimate of the expected error in the elements $\phi_{ij}$ of the parameter matrix $\boldsymbol{\phi}$, and hence of $\mathbf{a}$ is of the order of magnitude of $\psi_{ij}$, to yield:

$$\hat{\mathbf{a}}(0) = \mathbf{0} \tag{12.65}$$

$$\mathbf{P}'(\mu) = [\boldsymbol{\psi}_1(\mu) \cdots \boldsymbol{\psi}_m(\mu)] \cdot [\boldsymbol{\psi}_1(\mu) \cdots \boldsymbol{\psi}_m(\mu)]^T \tag{12.66}$$

$\mathbf{P}(0)$ is thus given by:

$$\mathbf{P}(0) = E[\mathbf{P}'(\mu)] \tag{12.67}$$

such that it represents the average of $\mathbf{P}'(\mu)$ over several sets of $m$ intervals where $\boldsymbol{\psi}(\mu)$ is computed.

We further mention that because of the convergent nature[6] of the estimation model of equations (12.60) to (12.62), an initial estimate where $\mathbf{a}(0) = \mathbf{0}$ and $\mathbf{P}(0)$ being an arbitrary positive diagonal matrix, is usually preferable. The similarity in form of equations (12.63) and (6.37) points to a choice of high equal values for the diagonal terms in $\mathbf{P}(0)$, if no other information is available, to indicate a pessimistic error estimate, as suggested at the end of Section 12.3.

We subsequently guess the value of $\mathbf{Q}(t)$ as follows:

$$\mathbf{Q}(t) \cong E[\mathbf{Q}'(\mu)] = E[\mathbf{U}(\mu)\mathbf{U}^T(\mu)] \tag{12.68}$$

where, using estimates $X_i(\mu + 1 \mid \mu)$ based on Equation (12.64):

$$u_i(\mu) = X_i(\mu + 1 \mid \mu + 1) - X_i(\mu + 1 \mid \mu) \tag{12.69}$$

However, this is again a vague estimate of $\mathbf{Q}$ the better one being given, in the absence of prior knowledge, by Section 12.8, where the matrix $\mathbf{a}$ of Equation (12.55) is also estimated.

To illustrate the employment of the procedure of the present section, we examine the following two examples.

EXAMPLE 12.2

Consider a one-dimensional signal $x(k)$ which satisfies:

$$x(k + 1) = \phi x(k) + v(k)$$

Noting equations (12.52) to (12.55), $D(k)$ of Equation (12.59) becomes:

$$D(k) = \frac{P(k)x(k)}{P(k)x^2(k) + Q(k)}$$

$$P(k + 1) = P(k) - \frac{P^2(k)x^2(k)}{P(k)x^2(k) + Q(k)}$$

$$\phi^*(k + 1) = \phi^*(k) + D(k)\tilde{z}(k) = \frac{P(k + 1)\phi^*(k)}{P(k)} + \frac{P(k + 1)x(k + 1)x(k)}{Q(k)}$$

$$= \phi^*(k) - \frac{P(k)\phi^*(k)x^2(k)}{P(k)x^2(k) + Q(k)} + \frac{P(k)x(k + 1)x(k)}{Q(k)}$$

$$- \frac{P^2(k)x^3(k)x(k + 1)}{Q(k)P(k)x^2(k) + Q^2(k)}$$

such that $\phi^*(k + 1)$ depends on $\phi^*(k)$, $P(k)$, $Q(k)$ and on measurements $x(k + 1)$, $x(k)$.

EXAMPLE 12.3

Consider a signal having a two-dimensional state vector $x = [x_1, x_2]^T$, and obeying a linear discrete state equation:

$$\begin{bmatrix} x_1(k + 1) \\ x_2(k + 1) \end{bmatrix} = \begin{bmatrix} \phi_{11} & \phi_{12} \\ \phi_{21} & \phi_{22} \end{bmatrix} \begin{bmatrix} x_1(k) \\ x_2(k) \end{bmatrix} + \begin{bmatrix} v_1(k) \\ v_2(k) \end{bmatrix}$$

$\phi_{ij}$ being unknown.

For the purpose of parameter estimation as discussed in the present section, the latter state equation is rewritten as follows:

$$\begin{bmatrix} x_1(k+1) \\ x_2(k+1) \end{bmatrix} = \begin{bmatrix} x_1(k) & x_2(k) & 0 & 0 \\ 0 & 0 & x_1(k) & x_2(k) \end{bmatrix} \begin{bmatrix} \phi_{11} \\ \phi_{12} \\ \phi_{21} \\ \phi_{22} \end{bmatrix} + \begin{bmatrix} v_1(k) \\ v_2(k) \end{bmatrix}$$

$$= \begin{bmatrix} \phi_{11} x_1(k) + \phi_{12} x_2(k) \\ \phi_{21}(x_1 k) + \phi_{22} x_2(k) \end{bmatrix} + \begin{bmatrix} v_1(k) \\ v_2(k) \end{bmatrix}$$

## 12.5 APPLICATION OF KALMAN'S PREDICTOR TO SEQUENCES WITH KNOWN PARAMETERS

When the parameters of a state-space model of a time sequence are available, its prediction into the future may be performed by substituting present state values into this model, assuming that the states are accessible. If the values of $\mathbf{Q}(t)$ and of $\mathbf{P}(0)$ are also available, prediction of the latter time sequence into the future may be performed by employing a Kalman filter approach[3] to the signal model. Hence, the resulting predictions are sequentially corrected (according to new incoming measurements) in a manner that is optimal with respect to the signal model that is used. In cases where the parameters $\boldsymbol{\phi}$ are derived as in Section 12.4, these may be further employed in a Kalman-type prediction. Consequently, the assumption of future state availability, as was made for identification, is waived at the prediction stage. Prediction is therefore performed as follows.

Let:

$$\mathbf{x}(t+\theta) = \mathbf{\Phi}(t)\mathbf{x}(t) + \mathbf{u}(t) \tag{12.70}$$

represent the signal states, and:

$$\mathbf{y}(t) = \mathbf{M}\mathbf{x}(t) + \mathbf{w}(t); \qquad E[\mathbf{w}(t)] = \mathbf{0}; \qquad E[\mathbf{u}(t)\mathbf{w}^T(\tau)] \triangleq \mathbf{0} \tag{12.71}$$

$\mathbf{y}$, $\mathbf{w}$ denoting measurements and white measurement noise, respectively. In analogy to Section 12.3, the optimal prediction $\mathbf{x}^*$ of $\mathbf{x}$ satisfies:[3]

$$\mathbf{x}^*(t+\theta \mid t) = \mathbf{\Phi}(t) \cdot \mathbf{x}^*(t \mid t-\theta) + \mathbf{D}(t)\tilde{\mathbf{y}}(t \mid t-\theta) \tag{12.72}$$

where:

$$\tilde{\mathbf{y}}(t \mid t-\theta) \triangleq \mathbf{y}(t) - \mathbf{M}\,\mathbf{x}^*(t \mid t-\theta) \tag{12.73}$$

and $\mathbf{x}^*(t \mid t-\theta)$ being the optimal prediction of $\mathbf{x}(t)$ on the basis of measurements up to $(t-\theta)$, which is fully optimal in the Gaussian case.

We further define:

$$E[\mathbf{w}(t)\mathbf{w}^T(\tau)] \triangleq \mathbf{R} \cdot \delta(t-\tau) \tag{12.74}$$

$$\tilde{\mathbf{x}}(t+\theta \mid t) \triangleq \mathbf{x}^*(t+\theta \mid t) - \mathbf{x}(t) \tag{12.75}$$

$$\mathbf{P}(t+\theta) \triangleq E[\tilde{\mathbf{x}}(t+\theta \mid t)\tilde{\mathbf{x}}(t+\theta \mid t)] \tag{12.76}$$

to derive, in analogy to the derivation of 12.3, but noting the difference in formulation between the measurement equation of the present section and of Section 12.3:

$$\mathbf{D}(t) = \mathbf{P}(t)\mathbf{M}^T\mathbf{R}^{-1}(t) \tag{12.77}$$

$$\mathbf{P}(t+\theta) = \mathbf{\Phi}\mathbf{P}(t) + \mathbf{P}(t)\mathbf{\Phi}^T + \mathbf{Q}(t) + \mathbf{P}(t)\mathbf{M}^T\mathbf{R}^{-1}(t)\mathbf{M}\mathbf{P}(t) \tag{12.78}$$

where $\mathbf{Q}(t)$ is as in Equation (12.51). $\mathbf{R}(t)$ could be obtained from the initial errors between the measurements and the respective curve-fitted values. This estimation of $\mathbf{R}$ is obviously vague. However, the inclusion of $\mathbf{w}(t)$ and of $\mathbf{R}(t)$ is not always essential (see Section 12.8) if no prior knowledge of them exists, and $\mathbf{D}(t)$, $\mathbf{P}(t)$ may then be derived as in Section 12.3.

## 12.6 IDENTIFICATION OF MIXED AUTOREGRESSIVE-MOVING-AVERAGE PREDICTOR MODELS

### 12.6.1 Properties of Mixed Autoregressive-Moving-Average Models

A fundamental property of random signals with Gaussian (normal) distribution is that when passed through a linear dynamic system, the resulting output is also Gaussian.[3] Consequently, any Gaussian time sequence may be considered to be the output of some linear system *whose input is an independent Gaussian time sequence*. Furthermore, the optimal predictor for predicting a Gaussian process is the optimal linear predictor, as has already been stated when discussing the Wiener and the Kalman filters. In cases where non-Gaussian time sequences are to be predicted, the respective linear optimal predictor models may not be the fully optimal predictors for these sequences, although, as said, they are the optimal linear predictors for these sequences.

A general linear model for a stationary time sequence may be expressed in terms of the following transfer function:

$$G(s) = \frac{D_m s^m + D_{m-1}s^{m-1} + \cdots D_1 s + D_0}{A_n s^n + A_{n-1}s^{n-1} + \cdots A_1 s + A_0} = \frac{x(s)}{u(s)} \tag{12.79}$$

$s$ being the Laplace transform variable. Equation (12.79) may be written in discrete form as

$$G(z) = \frac{\beta_0 + \beta_1 z^{-1} + \cdots \beta_m z^{-m}}{\alpha_0 + \alpha_1 z^{-1} + \cdots \alpha_n z^{-n}} = \frac{x(z)}{u(z)} \tag{12.80}$$

$z^{-1}$ denoting the back-shift operator as defined in Section 2.5.1, such that $z^{-n}x_k = x_{k-n}$, and $x$, $u$ denoting output and input to the transfer function model $G(z)$, the poles (for stability) *and* the zeros (for invertibility) of $G(z)$ lying outside the unit circle of the $z^{-1}$ plane*. Further defining:

$$\alpha_0/\beta_0 \triangleq K \tag{12.81-a}$$

$$\beta_i/\beta_0 \triangleq b_i \tag{12.81-b}$$

$$\alpha_i/\alpha_0 \triangleq a_i \tag{12.81-c}$$

$$z^{-1} = B \tag{12.81-d}$$

Equation (12.80) becomes

$$G(B) = K\frac{1 + b_1B + \cdots b_m B^m}{1 + a_1 B + \cdots a_n B^n} \tag{12.82}$$

Since we are presently concerned with deriving models of messages for prediction purposes, $x$ is considered to denote the message whereas $u$ represents an inaccessible input which is assumed to be a Gaussian random signal having zero average.[4] (For example, when the transfer function model of equations (12.79), (12.80) is employed to predict the sales $x(t)$ of a certain product from past sales data only, then no measurable input $u(t)$ can be defined.) Consequently, the identification problem is not only concerned with deriving the parameters $A_i$, $D_j$ or $\alpha_i$, $\beta_j$ of equations (12.79), (12.80), respectively, but it also requires the determining $u(t)$. For this purpose, we must assume that the input $u(t)$ be considered as white (uncorrelated) noise with a variance $\sigma_u^2$. For computational convenience we may further assume that the variance $\sigma_u^2$ of $u$ is unknown but that $K$ of equation (12.82) is unity. This formulation is equivalent to passing an input of unity variance through an amplifier with a linear gain of $K$ before feeding it to the process $G(z)$ of Equation (12.82), such that the amplifier's output variance, which is the input to $G(z)$ of Equation (12.82), is of $K^2$ times the variance of the input to the amplifier and is therefore $\sigma^2 = K^2 \cdot 1 = K^2$, $K^2$ being unknown. Hence, the assumption of known variance of the input and unknown $\alpha_0/\beta_0$, or the assumption of $\alpha_0/\beta_0 = 1$ and unknown variance are fully equivalent. We emphasize that the Gaussian and zero average assumptions of the present Section are required for obtaining optimal prediction and are sometimes waived in Sections 12.6.5, 12.7, for obtaining linear-optimal results.

To illustrate the identification procedure for the transfer function model above,[8] we consider the discrete transfer-function representation of Equation (12.80) as follows:

Cross multiplying Equation (12.82) and noting the definition of $B$, we further obtain:

$$x_k + a_1x_{k-1} + \cdots a_n x_{k-n} = u_k + b_1u_{k-1} + \cdots b_m u_{k-m} \tag{12.83}$$

*Invertibility must be assumed since, without prior information, an invertible model is always identified, even for non-invertible processes. Hence, for processes with zeros inside the unit circle, reciprocals of these zeros are identified.[7]

or:

$$x_k = \sum_{i=1}^{n} \phi_i x_{k-i} + \sum_{j=0}^{m} \theta_j u_{k-j} \tag{12.84}$$

where:

$$k = 0, 1, 2, \ldots; \qquad kT = t$$

and:

$$E[u_j] = 0 \qquad \forall j \tag{12.85-a}$$

$$E[(u_j)^2] = \sigma_u^2 \qquad \forall j; \quad E[u_i u_j] = 0 \qquad \forall i \neq j \tag{12.85-b}$$

$$\theta_0 = 1 \tag{12.85-c}$$

Equation (12.83) represents a mixed autoregressive-moving-average (ARMA) model of $x_k$, where $\phi_0 \ldots \phi_n$ denote the autoregressive coefficients (related to the history of the message itself) and where $\theta_0 \cdots \theta_m$ denote the moving-average coefficients (related to the history of the random input). An operator notation is subsequently applied to Equation (12.83) to yield

$$\phi(B)x_k = \theta(B)u_k \tag{12.86}$$

The process of Equation (12.83) may therefore be expressed as a convergent infinite pure autoregressive process

$$\theta^{-1}(B)\phi(B)x_k = u_k \tag{12.87}$$

or, as a convergent infinite pure moving-average process,

$$x_k = \phi^{-1}(z)\theta(z)u_k \tag{12.88}$$

the convergence being due to the conditions on the roots of Equation (12.80) above. We note that Equation (12.88) is basically a discrete formulation of the convolution integral of Equation (3.4). The convergence features of the infinite models facilitate them to be expressed in terms of finite orders. The finite order model thus becomes, for the pure moving-average formulation of Equation (12.88):

$$x_k = \sum_{i=0}^{\infty} \theta_i' u_{k-i}$$

$$= \sum_{i=0}^{p} \theta_i' u_{k-i} + \varepsilon_k' \tag{12.89}$$

where $\varepsilon_k'$ may be made arbitrarily small for finite $p$. Similarly, the finite pure autoregressive process (identical to Wiener's predictor[2] model) is derived as:

$$x_k = \sum_{j=1}^{\infty} \phi_j' x_{k-j} + u_k$$

$$= \sum_{j=1}^{q} \phi_j' x_{k-j} + u_k + \varepsilon_k'' \tag{12.90}$$

Again, $\varepsilon_k''$ may be made arbitrarily small by an appropriate choice of $q$[7]. If, however, the number of autoregressive terms of Equation (12.83) is reduced, but not to zero, Equation (12.83) becomes, in analogy to Equation (12.89),

$$x_k = \sum_{j=1}^{n-w} \phi_j'' x_{k-j} + \sum_{i=0}^{\infty} \theta_i'' u_{k-1}$$

$$= \sum_{j=1}^{n-w} \phi_j'' x_{k-j} + \sum_{i=0}^{v \gg 1} \theta_i'' u_{k-i} + \varepsilon^* \tag{12.91}$$

where $w$ may take arbitrarily values of 1, 2, ..., $n$. We thus observe that for a true model of $n + m + 1$ parameters, if either the number of the autoregressive or of the moving-average parameters is reduced by one or more, we ideally require an infinite number of parameters to describe the system, as indicated by equations (12.89) to (12.91). Furthermore, a model for a mixed autoregressive-moving-average process where the order of the autoregressive part is $n' = n + i$ and that of the moving-average part is $m' = m + j$, adequately represents the process [4] for any $i, j, \geq 0$. However, since any overfitting of orders ($i > 0$ or $j > 0$) leads to increasing round-off errors, identification should aim at the minimum adequate order.

### 12.6.2 The Identification Procedure

Having discussed the problem of overfitting and underfitting of orders, we now consider the identification itself.* We first discuss the possibility of applying sequential regression to identifying only the autoregressive terms of a mixed autoregressive-moving-average process. (Regression identification is considered due to its maximum likelihood properties, shown in Section 5.5 for Gaussian pure autoregressive models. Other techniques may be employed if rapid convergence is not essential.) The regression identification implies the minimization of the residual $w_k$ of a time series given by:

$$x_k = \sum_{i=1}^{n'} \phi_i x_{k-i} + w_k \tag{12.92}$$

where $w_k$ denotes the moving-average terms

$$w_k' = \sum_{j=0}^{m'} \theta_j u_{k-j} \tag{12.93}$$

in full analogy to Equation (12.84), but where $n' \geq n$, $m' \geq m$. Equation (12.93) thus indicates that $w_k$ is correlated with $w_{k-m+i}$. However, a consistent estimate of $\phi_i$ on the basis of $x_k$ alone requires that $w_k$ of Equation (12.92) be a white noise sequence, as arises from the following analysis:

*Input/output/noise processes are treated in Section 5.4. For identifying closed loop stochastic processes,[9] whitening of the input noise and/or of the effects of the measurement noise as considered at the input, must take place, whitening implying the multiplication of any colored noise $n_k = a(\mathrm{B})w_k$ by $a^{-1}(\mathrm{B})$, $w_k$ being white noise. We note that even if only white noise is inputted into a closed loop system, the feedback implies a colored (correlated) noise effect at the input. Hence, in the closed loop case, the identification of the whitening model $a^{-1}(\mathrm{B})$, say via Section 12.6, is essential to avoid biases. Once whitening is accomplished, identification proceeds[9] as in Section 5.4.2.

Let $x_k$ be given by Equation (12.84) and let the estimate $\hat{x}_k$ of $x_k$ be derived from Equation (12.86) on the basis of measured $x_{k-i}$ such that

$$\hat{x}_k = \sum_{i=1}^{n} \hat{\phi}_i x_{k-i} \tag{12.94}$$

$\hat{\phi}_i$ denoting the parameters $\phi_i$ as identified by least-squares regression through minimizing $J$, where

$$\begin{aligned} J = E[(x_k - \hat{x}_k)]^2 &= E\left[\left(\sum_{i=1}^{n} \phi_i x_{k-i} + \sum_{j=0}^{m} \theta_j u_{k-j} - \sum_{i=1}^{n} \hat{\phi}_i x_{k-i}\right)^2\right] \\ &= E\left[\left(\sum_{i=1}^{n} \phi_i x_{k-i} - \sum_{j=1}^{n} \hat{\phi}_i x_{k-i}\right)^2\right] + 2E\left[\left(\sum_{j=0}^{m} \theta_j u_{k-j}\right)\left(\sum_{i=1}^{n} \phi_i x_{k-i} \right.\right. \\ &\quad \left.\left. - \sum_{i=1}^{n} \hat{\phi}_i x_{k-i}\right)\right] + E\left[\left(\sum_{j=0}^{m} \theta_j u_{k-j}\right)^2\right] \end{aligned} \tag{12.95}$$

When $\hat{\phi}_i = \phi_i$ then $J$ above is given by $E\left[\sum_{j=0}^{m} \theta_j u_{k-j}\right]^2$. However, when $\hat{\phi}_i \neq \phi_i$ then $J$ may be still of a lower value since $\sum_{j=0}^{m} \theta_j u_{k-j}$, which denotes $w_k$, is not white noise.

Since $w_k, w_{k-(m+1)}$ are correlated, we cannot obtain consistent regression estimates of $x_k$ even if sets $x_k \ldots x_{k-n}$ are taken at $(m+1)$ intervals. In that case not all available measurements can serve for parameter estimation and the identification is not consistent. The latter difficulty may, however, be overcome when reconsidering the infinite pure autoregressive model of Equation (12.87) where the residual $u_k$ is white noise and which has been shown to be equivalent to the model of Equation (11.84). Furthermore, we have shown that the infinite sequence of Equation (12.83) may be adequately represented by a finite pure autoregressive model of a sufficiently high order as in Equation (12.90). Hence, the parameters $\phi_i'$ $(i = 1 \cdots q)$ may be rapidly and, for Gaussian $u_k$, efficiently identified by a sequential regression algorithm as in Chapter 6. The order $q$ of the above pure autoregressive model may be chosen through checking if the residual $\hat{u}_k = u_k + \varepsilon_k''$ of Equation (12.90) is uncorrelated, thus advancing $q$ if $\hat{u}_k$ is not uncorrelated.

Subsequently to identifying $\phi_i'$ of the pure autoregressive model above, estimates $\hat{x}_k$ of $x_k$ may be computed from:

$$\hat{x}_k = \sum_{i=1}^{q} \phi_i' x_{k-i} \tag{12.96}$$

to yield

$$\hat{u}_k = x_k - \hat{x} \tag{12.97}$$

$$\hat{\sigma}_u^2 = \frac{1}{N} \sum_{k=1}^{N} \hat{u}_k^2 \tag{12.98}$$

Once $\hat{u}_k$ are available, the problem of identifying $\phi_i$, $\theta_j$ of Equation (12.84) becomes that of identifying an input-output process given by these equations where both the inputs $\hat{u}_k$ and the outputs $x_k$ are available.* The latter identification problem may now be unbiasedly, consistently and almost efficiently solved for cases of Gaussian sequences by regression, since $\hat{u}_k$ are efficient estimates of $u_k$ in the Gaussian case for a sufficiently high order $q$. We further note that the present approach yields adequate and unbiased linear estimates also for non-Gaussian processes. The analysis above is thus shown to yield a sequential identification algorithm that may continuously update the parameters for as long as measurements are obtained.

### 12.6.3 Estimation of Orders

In the discussion above we have not yet solved the problem of estimating the orders $m$, $n$ of the process, which are often a priori unknown. These orders may be estimated when considering some properties of mixed autoregressive-moving-average processes already discussed in Section 12.6.1 as follows:

It has been shown by Equation (12.91) that when the actual mixed autoregressive moving-average process is of orders $m, n$, as in Equation (12.84), then reducing the order of the autoregressive of the model by one or more would require an infinite number of moving-average parameters to adequately represent the process. Similarly, if the number of moving-average parameter is reduced by one or more, then an infinite number of autoregressive parameters would be required, whereas any overfitting of the order of one or of both parts, without underfitting another part, still yields adequate models. Since overfitting of orders leads to increased round-off errors, the correct (not overfitted) orders $m$, $n$ may be estimated when the following equation, that is derived from equations (12.87), (12.90), is satisfied:

$$\hat{\phi}_{n'}(B) = \hat{\theta}_{m'}(B) \cdot \hat{\phi}'_q(B) + \varepsilon_{q+m'}(B) \quad \cdots \quad (m', n', q \text{ denoting orders}) \tag{12.99}$$

such that $\sum_{i=1}^{q+m'} \varepsilon_i^2$ is minimal, or almost minimal for the smallest $m + n$, $\varepsilon_i$ denoting the elements of $\varepsilon(B)$. The latter statement on $\varepsilon(B)$ implies that if $\Sigma\varepsilon_i^2|_{m'+n'}$ is considerably smaller than $\Sigma\varepsilon_i^2|_{m'+n'-1}$ but just slightly higher than some $\Sigma\varepsilon_i^2|_{m'+n'+j}$ the latter being the minimum, then the orders given by

*Alternatively, once $\phi'_i$ are identified, polynomial division may be employed[7], via the relations between (12.87) and (12.89), to yield estimates of $\phi_i$ and $\theta_j$.

$m' + n'$ should be selected. We note that $\hat{\phi}'(B)$, $\hat{\phi}(B)$, $\hat{\theta}(B)$ are as identified according to Section 12.6.2.

The estimation of the orders above is performed by initially identifying $\hat{\phi}(B)$, $\hat{\theta}(B)$ from $\hat{u}_k$, $x_k$ as in Section 12.6.2, for sufficiently high orders $m' = m_0/2$, $n' = n_0$. Subsequently, identification of $\hat{\phi}(B)$, $\hat{\theta}(B)$, is repeated for $m' = m_0$, $n' = n_0$. This process is further continued, when the range of either $m'$ or $n'$ is halved at each iteration until $\varepsilon(B)$ is minimal or almost minimal for the lowest $m' + n'$. The maximum number of iterations required is given by:

$$\mu = 1 + \log_2(m_0 \cdot n_0) \tag{12.100}$$

(when $m_0 \cdot n_0 = 2^{\mu}$, then $\mu$ iterations are required to determine single square in an $m_0 \cdot n_0$ grid).

A lengthier but better determination of orders, requiring the same number of iterations may be performed through checking $I = \frac{1}{M}\sum_{k=1}^{M}(x_k - \hat{x}_k)^2$ for $\hat{\theta}(B)$, $\hat{\phi}(B)$ of each iteration as described in Section 5.4 (where no infinite model was available). Hence, the lowest $m' + n'$ for which $I$ is approximately equal to $\frac{1}{M}\sum_{j=1}^{M}\hat{u}_k^2$, $\hat{u}_k$ being the residual of the pure autoregressive model of Equation (12.90), yields the estimated orders.

### 12.6.4 Prediction via the Mixed Autoregressive-Moving-Average Identification Algorithm

The analysis in Section 12.6.1 to 12.6.3 was concerned with the derivation of estimates of the parameters of a mixed autoregressive-moving-average model of a time series. These estimates have been derived sequentially such that the parameter estimates are updated with each new measurement. Consequently, these parameter estimates may yield future values of the model output $x_{k+1}$ when employing past measurements and past input estimates $\hat{u}_{k-i}$, the latter being derived from past prediction errors, as in Section 12.6.2.

We observe that the prediction of $x_{k+1}$ according to the continuously updated model, as in Section 12.6.2, is consistent for Gaussian time series, due to the consistency of the parameter and input estimates that are employed. Consequently, once the parameters of the mixed autoregressive-moving-average model are available, it yields predictions that are comparable to those obtained from a Kalman filter whose parameters are known. The difference between the two approaches thus lies in the fact that prediction via autoregressive-moving-average models requires the reconstruction of inputs from least-squared prediction errors, whereas the equivalent Kalman filter avoids this reconstruction through sequentially updating gains associated with the last error term. Obviously, these differences relate to prediction alone, noting that the Kalman filter approach assumes that the parameters and orders are known, while the approach of Sections 12.6.2, 12.6.3 performs complete identification. (The employment of an extended Kalman filter as in Section 12.9 may also yield the identification required above, but it still usually assumes knowledge of orders and of covariances).

Once the parameter estimates derived from the algorithms of Sections 12.6.2, 12.6.3 are available, the resulting mixed autoregressive-moving-average model may be transformed into a state-space formulation to yield and to update a Kalman filter model for subsequent prediction without reconstruction of inputs. The latter transformation is further discussed in Section 12.8 below.

### 12.6.5 Indentification of Non-Gaussian Predictors

Both the Kalman filtering approach and the mixed autoregressive-moving-average methods that have been discussed above are in terms of linear models. Although linear predictor models with Gaussian white noise inputs are optimal for Gaussian sequences, this is not true for non-Gaussian sequences, where the optimal predictor is nonlinear (with an independent noise input). The approach of Sections 12.6.1 to 12.6.4 may, however, yield an *optimal linear prediction model* with a non-Gaussian white noise input for non-Gaussian sequences, that is usually quite adequate, but is *fully optimal* only when the non-Gaussian input is also independent. The estimates of the linear non-Gaussian parameters thus obtained are still consistent and unbiased,[10] though not efficient; namely, they converge to the true values with increasing the number of samples, but are not estimates of minimum variance properties. The resulting model implies the reconstruction of the input sequence via an infinite autoregressive model (such that the input is the residual of the infinite model and is therefore non-Gaussian white noise). Consequently, once the parameter estimates have converged, the resulting prediction is linear-optimal.

An *optimal nonlinear* autoregressive-moving-average predictor for non-Gaussian sequences $y_k$ that are (unknowingly) due to nonlinear measurements of Gaussian sequences or to passing these through nonlinear gains, may be obtained by transforming $y_k$ into a Gaussian $x_k$, as follows:

Consider an element $y_k$ with a marginal p.d.f. (probability density function) $f(y)$. The transformation of $y_k$ into $z_k$ with a p.d.f. $\phi(z)$ is given by[11]:

$$\phi(z) = f(y) \cdot \left|\frac{dy}{dz}\right|; \quad \frac{dz}{dy} \neq 0 \tag{12.101}$$

Hence, $y_k$ may be transformed into a uniformly distributed $u_k$ by:

$$u = \int_{-\infty}^{y} f(y)\, dy \tag{12.102}$$

$$\frac{du}{dy} = f(y) \tag{12.103}$$

thus satisfying the uniform p.d.f. $\phi(u)$ of $u$, where:

$$\phi(u) = \frac{f(y)}{f(y)} = 1 \tag{12.104}$$

Having formulated the transformation from an arbitrary into a uniform p.d.f., we continue to derive a transformation into a Gaussian $x_k$ assuming a given variance $\sigma_x^2$. The transformation from a uniform to a Gaussian p.d.f. form is accomplished, through evaluating Equation (12.102) when substituting $x$ for $y$ and a Gaussian p.d.f. with $\sigma_x = 1$ for $f(y)$, to obtain the relation of Figure 12.2 which uniquely yields $x_k$ for given $u_k$. We note that the Gaussian assumption applies to $x_k$ only if its joint distribution is Gaussian[3]. However, when considering Gaussian sequences with nonlinear measurements, this assumption is valid for $x_k$.

Following the transformation from $y_k$ to a Gaussian $x_k$, an optimal autoregressive-moving-average predictor for $x_k$ may be consistently identified as in Sections 12.6.1 to 12.6.4, in terms of a Gaussian white noise input $w_k$. Only if the reconstructed input is Gaussian, is our Gaussian assumption valid and the predictor optimal, since Gaussian white noise is independent in all moments such that its joint and marginal distributions are identical. The predictor model for $x_k$ is thus given by the linear relation of Equation (12.86), namely:

$$\phi(B)x_k = \theta(B)w_k \tag{12.105}$$

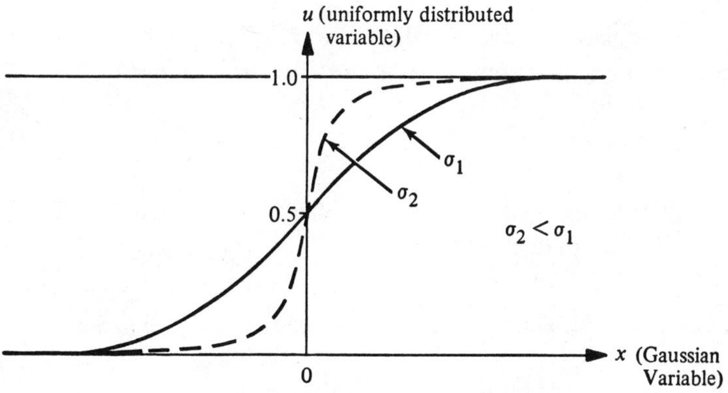


*Figure 12.2* Transformation from uniformly distributed to Gaussian variables.

which further yields an infinite autoregressive model given by:

$$\theta^{-1}(B)\phi(B)x_k = \gamma(B)x_k = \sum_i \gamma_i x_{k-i} = w_k \tag{12.106}$$

The variances $\sigma_w^2$, $\sigma_x^2$ are thus given by:

$$\sigma_w^2 = E[w_k^2] \tag{12.107-a}$$

$$\sigma_x^2 = E[x_k^2] = E[(\gamma(B)w_k)^2] = \sigma_w^2 \sum_i \gamma_i^2 \tag{12.107-b}$$

Equation (12.107-b) indicates that for any Gaussian sequence:

$$x_k' = Kx_k \tag{12.108}$$

the variance $\sigma_{x'}^2$ satisfies:

$$\sigma_{x'} = K\sigma_x \tag{12.109}$$

and, consequently:

$$\sigma_{w'} = K\sigma_w \tag{12.110}$$

Hence, the parameters $\phi(B)$, $\theta(B)$, as in Equation (12.105) are independent of the value of $\sigma_x$.

Once optimal estimates $\hat{x}_k$ of the Gaussian $x_k$ are available, an inverse transformation is required prior to evaluating the optimal prediction $\hat{y}_k$ of the non-Gaussian $y_k$. Denoting the transformation from $y_k$ to $x_k$ by:

$$x_k = T(y_k) \tag{12.111}$$

$T$ being a nonlinear function that may be numerically evaluated according to Equation (12.102) and Figure 12.2, the derivation of:

$$y_k = T^{-1}(x_k) \tag{12.112}$$

is again numerically possible. Furthermore, $T^{-1}(x_k)$ may be approximated to any accuracy by a polynomial fit, where (for $3\sigma_x \ll$ range of $x_k$):

$$T^{-1}(x_k) \cong \sum_{i=0}^{r} \eta_i x_k^i \tag{12.113}$$

Subsequently, the optimal prediction $\hat{y}_k$ of $y_k$ may be evaluated to minimize $E[(y_k - \hat{y}_k)^2]$, such that, for single valued $T^{-1}(x_k)$:

$$\hat{y}_k = E[y_k \mid y_{k-j}] = \sum_{i=1}^{r} \eta_i E[x_k^i \mid x_{k-j}]; \qquad j = 1, 2, \ldots \tag{12.114}$$

$\hat{y}_k$ is thus given by (see Section 5.5 of Ref. 12):

$$\hat{y}_k = \sum_{i=1}^{r} \eta_i \int_{-\infty}^{\infty} x_k^i \mathrm{P}(x_k \mid x_{k-j})\, dx_k; \qquad j = 1, 2, 3, \ldots \tag{12.115}$$

$P(x_k | x_{k-j})$ being a Gaussian p.d.f. with a mean of $x_k$ and a variance $\sigma_x^2$, due to the Gaussian nature of $x_k$. The latter Gaussian nature of $P(x_k | x_{k-j})$ implies that all its higher moments are uniquely determined by $\hat{x}_k$, $\sigma_x$.

The evaluation of $\hat{y}_k$ from Equation (12.115) is performed, noting Equation (12.113) through defining:

$$m_{k,i} \triangleq E(x_k^i | x_{k-j}) \tag{12.116}$$

where, according to Ref. 10:

$$m_{k,i} = \hat{x}_k^i + \frac{i(i-1)}{2} \int_0^{\sigma_x^2} m_{k,i-2}\, d(\sigma_x^2), \qquad i = 1, 2, 3, \ldots \tag{12.117}$$

to yield the optimal estimate for the type of system considered (see Figure 12.3):

$$\hat{y}_k = \sum_{i=1}^{r} \eta_i m_{k,i} \tag{12.118}$$

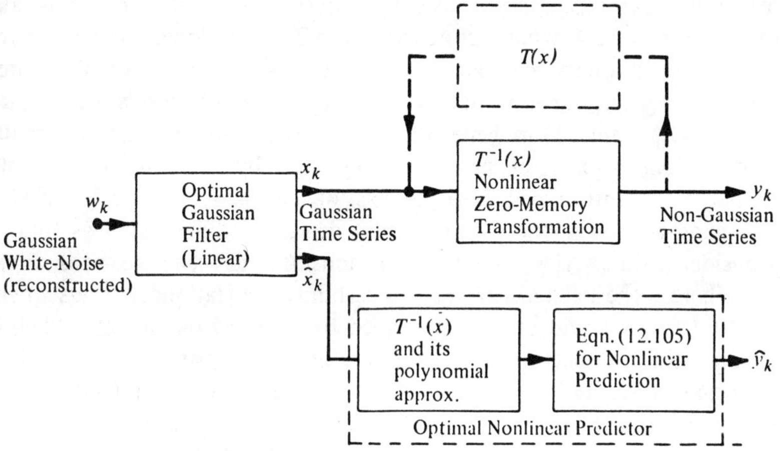


*Figure 12.3* Optimal predictor for a class of non-Gaussian sequences.

When $\sigma_x$ is not sufficiently smaller than the range of $x_k$, and noting the infinite integral in Equation (12.114), local low order polynomial fits near $\hat{x}_k$ may have to be considered to approximate $T^{-1}(x)$. Alternatively, $T^{-1}(x)$ may require low order extrapolations, say, based on its average slopes near the edges of the data range, or the addition of limiters at these edges, prior to its polynomial approximation, such that the range of $T^{-1}(x)$ is extended.

Although $\hat{y}_k$ is based on assuming $\sigma_x = 1$, we observe that for any $x_k' = Kx$, and noting Equation (12.108), the values of $m_{k,j}'$ corresponding to $m_{k,j}$ of Equation (12.117) are given by:

$$m_{k,i}' = K^i m_{k,i} \tag{12.119}$$

whereas:

$$y_k \cong \sum_{i=1}^{r} \frac{\eta_i}{K^i} m_{k,i}' \tag{12.120}$$

such that $\hat{y}_k$ of Equation (12.118) remains unchanged, to indicate the independence of $\hat{y}_k$ from the choice of $\sigma_x$. We further note that when $T^{-1}(x_k)$ yields a value that is not unique, the determination of the appropriate value may be accomplished through employing an optimal linear prediction, outlined earlier in this section. Hence, $\hat{y}_k$ that is closest to the linear prediction is selected, though not as an optimal prediction.

## 12.7 MIXED AUTOREGRESSIVE-MOVING-AVERAGE MODELS OF NONSTATIONARY SEQUENCES AND SYSTEMS

### 12.7.1 Nonperiodic Nonstationarities

Box and Jenkins[4] have shown that stationary mixed autoregressive-moving-average models may be applied to nonstationary sequences which demonstrate some homogeneity. Such sequences do frequently arise in many fields, as is shown in Figure 12.4, where sequence $x_a$ has a nonstationary slope, whereas $x_b$ has a nonstationary average. Sequence $x_a$ does, however, demonstrate a certain homogeneity around its various slopes, as does sequence $x_b$ around its averages. A similar homogeneity may exist around some long-term periodic patterns. Consequently, it has been suggested by Box and Jenkins that stationarity be introduced into models of nonstationary time series by differencing these sequences to a certain degree of differencing as follows:

Consider a time series $x_b(t)$ having a nonstationary average, as in Figure 12.4. Whereas the behavior of $x_b(t)$ is certainly nonstationary, the sequence $(1 - B)x_b(t)$ may be adequately described by a stationary model, ($B$ being a delay operator as in Section 12.6), since the difference $x_b(t_i) - x_b(t_{i-1})$ excludes the long-term average value. Similarly, stationarity may be introduced into the sequence $x_a$ of Figure 12.4 if it is differenced twice, namely, if $(1 - B)^2x_a(t)$ is considered. Once the order $q$ of differencing has been determined, a stationary model for $\xi(t) = (1 - B)^q x(t)$ results, which is similar to that of Equation

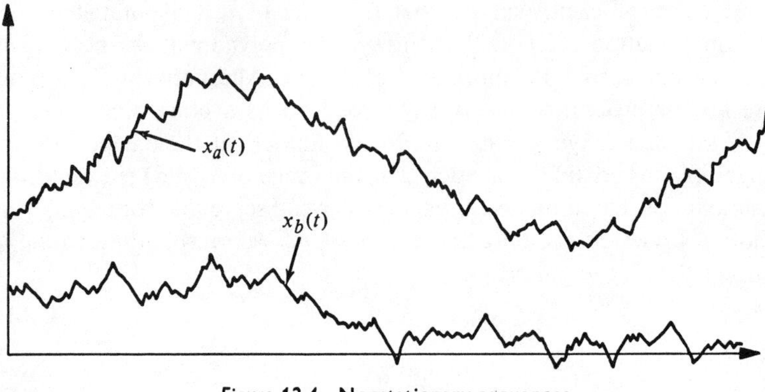


*Figure 12.4* Nonstationary sequences.

(12.83), as follows:

$$\alpha_0 \xi_k + \alpha_1 \xi_{k-1} + \cdots + \alpha_n \xi_{k-n} = \beta_0 u_k + \beta_1 u_{k-1} + \cdots + \beta_m u_{k-m} \qquad (12.121\text{-a})$$

or, employing the delay operator $B$:

$$(\alpha_0 + \alpha_1 B + \cdots \alpha_n B^n)\xi(t) = (\beta_0 + \beta_1 B + \cdots \beta_m B^m)u(t) \qquad (12.121\text{-b})$$

The identification of the (now stationary) parameters of Equation (12.121) thus proceeds according to the procedure of Section 12.6 where the parameters of Equation (12.83) are identified.

The determination of the differencing order $q$ requires the computation of the autocorrelation function as discussed in Chapter 4 for $x(t)$; $(1 - B)x(t)$; $\cdots (1 - B)^q x(t)$. The first order of differencing for which the autocorrelation function vanishes rapidly, namely, the first order for which $\phi_{\xi\xi}(t)$ converges to 0 for a relatively low $t$, yields $q$. (Obviously, the autocorrelation function for sequence $x_b(t)$ of Figure 12.4 cannot vanish rapidly, since the average of $x(t) \cdot x(t - rt)$ for fairly large $r$ would not be zero). We note that the number of samples of $x(t)$ that is required until the estimated parameters of a prediction model as in Section 12.6 converge is very large, since the input to the model is not available. Consequently, the introduction of stationarity as discussed in the present section is essential in cases of nonstationary sequences.

### 12.7.1-a Input-output processes

In the case of input/output systems where the input sequence is also available and not necessarily a zero average random sequence, the differencing of both input and output, and the examination of the autocorrelation functions for both, is required, to derive nonstationary input/output models[4]. We note that when a nonstationary input is applied to a stationary linear system, a nonstationary output results and the $(1 - B)^q$ terms for input and output cancel out.

### 12.7.2 Periodic Nonstationarities

In cases where periodic (seasonal) effects exist such that a nonstationary process presents a stationary behavior if sampled once every $M$ intervals (say monthly average weather measurement with a period of $M = 12$ months), we define:

$$\nabla_M \triangleq 1 - B^M \qquad (12.122)$$

$$B_M \triangleq B^M \qquad (12.123)$$

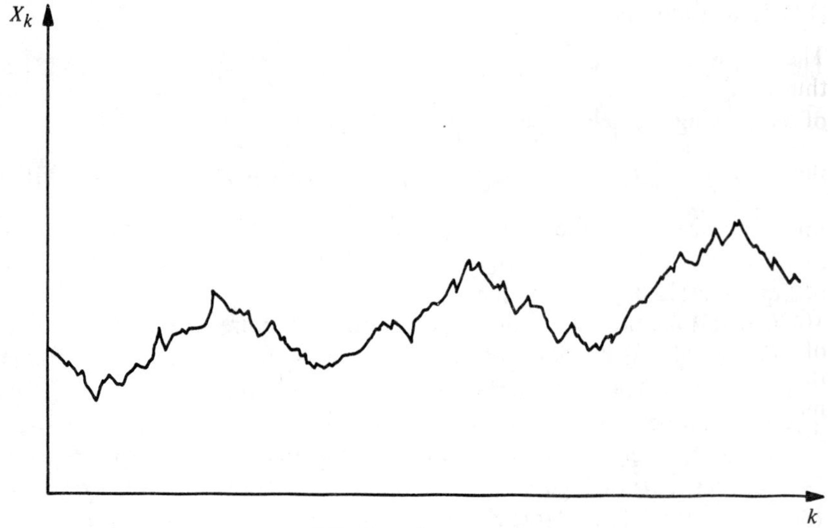


*Figure 12.5* Periodic nonstationarity.

Consequently,[4] a periodic process $x_k$ having a period of $M$ intervals as in Figure 12.5, may be described, in similarity to Equation (12.121-b), by:

$$[1 + a_{M,1}B_M + a_{M,2}B_M^2 + \cdots a_{M,p}B_M^p)\,\nabla_M^E x_k$$
$$= (c_{M,0} + c_{M,1}B_M + c_{M,2}B_M^2 + \cdots c_{M,q}B_M^q)u_k \quad (12.124)$$

where the $E$'th order differencing operator $(1 - B_M)^E$ is employed to eliminate nonperiodic nonstationarity as stated in Section 12.7.1. Furthermore, if $x_k$ is dependent on measurements $x_{k-M}, x_{k-2M}, x_{k-3M}, \ldots$ (namely, on a periodic effect) and also on the measurements at $x_k, x_{k-1}, x_{k-2}, \ldots$, we may write that:

$$(1 + \alpha_1 B - \alpha_2 B^2 + \cdots \alpha_r B^r)\nabla_1^D u_k = (\gamma_0 + \gamma_1 B + \gamma_2 B^2 + \cdots \gamma_s B^s)v_k \quad (12.125)$$

the $D$'th order differencing operator serving to eliminate nonperiodic nonstationarity. Substituting $u_k$ from Equation (12.125) into (12.124), we thus obtain, after cross-multiplication by $(1 - B)^D(1 + \alpha_1 B + \cdots \alpha_r B^r)$:

$$(1 + \alpha_1 B + \alpha_2 B^2 + \cdots \alpha_r B^r)(1 + a_{M,1}B_M + \cdots a_{M,p}B_M^p)\nabla_1^D \nabla_M^E x_k$$
$$= (\gamma_0 + \gamma_1 B + \cdots \gamma_s B^s)(c_{M,0} + c_{M,1}B_M + \cdots c_{M,q}B_M)v_k \quad (12.126)$$

In a similar manner, if several periodic effects with different periods appear (say, with periods 1, $M$, $N$), we obtain:

$$
\begin{aligned}
&(1+\alpha_1 B+\cdots+\alpha_r B^r)\\
&\quad\times(1+a_{M,1}B_M+\cdots a_{M,p}B_M^p)(1+a_{N,1}B_N+\cdots a_{N,w}B_N^w)\nabla_1^D\nabla_M^E\nabla_N^F x_k\\
&=(\gamma_0+\gamma_1 B+\cdots\gamma_s B^s)(c_{M,0}+c_{M,1}B_M+\cdots c_{M,q}B_M^q)\\
&\quad\times(c_{N,0}+c_{N,1}B_N+\cdots c_{N,\sigma}B_N^\sigma)v_k
\end{aligned} \tag{12.127}
$$

The identification of $M$, $N$ may be accomplished by examining the autocorrelation functions of $x_k$ to find periodically spaced peaks in the autocorrelation function, whereas the coefficients and orders as in Equation (12.127) are derived according to the procedure of Section 12.6, noting the differencing process discussed earlier in the present section that may be required to introduce stationarity.

## 12.8 DERIVATION OF KALMAN FILTER MODELS FROM AUTOREGRESSIVE-MOVING-AVERAGE PARAMETERS

We have stated in Section 12.6.4 that once tne parameters of a mixed autoregressive-moving-average sequence are identified, prediction may be performed through continuously updating the input sequence. We have further indicated that the parameters estimated in Section 12.6 may yield the corresponding Kalman filter parameters for subsequent prediction without updating of inputs. Consequently, a transformation as in Section 2.5.1 is to be employed, to yield the required state-space model. We note that the state-space model of equations (2.63), (2.64) is practically identical to that of equation (12.70), when $\boldsymbol{\Gamma}u(k)$ of Equation (2.63) stands for $\mathbf{u}(k)$ of Equation (12.70). Hence, the procedure of the present section will yield $\boldsymbol{\Phi}, \boldsymbol{\Gamma}$ of Equation (2.63), $\mathbf{C}$ of Equation (2.64) being given by Equation (2.67). We further note that if $w_k$ of equation (12.71) is also considered, the Kalman filter identification algorithm may be modified, as follows:[13,14] (for an alternative approach, see Ref. 15):

Consider a system with discrete scalar measurements $y_k$, where:

$$y_k = \mathbf{H}^T\mathbf{x}_k + w_k \; ; \mathbf{x}_k \triangleq [x_k, \ldots x_{k-n+1}]^T \; ; w_k = \text{white noise} \tag{12.128}$$

$$\sum_{i=0}^{n} \phi_i x_{k-i} = \sum_{j=1}^{n} \theta_j u_{k-j} \; ; \phi_0 = 1 \; ; u_k = \text{white noise} \tag{12.129}$$

$u_k$ being related to $\mathbf{u}_k$ of (12.70) via equation (2.66) and uncorrelated with $w_k$. Also, by Section 2.5:

$$\mathbf{H} = [1,0,0, \ldots 0]^T \tag{12.130}$$

Substituting for $x_k$ from equation (12.128) into (12.129), we obtain:

$$\sum_{i=0}^{n} \phi_i y_{k-1} = \sum_{i=0}^{n} \phi_i w_{k-i} + \sum_{j=1}^{m} \theta_j u_{k-j} = \sum_{i=0}^{n} \psi_i r_{k-i} \triangleq n_k \qquad (12.131)$$

$r_k$ being another discrete white noise process. The ARMA model of equation (12.131) between $y_k$ and $r_k$ can now be identified as in Section 12.6, to yield estimates $\hat{\phi}(B)$, $\hat{\psi}(B)$ and $\hat{\sigma}_r^2$ of $\phi(B)$, $\psi(B)$ and $\sigma_r^2$, where $\sigma_r^2$ denotes the variance of $r_k$. Subsequently,

$$E[n_k n_{k+h}] = \sigma_r^2 \sum_{i=0}^{n-h} \psi_i \psi_{i+h} = \begin{cases} \sigma_u^2 \sum_{j=1}^{m-h} \theta_j \theta_{j+h} + \sigma_w^2 \sum_{i=0}^{n-h} \phi_i \phi_{i+h} & \forall h \leqslant m \\ \sigma_w^2 \sum_{i=0}^{n-h} \phi_i \phi_{i+h} & \forall m < h \leqslant n \end{cases} \qquad (12.132)$$

$\sigma_u^2$ and $\sigma_w^2$ denoting the variances of $u_k$ and $w_k$, respectively, to yield estimates of $\sigma_u^2$, $\sigma_w^2$ and $\theta(B)$ via $\sigma_r^2$, $\phi(B)$ and $\psi(B)$ identified previously. The uniqueness of these estimates can be established when model stability and invertibility are assumed[13]. An assumption that $\phi_1 = 1$ can also be made without loss of generality. Hence, all the parameters and covariances of the Kalman filter model are available via the transformation of Section 2.5 and noting that $\sigma_w^2 = R$ of equation (12.71) for the scalar measurements case, and that Q of Section 12.5 is

$$Q = B\,B^T \sigma_w^2 \qquad (12.133)$$

B denoting the product of equation (2.77) when $a_i$, $\gamma_j$ of (2.77) are $\phi_i$, $\theta_j$. The estimates above are cosistent for consistent ARMA-model identification, and are bounded if the procedure of Section 12.6.2 is employed for ARMA identification, such that the bound can be reduced at will by increasing the order of the pure AR model employed in that procedure, the bound approaching zero for sufficiently high-order AR models.[7]

The present approach is extendable to vector measurements via reference 13.

## 12.9 JOINT STATE AND PARAMETER ESTIMATION VIA EXTENDED KALMAN FILTERING

Identification techniques based on Kalman's fiter may be extended to input-output-noise problems where measurable inputs also exist, as in Section 5.4.2. The latter techniques are also applicable to problems of joint state and parameter estimation and are known as extended Kalman filtering techniques, Since the Kalman filter formulation is in terms of a linear state space model. the application of the extended filter to nonlinear systems requires linearization around each last estimate prior to the next estimation. Furthermore, it is no more optimal in nonlinear cases, since the Gaussian assumption is no longer valid.

In similarity to the techniques of Section 12.4 and of Chapter 9, the extended Kalman filter is based on considering the elements of the parameter vector to be state variables. Although several formulations of the extended filter exist, we shall consider here only one such formulation, namely that based on iterating between parameter and state estimation. In the present formulation of the extended Kalman filter, the joint state and parameter estimation problem is thus treated such that the parameter estimation is performed prior to the state estimation to yield an estimated parameter vector. The latter parameters are subsequently employed for state estimation, such state predicted may be performed, as in Section 12.3 or 12.5. Further iterations between the parameter and state estimation are obviously possible.

For the parameter estimation stage, we consider an input-output-noise system, the deterministic input not being essential to the analysis:

$$\mathbf{x}(k+1) = \boldsymbol{\alpha}\mathbf{x}(k) + \boldsymbol{\beta}\mathbf{u}(k) + \mathbf{v}(k) \tag{12.134}$$

$\mathbf{u}(k)$ being an accessible input vector, and $\mathbf{v}(k)$ being a white noise vector. The state vector $\mathbf{x}(k)$ of Equation (12.134) is considered to be accessible as in Section 12.4. Since $\mathbf{u}$ is also accessible, Equation (12.134) may be rewritten in the form of Equation (12.50), where:

$$\mathbf{X}(k) = [\,\mathbf{x}^T(k), \mathbf{u}^T(k)]^T \tag{12.135}$$

and where $\boldsymbol{\Phi}$ contains the elements of $\boldsymbol{\alpha}$ and $\boldsymbol{\beta}$. Consequently, $\boldsymbol{\alpha}$, $\boldsymbol{\beta}$ may be derived in exactly the same manner as in Section 12.4.

Following the identification above, state estimation may be performed. Since $\mathbf{u}(k)$ is accessible, and since an approximation to $\boldsymbol{\alpha}$, $\boldsymbol{\beta}$ is now available from the parameter estimation, a set of equations similar to (12.70), (12.71) may now be considered as follows:

$$\mathbf{x}(k+1) = \boldsymbol{\alpha}\,\mathbf{x}(k) + \mathbf{U}(k) + \mathbf{v}(k) \tag{12.136}$$

$$\mathbf{y}(k) = \mathbf{M}\,\mathbf{x}(k) \tag{12.137}$$

$\mathbf{M}$, $\mathbf{y}(k)$ being as defined in Section 12.5, and:

$$\mathbf{U}(k) \triangleq \boldsymbol{\beta}\mathbf{u}(k) \tag{12.138}$$

$$E[\mathbf{v}(k)] = \mathbf{0} \tag{12.139}$$

$$E[\mathbf{v}(k)\mathbf{v}^T(k)] \triangleq \mathbf{Q} \tag{12.140}$$

$$E[\mathbf{U}(k)] \neq \mathbf{0} \tag{12.141}$$

Noting Equation (12.35) and the deterministic nature of $\mathbf{U}$, we may subsequently write that:

$$\mathbf{x}^*(k+1\,|\,k) = \boldsymbol{\alpha}\,\mathbf{x}^*(k) + \mathbf{D}\tilde{\mathbf{y}}(k\,|\,k-1) + \mathbf{U}(k) \tag{12.142}$$

where:

$$\tilde{\mathbf{y}}(k|k-1) \triangleq \mathbf{y}(k) - \mathbf{y}^*(k|k) \tag{12.143}$$

$$\mathbf{y}^*(k|k-1) \triangleq \mathbf{M}\mathbf{x}^*(k|k-1) \tag{12.144}$$

Consequently, and considering the derivation of Section 12.3, we obtain:

$$\tilde{\mathbf{x}}(k+1|k) = \mathbf{x}(k+1) - \mathbf{x}^*(k+1|k) \tag{12.145}$$

which is identical to Equation (12.42). However, noting Equation (12.112), the equivalent expression to Equation (12.43) becomes:

$$\begin{aligned}\tilde{\mathbf{x}}(k+1|k) &= \mathbf{\Phi}\mathbf{x}(k) + \mathbf{U}(k) + \mathbf{v}(k) - \mathbf{\Phi}^*\mathbf{x}^*(k|k-1) - \mathbf{D}(k)\mathbf{y}(k) - \mathbf{U}(k)\\ &= (\mathbf{\Phi} - \mathbf{DM})\tilde{\mathbf{x}}(k+1|k) + \mathbf{v}(k)\end{aligned} \tag{12.146}$$

such that the term $\mathbf{U}(k)$ is cancelled. Since the correction matrix $\mathbf{D}(k)$ of sections 12.3 and 12.5 is derived to minimize $\mathbf{P}(k)$ where:

$$\mathbf{P}(k) \triangleq E[\tilde{\mathbf{x}}(k+1|k)\tilde{\mathbf{x}}^T(k+1|k)] \tag{12.147}$$

and since $\tilde{\mathbf{x}}(k+1|k)$ is independent of $\mathbf{U}(k)$, the derivation of $\mathbf{D}(k)$, $\mathbf{P}(k)$ and, hence, of the feedback estimate $\mathbf{x}^*$ may be performed exactly as in Section 12.5. The latter feedback estimate may subsequently be re-employed in the parameter estimation stage further to improve identification.

In the linear Gaussian case, the present technique does not usually yield consistent estimates of all parameters and requires a priori knowledge of orders. Otherwise, it is comparable to the techniques of Sections 5.4.2, 12.6 and superior to them for given variance nonstationarities. Noting the latter comments, it may therefore replace regression identification in the Gaussian part of the transformation method of Section 12.6.5, or in Section 12.7.

## REFERENCES


1. Wiener, N. *Extrapolation, Interpolation on Smoothing of Stationary Time Series*, M.I.T. Press, Cambridge, Mass., 1966.
2. Levinson, N. "The Wiener Root-Mean-Square Error Criterion in Filter Design and Prediction," *Jour. Math. and Phys.*, Vol. 25, No. 4, pp. 261–278, 1947 (reprinted as Appendix B to Ref. 1 above).
3. Kalman, R. "A New Approach to Linear Filtering and Prediction Problems," *Trans. A.S.M.E., Jour. Basic Eng.*, Vol. 82, pp. 35–45, 1960.
4. Box, G. E. P., and Jenkins, G. M. *Time Series Analysis, Forecasting and Control*, Holden Day, San Francisco, 1970.
5. Mackinney, J. G. "Algorithm 28/29," *Comm. A.C.M.*, Vol. 3, No. 11, 1960.

6. Mayne, D. Q. "Optimal Non-Stationary Estimation of the Parameters of a Linear System with Gaussian Inputs," *Jour. Elect. Cont.*, Vol. 14, pp. 101–112, Jan. 1963.
7. Graupe, D., Krause, D. J. and Moore, J. B., "Identification of Autoregressive Parameters of Time Series," *Trans. IEEE*, Vol. AC-20, pp. 104-107, Feb. 1975.
8. Graupe, D., and Krause, D. J. "Sequential Regression Identification Procedure for Predictor and Nonlinear Systems Parameters," *Proc. 14th Midwest Symp. on Circuit Theory*, Denver, 1971.
9. Graupe, D. "On Identifying Stochastic Closed Loop Systems," *Trans. IEEE*, Vol. AC-20, Aug. 1975.
10. Mann, H. B. and Wald, W. A. "On the Statistical Treatment of Linear Stochastic Difference Equations," *Econometrica*, Vol. 11, pp. 173–200, 1943.
11. Freund, J. E. *Mathematical Statistics*, Prentice-Hall, Inc., Englewood Cliffs, N.J., 1971.
12. Papoulis, A. *Probability, Random Variables and Stochastic Processes*, McGraw-Hill, New York, 1967.
13. Graupe, D. "Identification of Time Series by ARMA Methods," *Proc. 5th Pittsburgh Conf. on Modeling and Simulation*, pp. 1013-1019, Apr. 1974.
14. Krause, D. J. and Graupe, D.: "Estimation of the Statistical Parameters of the Kalman-Bucy Filter," *Proc. 3rd Symp. on Nonlinear Estimation Theory*, pp. 135-137, San Diego, 1972.
15. Mehra, R. K.: "On-Line Identification of Linear Dynamic Systems with Applications to Kalman Filtering," *Trans. IEEE*, Vol. AC-16, pp. 12-21, 1971.

## PROBLEMS

**1.** Employ the approach of Section 12.3 to predict the sequence $y(t)$ at $t + \theta \; @ \; \theta = 4$.

| | | | | | | | | | |
|---|---|---|---|---|---|---|---|---|---|
| $t$ | 14 | 15 | 16 | 17 | 18 | 19 | 20 | 21 | |
| $y(t)$ | .8372 | .8895 | .89 | .9073 | .9556 | .967 | .9776 | .9704 | |
| $t$ | 22 | 23 | 24 | 25 | 26 | 27 | 28 | 29 | |
| $y(t)$ | .9918 | 1.0151 | 1.0118 | .9729 | .9538 | .9073 | .9098 | .8846 | |
| $t$ | 30 | 31 | 32 | 33 | 34 | 35 | 36 | 37 | |
| $y(t)$ | .8383 | .8096 | .7828 | .7599 | .7076 | .6637 | .6227 | .5418 | |
| $t$ | 38 | 39 | 40 | 41 | 42 | 43 | 44 | 45 | |
| $y(t)$ | .4799 | .4064 | .3513 | .2797 | .2344 | .1469 | .0881 | −.0114 | |
| $t$ | 46 | 47 | 48 | 49 | 50 | 51 | 52 | 53 | 54 |
| $y(t)$ | −.081 | −.1503 | −.209 | −.2717 | −.3556 | −.4090 | −.4612 | −.5313 | −.609 |

Compare the predicted values with those obtained from a Taylor extrapolation of a curve fit to the measurement. Employ the same curve fit in both cases. Observe that $y(t)$ is a sine wave with superimposed noise.

2. Identify the autoregressive-moving-average prediction model for the following time sequence with $x(k)$ given at $k = 1, 2, 3, \ldots$:

$x(k) = 0.0, 0.0, 1.18, 2.18, 2.35, -1.6, -4.63, -3.06, -.224, 2.04, 3.16,$
$2.68, .677, .074, .688, 1.03, 1.43, 1.57, 2.31, 1.09, -1.16, -3.56,$
$-3.13, -.56, 2.03, 2.13, .705, 1.66, 1.58, 1.46, -.466, -2.29,$
$-2.04, -.238, -.786, -.607, -.03, .17, 1.09, 3.72, 2.08, .114,$
$-1.21, 1.09, 3.03, 3.88, 2.41, .54, -1.63, -3.92, -4.04, -1.88,$
$2.11, 5.08, 5.41, 2.57, -.88, -1.88, -2.53, 1.52, 2.03, .89, -.4,$
$.15, 1.03, 2.17, 1.51, -.75, -1.41, .01, .59, -.025, -1.37, -.42,$
$-1.6, -1.52, -.08, 89, -.04, .56, -.04, -.65, .72, 1.88, .33,$
$-1.63, -1.89, -1.83, -.28, 2.1, 4.37, 3.06, 1.27, -.27, -2.47,$
$-3.63, -2.56, .88, 2.0, .395, .356, 1.33, .81, .51, .64, .9, .99, 1.35,$
$.17, -1.76, -2.58, -1.43, -.95, -1.02, -.36, 1.14, .98, -.36,$
$-1.65, -1.41, -2.26, -1.74, -2.45, -1.45, 1.4, 1.99$

Assume that the autoregressive part of the model is of second order.

3. Employ the extended Kalman filtering method of Section 12.9 to identify the model of the sequence given in Problem 2 above.
4. Repeat Problem 3 with the method of Section 12.3.
5. Apply a Gaussian white noise sequence of 1000 numbers $u_k$ to a linear filter $x_{k+1} = 0.95x_k - 0.5x_{k-1} + u_k$ and generate $y_k = x_k^3$. Identify a nonlinear predictor as in Section 12.6.5 and use the first 900 $y_k$ to predict further $y_k$. Repeat with a linear filter and compare prediction errors.

# 13

# PERFORMANCE SENSITIVITY TO IDENTIFICATION ERRORS

## 13.1 CONCEPTS OF PARAMETER SENSITIVITY

When performing parameter identification, one is often faced with situations where the identified parameter vector or matrix $\hat{\mathbf{p}}$ differs from the actual $\mathbf{p}$ by $\delta\mathbf{p}$, for reasons of identification errors or of parameter nonstationarity. It is therefore of interest to evaluate the effect of a discrepancy $\delta\mathbf{p}$ in the identified $\hat{\mathbf{p}}$ from $\mathbf{p}$ on the performance of the system for cases where the control policy has been based on assuming that $\hat{\mathbf{p}} = \mathbf{p}$. These differences $\delta J$ in performance are of particular importance if optimal performance-cost $J^*$ was designed to be achieved, this optimum requiring a feedback policy $\mathbf{F}^*(\hat{\mathbf{p}})$ based on the identified parameters ($\mathbf{F}$ denoting feedback gain). In that case, two types of information are usually required, namely:

(a) By how much does the actual performance-cost $J(\mathbf{p})$ that results from employing the (erroneously) designed policy $\mathbf{F}^*(\hat{\mathbf{p}})$, differ from the design-cost $J^*(\hat{\mathbf{p}})$, which should have been achieved had $\hat{\mathbf{p}}$ been equal to the true $\mathbf{p}$? (See cost difference $J(\mathbf{p}) - J^*(\hat{\mathbf{p}})$ of Figure 13.1).

(b) By how much could one practically improve the performance-cost from the actual $J(\mathbf{p})$ above (based on $\mathbf{F}^*(\hat{\mathbf{p}})$), had one known the true $\mathbf{p}$ and had one therefore designed a truly optimal policy $\mathbf{u}^*(\mathbf{p})$ based on the actual $\mathbf{p}$, to reach the true optimal cost $J^*(\mathbf{p})$ related to the actual $\mathbf{p}$? (See cost difference $J(\mathbf{p}) - J^*(\mathbf{p})$ of Figure 13.1).

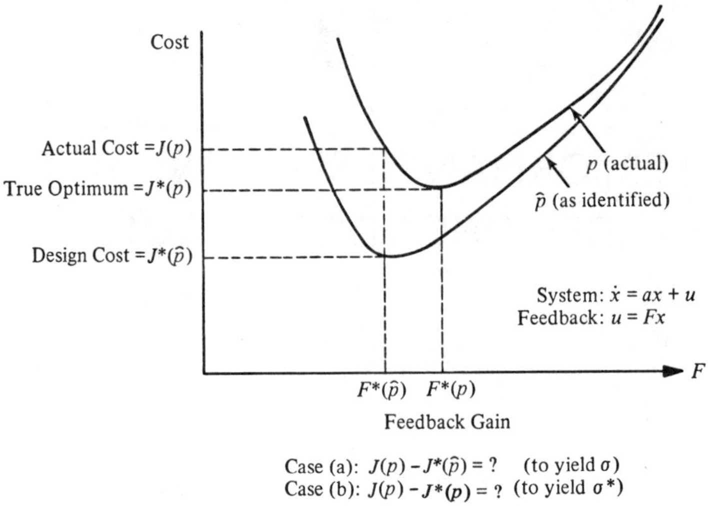


*Figure 13.1* Cost differences due to identification errors (case of scalar *F*).

The answer to the questions above depends on knowing the true $\mathbf{p}$. However, it is possible to evaluate how sensitive the performance-cost of the system is to errors $\delta\mathbf{p}$, through evaluating sensitivity matrices (assuming that the elements of $\mathbf{p}$ are arranged in the form of a matrix and not in form of a vector) for small $\delta\mathbf{p}$:

$$\boldsymbol{\sigma} \triangleq \left.\frac{\partial J}{\partial \mathbf{p}}\right|_{J^*(\hat{\mathbf{p}})} \quad @ \quad \mathbf{F} = \mathbf{F}^*(\hat{\mathbf{p}}) = \text{const.} \tag{13.1}$$

and:

$$\boldsymbol{\sigma}^* = \frac{\partial J^*}{\partial \mathbf{p}} \tag{13.2}$$

$\boldsymbol{\sigma}$ and $\boldsymbol{\sigma}^*$ denoting the design-performance sensitivity matrix and the optimal-performance sensitivity matrix, respectively. Equation (13.1) above thus describes the sensitivity related to the difference between the design optimum $J^*(\hat{\mathbf{p}})$ and the actual performance, as in case (a) above, whereas Equation (13.2) above describes the sensitivity related to the difference between the possible optimum and the actual performance as in case (b) above. It should be noted that $J^*(\hat{\mathbf{p}}) - J(\mathbf{p})$ of case (a) need not be negative, since different systems (with different $\mathbf{p}$) but with the same control policy may have either better or worse performances, as is illustrated in Figure 13.2 for a scalar case. However, $J^*(\mathbf{p}) - J(\mathbf{p})$ of case (b) is always negative, the true optimum being always better (of lower cost) than anything else.

Obviously, not every performance sensitivity evaluation must relate to the optimal performance. Yet, since optimal performance is usually the target

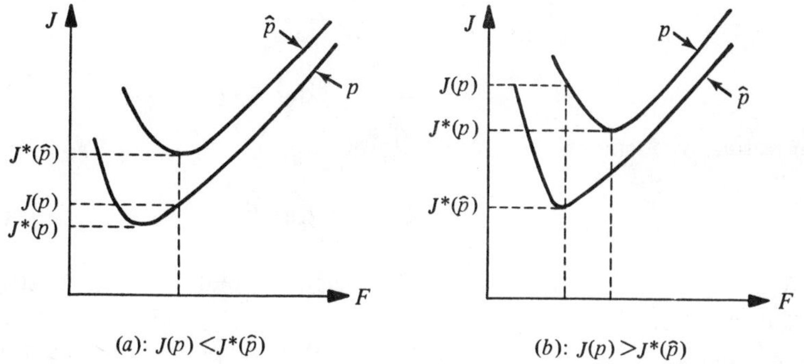


*Figure 13.2* Performance vs. feedback in scalar case.

of good design, sensitivity near the optimum is of major interest, and is usually indicative of the trend in performance sensitivity evaluation. Consequently, an answer to questions (a) and (b) above indicates which parameters require more effort in identification (such that they are more accurately identified). This kind of information may serve to concentrate the identification and instrumentation effort to where it is most required, thus facilitating the saving of considerable time and expenditure in both on-line and off-line identification. We note that if $J(\mathbf{p}) < J^*(\hat{\mathbf{p}})$, then the answer to question (a) is uninteresting. However, if $J^*(\hat{\mathbf{p}}) < J(\mathbf{p})$ and if $J^*(\hat{\mathbf{p}})$ is a certain a priori cost requirement to be satisfied, then the answer to question (a) may be important, especially in the multi-parameter case. Furthermore, the calculation of $\boldsymbol{\sigma} - \boldsymbol{\sigma}^*$ may point out if and where a slight parameter change is best rewarded in terms of performance, such that a better optimum may be reached.

The analysis below is related to linear processes and to performance measured from $t = 0$ to $\infty$. The latter case is *the only one* where analytical treatment is available (in the multi-variable case). This analytical treatment is inaccurate in nonlinear processes, but it gives the sensitivity trend if linearization is valid or nearly valid. Furthermore, results for the time range from 0 to $\infty$ are representative if the actual range is long compared with the systems dynamics. We note that all sensitivity derivations below employ only data that are available from identification, whereas the true $\mathbf{p}$ is not assumed to be known.

## 13.2 EVALUATION OF DESIGN-PERFORMANCE SENSITIVITY MATRICES

The evaluation of the matrix $\boldsymbol{\sigma}$ of Equation (13.1), related to the cost differences $J(\mathbf{p}) - J^*(\hat{\mathbf{p}})$ of *case* (*a*) of Section 13.1 (see Fig. 13.1), is treated first,[1] for reasons of mathematical convenience.

Consider a linear system given by:

$$\dot{\mathbf{x}}(t) = \mathbf{Ax} + \mathbf{Bu}; \qquad \mathbf{x}(t_0) = \mathbf{x}_0 \tag{13.3}$$

subject to a performance-cost $J$ as follows:

$$J = \int_0^\infty (\mathbf{x}^T\mathbf{Qx} + \mathbf{u}^T\mathbf{Ru})\, dt \tag{13.4}$$

$\mathbf{Q}$, $\mathbf{R}$ being positive definite symmetric weighting matrices and $\mathbf{A}$, $\mathbf{B}$ being parameter matrices.

Assuming that linear feedback control is being employed, such that:

$$\mathbf{u} = -\mathbf{Fx} \tag{13.5}$$

Equation (13.3) yields:

$$\dot{\mathbf{x}}(t) = (\mathbf{A} - \mathbf{BF})\mathbf{x}(t) \tag{13.6}$$

and hence:

$$\mathbf{x}(t) = e^{(\mathbf{A}-\mathbf{BF})t}\mathbf{x}_0 \tag{13.7}$$

Substituting $\mathbf{x}$ from Equation (13.7) into (13.4), we obtain that:

$$J = \mathbf{x}_0^T \int_0^\infty e^{\boldsymbol{\omega}^T t}\mathbf{M}e^{\boldsymbol{\omega} t}\, dt\, \mathbf{x}_0 \tag{13.8}$$

where:

$$\boldsymbol{\omega} \triangleq \mathbf{A} - \mathbf{B} \cdot \mathbf{F} \tag{13.9}$$

and:

$$\mathbf{M} \triangleq \mathbf{Q} + \mathbf{F}^T\mathbf{RF} \tag{13.10}$$

Equation (13.8) may be further written as:

$$J = \mathrm{tr}[\mathbf{SX}_0] \tag{13.11}$$

where:

$$\mathbf{S} \triangleq \int_0^\infty e^{\boldsymbol{\omega}^T t}\mathbf{M}e^{\boldsymbol{\omega} t}\, dt \tag{13.12}$$

and:

$$\mathbf{X}_0 = \mathbf{x}_0\mathbf{x}_0^T \tag{13.13}$$

*tr*[ ] denoting a trace. Equation (13.11) above yields that:

$$\frac{\partial J}{\partial \mathbf{A}} = \mathbf{X}_0 \frac{\partial\, tr\, \mathbf{S}}{\partial \mathbf{A}} \tag{13.14}$$

The term $\partial J/\partial \mathbf{A}$ of Equation (13.14) yields expected sensitivity when $\mathbf{X}_0$ represents the expectation $E[\mathbf{x}_0\mathbf{x}_0^T]$ rather than $\mathbf{x}_0\mathbf{x}_0^T$. The treatment to follow will thus consider X, $\partial J/\partial \mathrm{A}$ to denote expectations although the notation will not be changed.

We subsequently employ a basic feature of matrix equations of the form:

$$\boldsymbol{\alpha}^T\boldsymbol{\eta} + \boldsymbol{\eta}\boldsymbol{\alpha} + \boldsymbol{\mu} = \mathbf{0} \tag{13.15}$$

namely, that $\boldsymbol{\eta}$ of Equation (13.15) is given by:[2]

$$\boldsymbol{\eta} = \int_0^\infty e^{\alpha^T t}\boldsymbol{\mu} e^{\alpha t}\, dt \tag{13.16}$$

for $\boldsymbol{\alpha}$ with negative real eigenvalues (see Appendix 3). Consequently, Equation (13.12) satisfies:

$$\boldsymbol{\omega}^T\mathbf{S} + \mathbf{S}\boldsymbol{\omega} + \mathbf{M} = \mathbf{0} \tag{13.17}$$

or, noting Equation (13.9):

$$(\mathbf{A} - \mathbf{BF})^T\mathbf{S} + \mathbf{S}(\mathbf{A} - \mathbf{BF}) + \mathbf{M} = \mathbf{0} \tag{13.18}$$

Perturbing $\mathbf{A}$ by $\Delta\mathbf{A}$, and noting that $\mathbf{F}$ remains unchanged as has been designed for $\mathbf{A}$ and not for $\mathbf{A} + \Delta\mathbf{A}$, (i.e., at the optimum:[2] $\mathbf{F} = \mathbf{R}^{-1}\mathbf{B}^T\mathbf{S} =$ const.), we thus derive:

$$(\mathbf{A} + \Delta\mathbf{A} - \mathbf{B}\cdot\mathbf{F})^T(\mathrm{S} + \Delta\mathrm{S}) + (\mathrm{S} + \Delta\mathrm{S})^T(\mathbf{A} + \Delta\mathbf{A} - \mathbf{B}\cdot\mathbf{F}) + \mathbf{M} = \mathbf{0} \tag{13.19}$$

and, after substracting Equation (13.18) from (13.19):

$$\Delta\mathrm{A}^T\mathrm{S} + (\mathrm{A} - \mathrm{BF})^T\Delta\mathrm{S} + \Delta\mathrm{S}\mathrm{A} + \mathrm{S}\Delta\mathrm{A} = 0 \tag{13.20}$$

Obviously, Equation (13.20) is of the same form as Equation (13.15) when:

$$\mathbf{A} - \mathbf{BF} \triangleq \boldsymbol{\alpha} \tag{13.21}$$

$$\Delta\mathbf{S} \triangleq \boldsymbol{\eta} \tag{13.22}$$

$$\Delta\mathrm{A}^T\mathrm{S} + \mathrm{S}\Delta\mathrm{A} \triangleq \mu \tag{13.23}$$

Consequently, (noting Equation (13.16)):

$$\Delta\mathrm{S} = \int_0^\infty e^{(\mathbf{A}-\mathbf{BF})^T t}[\Delta\mathrm{A}^T\mathrm{S} + \mathrm{S}\Delta\mathrm{A}]\, e^{(\mathbf{A}-\mathbf{BF})t}\, dt \tag{13.24}$$

Employing Kleinman's Lemma,[3] by which:

$$\frac{\partial J}{\partial \mathrm{A}} = \frac{\partial\, tr\, \mathrm{SX}_0}{\partial \mathrm{A}} = \frac{\partial\, tr\, \Delta\mathrm{SX}_0}{\partial \Delta\mathrm{A}} \tag{13.25}$$

and since **A**, **B**, **F**, **M**, and **S** are independent of $\Delta\mathbf{A}$, equations (13.24) and (13.25) yield, according to the matrix differentiation principles as in Appendix 2:

$$\frac{\partial J}{\partial \mathbf{A}} = \int_0^\infty e^{(\mathbf{A}-\mathbf{BF})t} \cdot 2 \cdot \mathbf{X}_0 \cdot e^{(\mathbf{A}-\mathbf{BF})^T t} dt \tag{13.26}$$

Defining:

$$\boldsymbol{\Gamma} \triangleq \int_0^\infty e^{(\mathbf{A}-\mathbf{BF})t} 2\mathbf{X}_0 e^{(\mathbf{A}-\mathbf{BF})^T t} dt \tag{13.27}$$

and noting that Equation (13.26) is of the form of (13.16) we obtain that:

$$\boldsymbol{\omega}^T \boldsymbol{\Gamma} + \boldsymbol{\Gamma}\boldsymbol{\omega} + 2\mathbf{X}_0 = 0 \tag{13.28}$$

and:

$$\frac{\partial J}{\partial \mathbf{A}} = \mathbf{S}\boldsymbol{\Gamma} \tag{13.29}$$

A similar expression is available for $\partial J/\partial \mathbf{B}$, following an exactly analogous derivation.

We note that our interest in the present chapter is restricted to sensitivity around the optimal cost. In that case, the optimal **S**, namely **S*** is derived through perturbing Equation (13.18) by $\Delta\mathbf{F}$, such that:

$$(\mathbf{A} - \mathbf{BF})^T \Delta\mathbf{S} + \Delta\mathbf{S}(\mathbf{A} - \mathbf{BF}) - \Delta\mathbf{F}^T\mathbf{B}^T\mathbf{S} - \mathbf{SB}\,\Delta\mathbf{F} + \Delta\mathbf{F}^T\mathbf{RF} + \mathbf{F}^T\mathbf{R}\,\Delta\mathbf{F} = 0 \tag{13.30}$$

Since Equation (13.30) is of the form of Equation (13.15), we obtain:

$$\begin{aligned}\Delta\mathbf{S} &= \int_0^\infty e^{\boldsymbol{\omega}^T t}[\Delta\mathbf{F}^T(\mathbf{RF} - \mathbf{B}^T\mathbf{S}) + (\mathbf{F}^T\mathbf{R} - \mathbf{SB})\Delta\mathbf{F}]\, e^{\boldsymbol{\omega} t}\, dt \\ &= \int_0^\infty e^{\boldsymbol{\omega}^T t}[\Delta\mathbf{F}^T(\mathbf{RF} - \mathbf{B}^T\mathbf{S}) - (\mathbf{RF} - \mathbf{B}^T\mathbf{S})^T\Delta\mathbf{F}]\, e^{\boldsymbol{\omega} t}\, dt \end{aligned} \tag{13.31}$$

and:

$$\Delta\mathbf{J} = tr[\Delta\mathbf{S} \cdot \mathbf{X}_0] \tag{13.32}$$

Subsequently, at the optimum (according to Kleinman's Lemma):

$$\frac{\partial J}{\partial \mathbf{F}} = \frac{\partial \Delta J}{\partial \Delta\mathbf{F}} = \mathbf{0} \tag{13.33}$$

which is satisfied through employing a feedback matrix given by:

$$\mathbf{F}^* = \mathbf{R}^{-1}\mathbf{B}^T\mathbf{S}^* \tag{13.34}$$

where, $\mathbf{S}^*$, $\mathbf{F}^*$ denote $\mathbf{S}$, $\mathbf{F}$ at the optimum. Substituting the optimal $\mathbf{F} = \mathbf{F}^*$ from Equation (13.34) into (13.18), we obtain the following algebraic Riccati matrix equation for deriving $\mathbf{S} = \mathbf{S}^*$ at the optimum, from $\mathbf{A}$, $\mathbf{B}$, $\mathbf{Q}$, $\mathbf{R}$:

$$\mathbf{A}^T\mathbf{S}^* + \mathbf{S}^*\mathbf{A} + \mathbf{Q} - \mathbf{S}^*\mathbf{B}\mathbf{R}^{-1}\mathbf{B}^T\mathbf{S}^* = \mathbf{0} \tag{13.35}$$

Consequently, the sensitivity matrix $\boldsymbol{\sigma}$ in the vicinity of $\mathbf{F}^*$ may be evaluated by solving two matrix equations, namely, the algebraic *Riccati matrix* equation (13.35) for evaluating $\mathbf{S}$ at the optimum, and the *linear matrix* equation (13.28) for evaluating $\Gamma$ once $\mathbf{S}$ is available (see solution to Problem 1, Chapter 13). We note that when optimal $J$ is required, $\mathbf{S}^*$ must be derived regardless of any sensitivity analysis. Hence, the derivation of $\boldsymbol{\sigma}$ involves only a solution of an additional linear matrix equation, (i.e., a set of linear simultaneous equations for the elements of $\boldsymbol{\Gamma}$).

Obviously, the elements of the matrices $\dfrac{\partial J}{\partial \mathbf{A}}, \dfrac{\partial J}{\partial \mathbf{B}}$ are those of $\dfrac{\partial J}{\partial \mathbf{p}}$. The evaluation of $\boldsymbol{\Gamma}$ above is only possible if $\mathbf{A}$, $\mathbf{B}$ are available. When $\hat{\mathbf{A}}$, $\hat{\mathbf{B}}$ of $\hat{\mathbf{p}}$, as resulting from an identification procedure, are substituted for $\mathbf{A}, \mathbf{B}$ of equations (13.3) to (13.35) and if $\partial\mathbf{A}$, $\partial\mathbf{B}$ are not too large, then the derivation above yields $\boldsymbol{\sigma}$ of Equation (13.1) as is required.

EXAMPLE 13.1

Consider a system given by $\dot{\mathbf{x}} = \mathbf{A}\mathbf{x} + \mathbf{B}u$ with $E[\mathbf{x}_0\,\mathbf{x}_0^T] = \mathbf{I}$, where $\mathbf{A}$, $\mathbf{B}$ have been identified as follows:

$$\hat{\mathbf{A}} = \begin{bmatrix} 0 & 1 \\ -2 & -3 \end{bmatrix}; \qquad \hat{\mathbf{B}} = \begin{bmatrix} 0 \\ 1 \end{bmatrix}$$

and where $J = \int_0^\infty (\mathbf{x}^T\mathbf{Q}\mathbf{x} + \mathbf{u}^T\mathbf{R}\mathbf{u})\,dt$ with $\mathbf{Q} = \mathbf{I}$; $\mathbf{R} = 1$. The above system is controlled by a linear policy $u = -\mathbf{F}\mathbf{x}$, where $\mathbf{F} = [1, 1]$. (Note that although we are usually concerned with an optimal policy, the derivation of Section 13.2 is valid for any linear feedback control and yields the sensitivity matrix around the respective, not necessarily optimal, cost). From Equation (13.29) we thus obtain that $\partial J/\partial\mathbf{A} = \mathbf{S}\Gamma$, where $\mathbf{X}_0$ is given to be equal to $\mathbf{I}$ and $\boldsymbol{\Gamma}$ is derived from Equation (13.28) as follows:

$$\left\{\begin{bmatrix} 0 & 1 \\ -2 & -3 \end{bmatrix} - \begin{bmatrix} 0 \\ 1 \end{bmatrix}[1;1]\right\} \cdot \boldsymbol{\Gamma} + \boldsymbol{\Gamma}\left\{\begin{bmatrix} 0 & 0 \\ -2 & -3 \end{bmatrix} - \begin{bmatrix} 0 \\ 1 \end{bmatrix}[1;1]\right\}^T + 2\cdot\mathbf{I}$$

$$= \begin{bmatrix} 0 & -3 \\ 1 & -4 \end{bmatrix}\boldsymbol{\Gamma} + \boldsymbol{\Gamma}\begin{bmatrix} 0 & 1 \\ -3 & -4 \end{bmatrix} + 2\cdot\mathbf{I} = \mathbf{0}$$

Since $\mathbf{S}$ satisfies Equation (13.18), we derive:

$$\begin{bmatrix} -0 & -3 \\ 1 & -4 \end{bmatrix}\mathbf{S} + \mathbf{S}\begin{bmatrix} 0 & 1 \\ -3 & -4 \end{bmatrix} + \mathbf{I} + \begin{bmatrix} 1 & 1 \\ 1 & 1 \end{bmatrix} = \mathbf{0}$$

such that, noting the symmetry of $S$:

$$\begin{bmatrix} -3S_{12}; & -3S_{22} \\ S_{11}-4S_{12}; & S_{12}-4S_{22} \end{bmatrix} + \begin{bmatrix} -3S_{12}; & S_{11}-4S_{12} \\ -3S_{22}; & S_{12}-4S_{22} \end{bmatrix} + \begin{bmatrix} 2 & 1 \\ 1 & 2 \end{bmatrix} = \mathbf{0}$$

and:

$$\begin{aligned} -6S_{12}+2=0; &\quad S_{12}=\tfrac{1}{3} \\ 2S_{12}-8S_{22}+2=0; &\quad S_{22}=\tfrac{1}{3} \\ S_{11}-4S_{12}-3S_{22}+1=0; &\quad S_{11}=\tfrac{4}{3} \end{aligned}$$

Furthermore:

$$\begin{bmatrix} -3\Gamma_{12}; & -3\Gamma_{22} \\ \Gamma_{11}-4\Gamma_{12}; & \Gamma_{12}-4\Gamma_{22} \end{bmatrix} + \begin{bmatrix} -3\Gamma_{12}; & \Gamma_{11}-4\Gamma_{12} \\ -3\Gamma_{22}; & \Gamma_{12}-4\Gamma_{22} \end{bmatrix} + \begin{bmatrix} 2 & 0 \\ 0 & 2 \end{bmatrix} = \mathbf{0}$$

such that:

$$\begin{aligned} -6\Gamma_{12}+2=0; &\quad \Gamma_{12}=\tfrac{1}{3} \\ 2\Gamma_{12}-8\Gamma_{22}+2=0; &\quad \Gamma_{22}=\tfrac{1}{3} \\ \Gamma_{11}-4\Gamma_{12}-3\Gamma_{22} \quad =0; &\quad \Gamma_{11}=\tfrac{7}{3} \end{aligned}$$

Obviously, for optimal control, the derivation of $\mathbf{S}=\mathbf{S}^*$ (and, hence, of an optimal $\mathbf{F}=\mathbf{F}^*$) is essential, regardless of any sensitivity analysis. With $\mathbf{S}^*$ thus available, Equation (13.28) is linear in $\Gamma_{ij}$ and its solution is immediate as is indicated by the last computation step of the present example.

## 13.3 EVALUATION OF OPTIMAL-PERFORMANCE SENSITIVITY MATRICES

Considering equations (13.1) and (13.2), we derive:

$$tr[\boldsymbol{\sigma}\cdot\delta\mathbf{p}^T] = J(\mathbf{p}) - J^*(\hat{\mathbf{p}}) \tag{13.36-a}$$

and:

$$tr[\boldsymbol{\sigma}^*\cdot\delta\mathbf{p}^T] = J(\mathbf{p}) - J^*(\mathbf{p}) \tag{13.36-b}$$

$J$ being the actual performance, $J^*(\hat{\mathbf{p}})$ being the design optimum assuming (erroneously) that $\hat{\mathbf{p}}=\mathbf{p}$ and $J^*(\mathbf{p})$ denoting the actually-possible optimum.

Equations (13.36-a), (13.36-b) yield:

$$tr[(\boldsymbol{\sigma}-\boldsymbol{\sigma}^*)\,\delta\mathbf{p}^T] = J^*(\mathbf{p}) - J^*(\hat{\mathbf{p}}) \tag{13.37}$$

We thus define:

$$\boldsymbol{\sigma}-\boldsymbol{\sigma}^* \triangleq \boldsymbol{\Sigma}^* \tag{13.38}$$

Since $\boldsymbol{\sigma}$ has already been derived (in Section 13.2), the evaluation of $\boldsymbol{\sigma}^*$ is now analytically performed through deriving $\boldsymbol{\Sigma}^*$ as follows:[1]

Assuming that $J^*(\hat{\mathbf{p}})$ is the *optimum* of $J$ of Equation (13.8) for $\hat{\mathbf{A}}$, $\hat{\mathbf{B}}$ as identified, we restate Equation (13.35) as follows:

$$\hat{\mathbf{A}}^T\hat{\mathbf{S}}^* + \hat{\mathbf{S}}^*\hat{\mathbf{A}} + \mathbf{Q} - \hat{\mathbf{S}}^*\hat{\mathbf{B}}\mathbf{R}^{-1}\hat{\mathbf{B}}^T\hat{\mathbf{S}}^* = \mathbf{0} \tag{13.39}$$

to yield an estimated optimal cost:

$$J^*_{\hat{\mathbf{p}}} = J^*(\hat{\mathbf{A}}, \hat{\mathbf{B}}) = J^*(\hat{\mathbf{p}}) = tr[\hat{\mathbf{S}}\mathbf{X}_0] \tag{13.40}$$

$$\mathbf{X}_0 \triangleq E(\mathbf{x}_0\mathbf{x}_0^T) \tag{13.41}$$

If $\hat{\mathbf{F}}$ is changed by $\Delta\mathbf{F}$ such that $\hat{\mathbf{F}} + \Delta\mathbf{F}$ is the new $\mathbf{F}$, a new cost will be achieved given by $J^*_{\hat{\mathbf{p}}}(\hat{\mathbf{F}} + \Delta\mathbf{F})$, which satisfies the following perturbed Equation (13.18):

$$(\hat{\mathbf{A}} - \hat{\mathbf{B}}(\hat{\mathbf{F}} + \Delta\mathbf{F}))^T(\hat{\mathbf{S}}^* + \Delta\mathbf{S}') + (\hat{\mathbf{S}}^* + \Delta\mathbf{S}')(\hat{\mathbf{A}} - \hat{\mathbf{B}}(\hat{\mathbf{F}} + \Delta\mathbf{F}))$$

$$+ \mathbf{Q} + (\hat{\mathbf{F}} + \Delta\mathbf{F})^T\mathbf{R}(\hat{\mathbf{F}} + \Delta\mathbf{F}) = \mathbf{0} \tag{13.42}$$

such that:

$$J^*_{\hat{\mathbf{p}}}(\hat{\mathbf{F}} + \Delta\mathbf{F}) = tr[\hat{\mathbf{S}}^* + \Delta\mathbf{S}')\mathbf{X}_0] \tag{13.43}$$

Substructing Equation (13.39) from (13.42) and omitting second-order differences of the form of $\Delta\mathbf{F}$, $\Delta\mathbf{S}'$, we derive:

$$\Delta\mathbf{S}'(\hat{\mathbf{A}} - \hat{\mathbf{B}}\hat{\mathbf{F}}) + (\hat{\mathbf{A}}^T - \hat{\mathbf{F}}^T\hat{\mathbf{B}}^T)\Delta\mathbf{S}' + \Delta\mathbf{F}^T(\mathbf{R}\hat{\mathbf{F}} - \hat{\mathbf{B}}^T\hat{\mathbf{S}}^*) + (\hat{\mathbf{F}}^T\mathbf{R} - \hat{\mathbf{S}}^*\hat{\mathbf{B}})\Delta\mathbf{F} = \mathbf{0} \tag{13.44}$$

Equation (13.44) is of the form of Equation (13.15). However, if $\hat{\mathbf{A}}$ becomes $\mathbf{A} + \Delta\mathbf{A}$, then $\mathbf{S}$ of (13.44) is $\hat{\mathbf{S}}^* + \Delta\mathbf{S}_A = \hat{\mathbf{S}}^* + \Delta\mathbf{S}$ of Section 13.2. Hence by (13.34):

$$\Delta\mathbf{S}' = -\int_0^\infty e^{\omega^T t}(\Delta\mathbf{F}^T\mathbf{B}\Delta\mathbf{S} + \mathbf{B}^T\Delta\mathbf{S}\Delta\mathbf{F})e^{\omega t}\,dt \tag{13.45}$$

and:

$$\Delta\mathbf{S}_A = \Delta\mathbf{S}\Big|_{\mathbf{F} = \text{Constant}, \Delta\mathbf{A}} \tag{13.46}$$

Noting Equation (13.25), Equation (13.46) yields:

$$\frac{\partial J^{**}}{\partial \mathbf{F}} = \frac{\partial tr\Delta\mathbf{S}'\mathbf{X}_0}{\partial\Delta\mathbf{F}} = -2\mathbf{B}^T\Delta\mathbf{S}_A\int_0^\infty e^{\omega t}\mathbf{X}_0 e^{\omega^T t}dt = -2\mathbf{B}^T\Delta\mathbf{S}_A\Gamma \tag{13.47}$$

$\partial J^{**}$ denoting the difference between $J^*(\hat{\mathbf{p}})$ and $J^*(\hat{\mathbf{p}})$ related to $\Sigma^*$ above, as in Fig. 13.1. Consequently, via (13.29) and (13.38), we obtain $\Delta J^* = J(\mathbf{p}) - J^*(\hat{\mathbf{p}})$, as follows:

$$\Delta J^* = tr(\mathbf{S}\Gamma\Delta\mathbf{A}^T + 2\mathbf{B}^T\Delta\mathbf{S}_A\Gamma\Delta\mathbf{F}^T) \tag{13.48}$$

where, according to equations (13.20), (13.34):

$$\Delta \mathbf{F} = \mathbf{R}^{-1} \mathbf{B}^T \Delta \mathbf{S}_A \tag{13.49}$$

the latter being a *linear* equation in $\Delta\mathbf{A}$ via (13.20). Hence, once $\mathbf{S}^*$ is available, Equation (13.48) yields:

$$\frac{\partial J^*}{\partial \mathbf{A}} = \hat{\mathbf{S}}^* \lambda = 4\hat{\mathbf{S}}^* \int_0^\infty e^{\omega t} \left( \frac{\mathbf{X}_0}{2} - \mathbf{B}\Delta\mathbf{F}\Gamma - \Gamma\Delta\mathbf{F}^T\mathbf{B}^T \right) e^{\omega^T t} dt \tag{13.50}$$

$\lambda$ being computable in the same manner as $\hat{\mathbf{S}}^*$, $\Gamma$. In similarity to Section 13.2, an analogous derivation to that of equations (13.36) to (13.50) yields $\partial J^*/\partial \mathbf{B}$ to facilitate the complete evaluation of $\sigma^*$ whereas $\Sigma^*$ is derived via directly considering (13.47) for $\Delta\mathbf{A}$ and $\Delta\mathbf{B}$.

We observe that $\Sigma^*$ is not only useful for yielding $\sigma^*$; it is of further importance since it yields a qualitative indication of the difference between the designed and the actually-possible optimum. Furthermore, an evaluation of $\Sigma^*$ may indicate which parameters of $\mathbf{p}$ mostly affect the optimal cost, such that changes in these elements would result in a greater improvement of the optimum.

In conclusion, we emphasize that the sensitivity analysis for deriving $\sigma$, $\sigma^*$, $\Sigma^*$ involves only a solution of two linear matrix equations, assuming that $\mathbf{S}^*$ must be anyway available if optimal performance is sought.[4]

EXAMPLE 13.2

A further insight into identification sensitivity and into the relations between performance cost and control policy may be obtained from investigating the following one-dimensional system:

$$\dot{x} = ax + bu;\ E[x(0)] = 0;\ E[x^2(0)] = P_0$$

considering a performance cost $J = \frac{1}{2} \int_0^\infty (Cx^2 + Du^2)\, dt$.

The optimal feedback for the latter system is given by: $u = -kx$, $k$ being derived from substituting $-kx$ for $u$ into the expression of $J$ above, and solving $k$ from $\partial J/\partial k = 0$, to yield:

$$k = \frac{a}{b} \pm \sqrt{\frac{a^2}{b^2} + \frac{C}{D}}$$

since the latter $k$ yields:

$$\dot{x} = \pm \sqrt{a^2 + \frac{b^2 C}{D}} \cdot x,$$

and since:

$$\dot{x} = +\sqrt{a^2 + \frac{b^2 C}{D}} \cdot x$$

is unstable, the optimal $k$ is obviously:

$$k = \frac{a}{b} + \sqrt{\frac{a^2}{b^2} + \frac{C}{D}}$$

and the optimum cost becomes:

$$J^* = \frac{-(C + k^2 D)P_0}{4(a - bk)}$$

(See Figure 13.1.)

The elements of the design-performance sensitivity matrix $\boldsymbol{\sigma}$ for the latter system thus become:

$$\left.\frac{\partial J}{\partial a}\right|_{k=k^*} = \frac{C + k^2 D}{4(a - bk)^2} P_0 = \sigma_1$$

Similarly $\partial J/\partial b_{k=k^*}$ yields $\sigma_2$ to form $\boldsymbol{\sigma} = [\sigma_1; \sigma_2]^T$. Furthermore, the optimal performance sensitivity matrix $\boldsymbol{\sigma}^*$ for the above system is derived, in accordance with Section 13.3, by first evaluating $\boldsymbol{\Sigma}^*$. Consequently, we substitute $\frac{a}{b} + \sqrt{\frac{a^2}{b^2} + \frac{C}{D}}$ for $k$ into the expression for $J^*$ to yield:

$$\Gamma = \frac{P_0}{\sqrt{a^2 + \dfrac{Cb^2}{D}}}$$

and, noting Equation 13.50:

$$\frac{\partial J^*}{\partial a} = \frac{-DJ^* + 4b^2 \sigma_1^2 \Delta a / P_0}{D(a - bk)}$$

Similarly, $\partial J^*/\partial b$ yields $\sigma_2{}^*$ to form $\boldsymbol{\sigma}^* = [\sigma_1^*; \sigma_2^*]^T$, and noting Equation (13.38) we obtain $\boldsymbol{\Sigma}^* = \boldsymbol{\sigma} - \boldsymbol{\sigma}^*$, such that $\boldsymbol{\sigma}; \boldsymbol{\sigma}^*$ and $\boldsymbol{\Sigma}^*$ are all in terms of the identified $a$, $b$ of $P_0$, $C$, $D$ as defined above. Hence, if $a$, $b$ are identified, effects of errors between the true and the identified $a$, $b$ on the optimal performance are determined.

## 13.4 EXPERIMENTAL DERIVATION OF SENSITIVITY MATRICES

In nonlinear systems where linearization is not valid or in linear systems when performance must be considered over finite intervals only (namely: $J = \int_0^{t_f} \psi(\mathbf{x}, \mathbf{u})\, dt$) or is related to a changing target vector, an experimental derivation of the sensitivity matrices above is obviously required. The latter derivation may be performed by first computing the optimum $J^*(\hat{\mathbf{p}})$ with respect to the identified and hence available $\hat{\mathbf{p}}$. The optimum is then re-evaluated with respect to hypothetical systems with parameters $\hat{\mathbf{p}} + \Delta p_i \; \forall i = 1 \cdots v$; $v$ being the number of elements of $\hat{\mathbf{p}}$. The elements of the sensitivity matrices are thus derived from $J^*(\hat{\mathbf{p}} + \Delta p_i) - J^*(\hat{\mathbf{p}})$, where

$$\frac{J^*(\mathbf{p} + \Delta p_i) - J^*(\mathbf{p})}{\Delta p_i} \tag{13.51}$$

yields the $i$'th element of the sensitivity matrix, which is written in terms of a vector if $\mathbf{p}$ is considered to be a vector.

The numerous computations of optima required for the latter derivation are obviously very time-consuming, thus pointing to the advantage of employing the linear infinite-range formulations of Sections 13.2, 13.3 whenever possible.

## REFERENCES


1. Bobrovsky, B. Z., and Graupe, D. "Analysis of Optimal-Cost Sensitivity to Parameter Changes," *IEEE Trans.*, Vol. AC-16, Oct., pp. 487–488, 1971.
2. Levine, W. S., and Athans, M. "On the Determination of the Optimal Constant Output Feedback Gains for Linear Multivariable Systems," *IEEE Trans.*, Vol. AC-15, pp. 44–48, 1970.
3. Kleinman, D. L. "Suboptimal Design of Linear Regulator Systems Subject to Computer Storage Limitations," *M.I.T. Electronic Systems Lab. Rept. ESL-R-297*, Cambridge, Mass., 1967.
4. Lee, R. C. K. *Optimal Estimation, Identification and Control,* M.I.T. Press, Cambridge, Mass., 1964.


## PROBLEMS

1. Compute $\partial J/\partial \mathrm{A}$ of Equation (13.29) for the system $\dot{\mathbf{x}} = \mathbf{Ax} + \mathbf{Bu}$, where $\mathbf{A}$, $\mathbf{B}$ have been identified as follows:

$$\hat{\mathbf{A}} = \begin{bmatrix} 0 & 1 \\ -1 & -1 \end{bmatrix}; \qquad \hat{\mathbf{B}} = \begin{bmatrix} 0 \\ 1 \end{bmatrix}$$

and where: $\mathbf{Q} = \mathbf{I}$; $\mathbf{R} = 1$; $\mathbf{X} = E[\mathbf{x}_0 \mathbf{x}_0^T] = \mathbf{I}$.

**2.** Derive $\frac{\partial J}{\partial \mathbf{B}}$ to correspond to $\frac{\partial J}{\partial \mathbf{A}}$ of Equation (13.29).

**3.** Compute $\frac{\partial J^*}{\partial \mathbf{A}}$ for the system of Problem 1.

**4.** Derive $\frac{\partial J^*}{\partial \mathbf{B}}$ to correspond to $\frac{\partial J^*}{\partial \mathbf{A}}$.

# 14

# CONCLUDING COMMENTS

In conclusion to the present text, some general comments on the relative merits and applicability of the various identification approaches that have been discussed may be appropriate.

When coming to apply an identification technique to a specific problem, one must consider some basic aspects. These relate first to the classification of the problem, in terms of the categories discussed in Chapter 1. Furthermore, it is most important to employ as much a priori knowledge as is possible and to evaluate the subsequent identification results when considering this prior knowledge. It is not only practical but also essential to employ the simplest technique possible, in terms of computational difficulty. This requirement is particularly important in on-line application where any saving in computational time may make the difference between adequate and inadequate control. The latter consideration would also avoid unnecessary computational errors which increase with the complexity of the problem. Obviously, if a simple technique is not accurate enough, a more complex one may be required. If the employment of specific identification inputs is possible, as in the cases of chapters 3 and 4, they may yield fast and accurate identification. Otherwise, sequential techniques are probably the best in terms of speed and computational complexity. Here simplicity would point to the sequential learning and stochastic approximation techniques, whereas considerations of rapid convergence point to sequential least squares regression, which yields efficient estimates if the noise terms add up to Gaussian white noise, because of the maximum likelihood properties of that case. (These maximum likelihood properties of least squares also apply when moving-average noise terms are eliminated by reformulation whenever they appear.) Techniques where matrix inversion is required should be avoided if possible, since ill-conditioning of matrices is a cause of endless headaches to programmers of any estimation and control problems, or, indeed, to programmers in general. This again points to sequential identification approaches. The recommendations above hold for both linear and nonlinear processes, which may be continuous or discrete. They hold also for nonstationary processes to which sequential regression or sequential learning techniques* may be applicable, as indicated in chapters 6, 7 and 12.

Invariant imbedding techniques should be mainly employed in cases of nonlinear systems, when both states and parameters require estimation. They however require some reasonable guess of the parameter values (usually within 2:1 to 1:2 range of the true values), and an order of magnitude guess of the other initial conditions that are involved, in order that adequate convergence be accomplished. When joint state and parameter estimation is required in linear cases, the extended Kalman filtering approach or the mixed autoregressive-moving-average approach of Chapter 12 may be preferable to invariant imbedding, especially when no a priori information is available. The employment of autoregressive-moving-average input-output-noise techniques in these cases is however, preferable to both, in terms of computational speed and simplicity, especially when the order of the system is also unknown and Gaussian sequences are considered.

Predictive approaches may find their main field of applications in nonstationary cases where the only consideration is adequate control, and when state-space or transfer-function formulations are not required. Their disadvantage is in the need for performing prediction at every control interval, which results in additional computer time and program complexity. However, when nonstationary systems are considered where only measurements of the inputs and of the control performance index are available, they may be the answer.

In cases where the dimension of the state vector is unknown, state-space models should usually be derived via transfer-function identification and subsequent transformation. Whenever autoregressive-moving-average models are derived, care must be taken that common roots of the autoregressive and moving-average polynomials are cancelled.

The identification of the parameters of linear state-space models of time series, for subsequent prediction purposes, in the absence of any state equation parameter knowledge may be obtained by means of a modified

*The sequential learning and least squares regression methods converge also for unstable processes, as indicated in Chapter 7.

Kalman filter (Mayne's estimator). The identification of a mixed autoregressive-moving-average model of time series by a technique based on sequential regression (or, on techniques as in Chapter 7, when rapid convergence is not of main importance) is applicable to cases where prediction of measured data is required, and where no information on the states themselves is available, or, indeed, required. The latter facilitates the consistent, and almost efficient derivation of parameters and orders of a discrete transfer-function model for stationary and for several nonstationary sequences or systems. The mixed autoregressive-moving-average model therefore yields optimal linear prediction of measured data for unknown parameters and orders via input reconstruction, in contrast to the Kalman filter approach where the parameters and orders must be known and where reconstruction is avoided through sequentially updating error gains. Furthermore, once identification is assumed to be complete, the autoregressive-moving-average model may be transformed into a state space formulation, as in Section 2.5, to yield a model for prediction via the Kalman filtering techniques discussed earlier, such that further input reconstruction is avoided. Both the Kalman filter formulation and the auto-regressive-moving-average formulation yield optimal prediction of Gaussian sequences, the former also directly filtering measurement noise. Both (and also the methods of Chapters 8 and 9) may be combined with transformation procedures as in Section 12.6.5 to identify the parameters of optimal predictors of certain non-Gaussian sequences.

Problems of filtering can be reformulated as prediction problems such that identification techniques of Chapter 12 (especially, of Section 12.8) are also applicable to them. The extension to homogeneous nonstationary processes as in Section 12.7 is also possible with both techniques. However, unbiased and consistent identification of all parameters jointly is not facilitated by extended Kalman filtering.

The main purpose of the sensitivity analysis of Chapter 13 is to indicate which parameters of a (linear) system require the greatest identification effort. Such sensitivity information may serve to speed up identification of parameters having low sensitivity indices.

A comment may be helpful at this point to further clarify the relation between the major types of filter and process formulations. We have noted in Chapter 12 that the discrete Wiener predictor formulation is in fact a pure (ideally infinite) autoregressive formulation, which is, therefore, efficiently identifiable. The mixed autoregressive-moving-average formulation is therefore directly related to the Wiener filter, but is of minimum number of parameters. The Kalman predictor, which is related to the autoregressive-moving-average predictor by transformation is thus also a minimum parameter formulation. Moreover, the two last formulations have been shown to be again directly related to the transfer function and the state space formulation in general.

We further comment on the concepts of efficient, consistent and unbiased identification. Although efficient identification should be reached whenever possible without over-complicating the computation, one should keep in mind that consistent sequential and asymptotically unbiased identification is usually just as satisfactory since it converges to the true parameters.

We re-emphasize that no identification of dynamic parameters from measurements is possible unless these measurements include transient effects. Therefore, steady state data cannot yield dynamic identification by any approach. We also stress again that identification of parameters of nonlinear systems must relate to a specific nonlinear formulation or approximation, since an infinite number of nonlinear functions does exist and a parameter which fits one function to measurements is not best for another nonlinear function.

The general considerations outlined in this chapter are partly based on the subjective experience and observations of the author. They should merely serve as a guide for the reader, who may wish to get a general comparative evaluation. For deeper insight, it is advisable to apply different techniques to the various specific problems. Further information to this end may be found when one scans the literature on identification and its application, as it is available in the scientific press. This literature deals with the techniques of the present text and with several other techniques, which are often derived or extended from the techniques outlined in chapters 3 to 13.

Noting that all identification approaches, as discussed in the present text or applied in practice, must be based on measured phenomena, we may find it worthwhile to keep in mind Immanuel Kant's words:

> What things may be by themselves we know
> not, nor need we care to know, because,
> after all, a thing can never come before me
> otherwise than as a phenomenon.
>
> (*Critique of Pure Reason*, 1781)

# APPENDIX 1
# Linearization of Nonlinear Processes

A nonlinear process may be linearized, near a certain operation-state, if only small input perturbations are applied to it at this state. Consequently, the identification inputs discussed in Chapters 3, 4, 10, in relation to linear systems may be applicable to the linearized formulation of nonlinear systems if the inputs are kept low enough. The linearized characteristics of a nonlinear process, for small perturbations, are derived as follows:

Consider a nonlinear process given by:

$$\dot{\mathbf{x}} = \mathbf{f}(\mathbf{x}, \mathbf{u}) \tag{A-1.1}$$

$\mathbf{f}$ being a nonlinear $n \cdot 1$ vector function of $\mathbf{x}$, $\mathbf{u}$, and $\mathbf{x}$, $\mathbf{u}$ being an $n \cdot 1$ state-vector and an $m \cdot 1$ control-vector, respectively. If only small perturbations in $\mathbf{u}$, $\mathbf{x}$ are assumed, we obtain:

$$\dot{\mathbf{x}} + \delta\dot{\mathbf{x}} = \mathbf{f}(\mathbf{x} + \delta\mathbf{x} : \mathbf{u} + \delta\mathbf{u}) \tag{A-1.2}$$

Subtracting Equation (A-1.1) from (A-1.2) gives:

$$\delta\dot{\mathbf{x}} = \mathbf{f}(\mathbf{x} + \delta\mathbf{x}, \mathbf{u} + \delta\mathbf{u}) - \mathbf{f}(\mathbf{x}, \mathbf{u}) = \left[\frac{\partial \mathbf{f}^T}{\partial \mathbf{x}}\right]_{\mathbf{x}_0, \mathbf{u}_0} \cdot \delta\mathbf{x} + \left[\frac{\partial \mathbf{f}^T}{\partial \mathbf{u}}\right]_{\mathbf{x}_0, \mathbf{u}_0} \cdot \delta\mathbf{u} \tag{A-1.3}$$

$[\cdots]_{\mathbf{x}_0, \mathbf{u}_0}$ denoting $[\cdots]$ near $\mathbf{x}_0$, $\mathbf{u}_0$, and $T$ denoting a transpose.

Defining:

$$A^T = \frac{\partial \mathbf{f}}{\partial \mathbf{x}} = \begin{bmatrix} \frac{\partial f_1}{\partial x_1} & \frac{\partial f_2}{\partial x_1} & \cdots & \frac{\partial f_n}{\partial x_1} \\ \frac{\partial f_1}{\partial x_2} & & \cdots & \vdots \\ \vdots & & & \vdots \\ \frac{\partial f_1}{\partial x_n} & & \cdots & \frac{\partial f_n}{\partial x_n} \end{bmatrix} = n \cdot n \text{ matrix} \qquad \text{(A-1.4)}$$

and:

$$\mathbf{B}^T \triangleq \frac{\partial \mathbf{f}}{\partial \mathbf{u}} = \begin{bmatrix} \frac{\partial f_1}{\partial u_1} & \cdots & \frac{\partial f_n}{\partial u_1} \\ \vdots & & \vdots \\ \frac{\partial f_1}{\partial u_m} & & \frac{\partial f_n}{\partial u_m} \end{bmatrix} = n \cdot m \text{ matrix} \qquad \text{(A-1.5)}$$

Equation (A-1.3) yields the following linearized small-perturbations expression:

$$\delta\dot{\mathbf{x}} = \mathbf{A} \cdot \delta\mathbf{x} + \mathbf{B} \cdot \delta\mathbf{u} \qquad \text{(A-1.6)}$$

The derivation of $\frac{\partial \mathbf{f}}{\partial \mathbf{x}}, \frac{\partial \mathbf{f}}{\partial \mathbf{u}}$ is further discussed in Appendix 2.

EXAMPLE

Consider the following nonlinear process:

$$\left.\begin{aligned} \dot{x}_1 &= 2 \cdot x_1^2 + 3 \cdot x_1 \cdot u \\ \dot{x}_2 &= x_1 \cdot x_2 + u^3 \end{aligned}\right\}$$

For small perturbations, the latter process may be described as follows (employing conventional scalar partial differentiation):

$$\left.\begin{aligned} \delta\dot{x}_1 &= (2x_{1,0} + 3u_0)\,\delta x_1 + 3x_{1,0}\,\delta u \\ \delta\dot{x}_2 &= x_{2,0}\,\delta x_1 + x_{1,0}\,\delta x_2 + 3u_0^2\,\delta u \end{aligned}\right\}$$

or, in vector form:

$$\delta\dot{\mathbf{x}} = \begin{bmatrix} 2 \cdot x_{1,0} + 3 \cdot u_0\,; & 0 \\ x_{2,0} & ; \; x_{1,0} \end{bmatrix} \delta\mathbf{x} + \begin{bmatrix} 3 \cdot x_{1,0} \\ 3 \cdot u_0^2 \end{bmatrix} \delta\mathbf{u} = \mathbf{A}\,\delta\mathbf{x} + \mathbf{B}\,\delta\mathbf{u}$$

We observe that **f** of the original system of this example is given by:

$$\mathbf{f} = \begin{bmatrix} f_1 \\ f_2 \end{bmatrix} = \begin{bmatrix} 2x_1 + 3x_1 \cdot u \\ x_1 x_2 + u^3 \end{bmatrix}$$

Consequently:

$$\left[\frac{\partial \mathbf{f}}{\partial \mathbf{x}}\right]^T = \begin{bmatrix} \dfrac{\partial f_1}{\partial x_1}; & \dfrac{\partial f_1}{2x_2} \\[2ex] \dfrac{\partial f_2}{\partial x_1}; & \dfrac{\partial f_2}{2x_2} \end{bmatrix} = \begin{bmatrix} 3x_1; & 0 \\ x_2; & x_1 \end{bmatrix} \triangleq \mathbf{A}$$

$$\left[\frac{\partial \mathbf{f}}{\partial \mathbf{u}}\right]^T = \begin{bmatrix} \dfrac{\partial f_1}{\partial u} \\[2ex] \dfrac{\partial f_2}{\partial u} \end{bmatrix} = \begin{bmatrix} 3x_1 \\ 3u_2 \end{bmatrix} \triangleq \mathbf{B}$$

yielding the same **A**, **B** matrices as derived through conventional (scalar) partial differentiation of the nonlinear process equations.

# APPENDIX 2
# Differentiation of Trace Functions with Respect to Matrices

The discussion below is based on derivations of gradients as described by Kleinman and Athans (see Refs. 8 and 9 to Chapter 5).

In the present discussion we consider a scalar $J$ that is a function of any $n \cdot m$ matrix $\mathbf{x}$. The gradient of $J$ with respect to $\mathbf{x}$ is given by:

$$\nabla J_{\mathbf{x}} \triangleq \frac{\partial J}{\partial \mathbf{x}} = \begin{bmatrix} \dfrac{\partial J}{\partial x_{11}} & \cdots & \dfrac{\partial J}{\partial x_{1m}} \\ \vdots & & \vdots \\ \dfrac{\partial J}{\partial x_{n1}} & \cdots & \dfrac{\partial J}{\partial x_{nm}} \end{bmatrix} \tag{A-2.1}$$

where

$$\mathbf{x} \triangleq \begin{bmatrix} x_{11} & \cdots & x_{m1} \\ \vdots & & \vdots \\ x_{n1} & \cdots & x_{nm} \end{bmatrix} \tag{A-2.2}$$

When $J$ represents a trace of a matrix, this matrix being a function of $\mathbf{x}$ the gradient, $\partial J/\partial \mathbf{x}$ becomes a gradient with respect to this trace function. The latter gradient expressions may be obtained through long-hand differentiation, considering Equation (A-2.1). Some of the more common such gradients are given in Ref. 9 to Chapter 5 of this text, and a somewhat extended list of these gradients is presented below, as follows (assuming that a trace exists):

$$\frac{\partial tr(\mathbf{x})}{\partial \mathbf{x}} = \mathbf{I} \tag{A-2.3}$$

$$\frac{\partial tr(\mathbf{Ax})}{\partial \mathbf{x}} = \mathbf{A}^T \tag{A-2.4}$$

$$\frac{\partial tr(\mathbf{Ax}^T)}{\partial \mathbf{x}} = \mathbf{A} \tag{A-2.5}$$

$$\frac{\partial tr(\mathbf{AxB})}{\partial \mathbf{x}} = \mathbf{A}^T\mathbf{B}^T \tag{A-2.6}$$

$$\frac{\partial tr(\mathbf{Ax}^T\mathbf{B})}{\partial \mathbf{x}} = \mathbf{BA} \tag{A-2.7}$$

$$\frac{\partial tr(\mathbf{x}^T\mathbf{Ax})}{\partial \mathbf{x}} = (\mathbf{A} + \mathbf{A}^T)\,\mathbf{x} \tag{A-2.8}$$

$$\frac{\partial tr(\mathbf{xAx}^T)}{\partial \mathbf{x}} = \mathbf{x}(\mathbf{A} + \mathbf{A}^T) \tag{A-2.9}$$

$$\frac{\partial tr(\mathbf{AxBx})}{\partial \mathbf{x}} = \mathbf{A}^T\mathbf{x}^T\mathbf{B}^T + \mathbf{B}^T\mathbf{x}^T\mathbf{A}^T \tag{A-2.10}$$

$$\frac{\partial tr(\mathbf{AxBx}^T)}{\partial \mathbf{x}} = \mathbf{AxB} + \mathbf{A}^T\mathbf{xB}^T \tag{A-2.11}$$

$$\frac{\partial tr(\mathbf{Axx}^T\mathbf{B})}{\partial \mathbf{x}} = (\mathbf{A}^T\mathbf{B}^T + \mathbf{BA})\mathbf{x} \tag{A-2.12}$$

$$\frac{\partial tr(e^{\mathbf{x}})}{\partial \mathbf{x}} = e^{\mathbf{x}^T} \tag{A-2.13}$$

$$\frac{\partial tr[\det|\mathbf{x}|]}{\partial \mathbf{x}} = \det|\mathbf{x}| \cdot (\mathbf{x}^{-1})^T \tag{A-2.14}$$

$$\frac{\partial tr[\det|\mathbf{AxB}|]}{\partial \mathbf{x}} = \det|\mathbf{AxB}| \cdot (\mathbf{x}^{-1})^T \tag{A-2.15}$$

$$\frac{\partial tr(\mathbf{x}^{-1})}{\partial \mathbf{x}} = -[(\mathbf{x}^{-1})(\mathbf{x}^{-1})]^T \tag{A-2.16}$$

$$\frac{\partial tr(\mathbf{Ax}^{-1}\mathbf{B})}{\partial \mathbf{x}} = -(\mathbf{x}^{-1}\mathbf{BAx}^{-1})^T \tag{A-2.17}$$

$\partial J/\partial \mathbf{x}$ may be simplified by employing Kleinman's Lemma (see Ref. 8 to Chapter 5), that is briefly re-stated as follows:

Let $f(\mathbf{x})$ be a trace function. Consequently, if the relation:

$$f(\mathbf{x} + \varepsilon\,\Delta\mathbf{x}) - f(\mathbf{x}) = \varepsilon\, tr[\mathbf{M}(\mathbf{x}) \cdot \Delta\mathbf{x}] \qquad @ \quad \varepsilon \to 0 \tag{A-2.18}$$

holds, $\mathbf{M}$, $\mathbf{x}$ being $n \cdot m$ and $m \cdot n$ matrices, respectively, we obtain:

$$\frac{\partial f(\mathbf{x})}{\partial \mathbf{x}} = \mathbf{M}^T(\mathbf{x}) \tag{A-2.19}$$

Employing Kleinman's Lemma, we may subsequently prove that if $\partial J/\partial \mathbf{x}$ exists, then (see also Ref. 10 to Chapter 5):

$$\frac{\partial J}{\partial \mathbf{x}} = \frac{\partial \, \Delta J}{\partial \, \Delta \mathbf{x}} \quad @ \quad J \to 0; \mathbf{x} \to \mathbf{0} \tag{A-2.20}$$

For proving Equation (A-2.20), we define:

$$\Delta J \triangleq f(\mathbf{x} + \Delta \mathbf{x}) - f(x) \tag{A-2.21}$$

Considering equations (A-2.18) and (A-2.19) we derive:

$$f(\mathbf{x} + \varepsilon \, \Delta \mathbf{x}) - f(\mathbf{x}) = \varepsilon \, \Delta J = \varepsilon \, tr[\mathbf{M}(\mathbf{x}) \cdot \Delta \mathbf{x}] \tag{A-2.22}$$

Consequently:

$$\Delta J = tr[\mathbf{M}(\mathbf{x}) \, \Delta \mathbf{x}] \tag{A-2.23}$$

Finally, noting that $\mathbf{x}$ is independent of $\Delta \mathbf{x}$, and observing Equation (A-2.6), we obtain, for $\Delta J \to 0$, $\Delta \mathbf{x} \to \mathbf{0}$:

$$\frac{\partial \, \Delta J}{\partial \, \Delta \mathbf{x}} = \mathbf{M}^T(\mathbf{x}) \qquad \text{Q.E.D.} \tag{A-2.24}$$

# APPENDIX 3

# The Integral Property of $\mathbf{Ax}+\mathbf{xA}^T+\mathbf{C}=\mathbf{0}$

The matrix equation:

$$\mathbf{Ax}+\mathbf{xA}^T+\mathbf{C}=\mathbf{0} \tag{A-3.1}$$

**x, A, B, C** being square matrices, arises in many identification, optimization and stability analysis problems.

When all the eigenvalues of **A** have a negative real part, **x** of Equation (A-3.1) has a unique solution given by:

$$\mathbf{x}=\int_0^\infty e^{\mathbf{A}t}\mathbf{C}e^{\mathbf{A}^T t}\,dt \tag{A-3.2}$$

The latter solution may be derived by proving that Equation (A-3.2) satisfies Equation (A-3.1), as follows:
Let:

$$\dot{\mathbf{U}} \triangleq \mathbf{A}e^{\mathbf{A}t} \tag{A-3.3}$$

$$\mathbf{V}=\mathbf{C}e^{\mathbf{A}^T t} \tag{A-3.4}$$

and, consider the following expression for $\mathbf{A}\cdot\mathbf{x}$ resulting from Equation (A-3.2):

$$\mathbf{Ax}=\int_0^\infty \mathbf{A}e^{\mathbf{A}t}\mathbf{C}e^{\mathbf{A}^T t}\,dt \tag{A-3.5}$$

Substituting for $\mathbf{A}e^{\mathbf{A}t}$, $\mathbf{C}e^{\mathbf{A}^Tt}$ from Equation (A-3.3), (A-3.4) into (A-3.5) we derive:

$$\mathbf{Ax} = \int_0^\infty \dot{\mathbf{U}}\mathbf{V}\,dt \tag{A-3.6}$$

and, through integration by parts:

$$\mathbf{Ax} = \mathbf{UV}\Big|_0^\infty - \int_0^\infty \mathbf{U}\dot{\mathbf{V}}\,dt \tag{A-3.7}$$

However, equations (A-3.3), (A-3.4) yield:

$$\mathbf{U} = \int \dot{\mathbf{U}}dt = e^{\mathbf{A}t} + \mathbf{K} \tag{A-3.8}$$

$$\dot{\mathbf{V}} = \mathbf{C}e^{\mathbf{A}^Tt}\mathbf{A}^T \tag{A-3.9}$$

(We note that when a Taylor series expansion of $\mathbf{A}e^{\mathbf{A}t}$ is considered, no inversion of $\mathbf{A}$ arises in integrating $\dot{\mathbf{U}}$). Substituting the latter expressions for $\mathbf{U}$, $\dot{\mathbf{V}}$ into Equation (A-3.7), we obtain:

$$\mathbf{Ax} = \underbrace{(e^{\mathbf{A}t} + \mathbf{K})}_{\mathbf{U}}\underbrace{\mathbf{C}e^{\mathbf{A}^Tt}}_{\mathbf{V}}\Big|_0^\infty - \int_0^\infty e^{\mathbf{A}t}\mathbf{C}e^{\mathbf{A}^Tt}\,dt \cdot \mathbf{A}^T - \mathbf{KC}e^{\mathbf{A}^Tt}\Big|_0^\infty \tag{A-3.10}$$

Considering the eigenvalue requirements on $\mathbf{A}$, the term $e^{\mathbf{A}t}$ satisfies:

$$e^{\mathbf{A}\infty} = \mathbf{0} \tag{A-3.11}$$

Consequently, and substituting for $\int_0^\infty e^{\mathbf{A}t}\mathbf{C}e^{\mathbf{A}^Tt}\,dt$ from Equation (A-3.2), Equation (A-3.10) becomes:

$$\mathbf{Ax} + \mathbf{xA}^T + \mathbf{C} = \mathbf{0} \tag{A-3.12}$$

Q.E.D.

# APPENDIX 4
# Solutions to Selected Problems

## CHAPTER 2

**3.** Uncontrollable, $\mathbf{V} = \begin{bmatrix} 1 & 1 \\ 1 & -1 \end{bmatrix}$; $\mathbf{V}^{-1} = \begin{bmatrix} 0.5 & 0.5 \\ 0.5 & -0.5 \end{bmatrix}$.

**5.** Unobservable.

**9.** $G(s) = \dfrac{s+7}{s^2 + 2s - 11}$.

## CHAPTER 3

**2.** $G(s)$ is approximately given by $\dfrac{1}{(s+1)(0.35s+1)}$.

**4.** $G(s)$ is approximately given by $\dfrac{10}{(16.4s+1)^4}$. The value of $n$ is approximated to the nearest integer to be 4 according to $\eta$ and according to $T_a/T_b$ or $T_e/T_b$ of Table 3.3. The value of $\tau$ is subsequently obtained from Table 3.4 as 16.8; 16.1, 16.0; 16.7 from $T_a/\tau$; $T_b/\tau$; $T_d/\tau$; $T_e/\tau$, respectively.

## CHAPTER 4

**1.** The sequence is given by: 1, 13, 69, 97, 61, 93, 9, 17, 21, 73, 49, 37, 81, 53, 89, 57, 41, 33, 29, 77, 1, 13, .... We note that the 21'st element of the sequence is identical to the first, and the sequence is repeated from that element.

**4.** $\phi_{xx}(0) = \frac{1}{N}\sum_{j=0}^{N-1} x_j x_j = \frac{1}{N}\sum_{j=0}^{N} (x_j)^2 = 1$ since $x_j$ are either 1 or $-1$ $\forall j, N$. Consequently, for a 15 element MLNSN, we obtain that $\phi_{xx}(0) = 1$; $\phi_{xx}(1) = -\frac{1}{15}$ and subsequently, $\phi_{xx}(k) = \pm\frac{1}{15}$ $\forall k = 2, 3, \ldots 14$. We note that the MLNSN is $+1, +1, +1, +1, -1, -1, -1, +1, -1, -1, +1, +1, -1, +1, -1$, as obtained from the MLNS of period 15 given in Section 4.2.2-a., when replacing all 0 by $-1$.

**5.** $+1, -1, +1, +1, +1, -1, -1, -1, +1, -1 \pm 1$.

## CHAPTER 5

**1.** $y = 29x_1 + 2.2x_2 + 0.5x_3$.

**3.** $\mathbf{A} = \begin{bmatrix} 0 & 1 \\ -4 & -2{,}6 \end{bmatrix} \quad \mathbf{B} = \begin{bmatrix} 0 \\ 1.5 \end{bmatrix}$.

**6.** Substituting $\xi = \cos\lambda$ into Equation (5.72), we obtain that arcos $\xi = \lambda$ and $T_\nu(\xi) = \cos(\nu\lambda)$. Consequently, Equation (5.73) becomes:

$$\int_{-1}^{1} \frac{\cos(\mu\lambda)\cdot\cos(\nu\lambda)}{\sqrt{1-\cos^2\lambda}}\, d\xi$$

However: $\sqrt{1-\cos^2\lambda} = \sin\lambda$, and $d\xi = d(\cos\lambda) = \sin\lambda\, d\lambda$ yielding:

$$\int_{-1}^{1} \frac{\cos(\mu\lambda)\cdot\cos(\nu\lambda)}{\sqrt{1-\cos^2\lambda}}\, d(\cos\lambda) = \int_{0}^{\pi} \frac{\cos(\mu\lambda)\cos(\nu\lambda)}{\sin\lambda} \sin\lambda\, \partial\lambda$$

$$= \int_{1}^{\pi} \cos(\mu\lambda)\cdot\cos(\nu\lambda)\, d\lambda = \left[\frac{\sin(\mu+\nu)\lambda}{2(\mu+\nu)} + \frac{\sin(\mu-\nu)}{2(\mu-\nu)}\right]_0^{\pi} = \begin{cases} 0 \ @\ \mu \neq \nu \\ \frac{\pi}{2} \ @\ \mu = \nu \neq 0 \\ \pi \ @\ \mu = \nu = 0 \end{cases}$$

**10.** $$\frac{\partial S}{\partial b_k} = \frac{\partial}{\partial b_k}\left[\sum_j y(\xi_j) - b_0 T_0(\xi_j) - b_1 T_1(\xi_j) - \cdots b_m T_m(\xi_j)\right]^2$$

$$= \frac{\partial}{\partial b_k}\left[\sum_j b_k^2 T_k^2(\xi_j) - 2y(\xi_j) b_k T_k(\xi_j)\right] = 0$$

(Because of the orthogonality property, all sums over other terms are zero). Consequently;

$$2\sum_j b_k^2 T_k^2(\xi_j) = 2\sum_j y(\xi_j) b_k T_k(\xi_j)$$

yielding:

$$b_k^2 \sum_j T_k^2(\xi_j) = b_k \sum_j y(\xi_j) T_k(\xi_j)$$

and:

$$b_k = \frac{\sum_j y(\xi_j) T_k(\xi_j)}{\sum_j T_k^2(\xi_j)}$$

and, noting Equation (5.79), the relations of equations (5.81-a), (5.81-b) are obtained.

**11.** $a = 20$; $b = 0.25$; $c = 3$.

## CHAPTER 6

**1.** For a maximum computer word of $10^{15}$ and for $1/\varepsilon = 10$, we obtain that:

$$\mathbf{P}_1 = \begin{bmatrix} 9.431 & -2.254 \\ -2.254 & 1.074 \end{bmatrix} \qquad \mathbf{a}_1 = \begin{bmatrix} -0.6421 \\ 2.5426 \end{bmatrix}$$

$$\mathbf{P}_2 = \begin{bmatrix} 0.084 & 0.0865 \\ 0.0865 & 0.4876 \end{bmatrix} \qquad \mathbf{a}_2 = \begin{bmatrix} -0.6209 \\ 2.8589 \end{bmatrix}$$

$$\mathbf{P}_{10} = \begin{bmatrix} 0.0109 & -0.0039 \\ -0.0039 & 0.0847 \end{bmatrix} \qquad \mathbf{a}_{10} = \begin{bmatrix} -0.5982 \\ 0.2974 \end{bmatrix}$$

$$\mathbf{P}_{30} = \begin{bmatrix} 0.002 & -0.0005 \\ -0.0005 & 0.03 \end{bmatrix} \qquad \mathbf{a}_{30} = \begin{bmatrix} -0.5997 \\ 2.991 \end{bmatrix}$$

For $1/\varepsilon = 10^3$, we obtain:

$$\mathbf{P}_1 = \begin{bmatrix} 940.1 & -237.3 \\ -237.3 & 60.456 \end{bmatrix}; \qquad \mathbf{a}_1 = \begin{bmatrix} 0.6759 \\ 2.6763 \end{bmatrix}$$

$$\mathbf{P}_2 = \begin{bmatrix} 0.0850 & 0.0917 \\ 0.0917 & 0.5131 \end{bmatrix}; \qquad \mathbf{a}_2 = \begin{bmatrix} -0.6002 \\ 2.9985 \end{bmatrix}$$

$$\mathbf{P}_{10} = \begin{bmatrix} 0.011 & -0.0039 \\ -0.0039 & 0.0855 \end{bmatrix}; \qquad \mathbf{a}_{10} = \begin{bmatrix} -0.59998 \\ 2.9996 \end{bmatrix}$$

For $1/\varepsilon = 10^{20}$ (above maximum computer number), we obtain:

$$\mathbf{P}_1 = \begin{bmatrix} 9.4 \cdot 10^{19} & -2.37 \cdot 10^{19} \\ -2.37 \cdot 10^{19} & 6.0 \cdot 10^{19} \end{bmatrix} \qquad \mathbf{a}_1 = \begin{bmatrix} -4.97 \cdot 10^5 \\ -3.72 \cdot 10^5 \end{bmatrix}$$

$$\mathbf{P}_2 = \begin{bmatrix} -5.24 \cdot 10^5 & -2.62 \cdot 10^5 \\ -2.62 \cdot 10^5 & -6.55 \cdot 10^4 \end{bmatrix} \qquad \mathbf{a}_2 = \begin{bmatrix} 3.48 \cdot 10^{12} \\ -1.49 \cdot 10^{12} \end{bmatrix}$$

$$\mathbf{P}_{30} = \begin{bmatrix} +0.0025 & -0.0008 \\ -0.0008 & 0.0332 \end{bmatrix} \qquad \mathbf{a}_{30} = \begin{bmatrix} 1.539 \cdot 10^4 \\ 4.775 \cdot 10^4 \end{bmatrix}$$

the actual a being $\mathbf{a} = [-0.6; 3.0]^T$.

**2.** $\mathbf{a} = [1.00002; 1.99995; 2.9994]$ in both cases, the true value being $[1, 2, 3]$. However, for $1/\varepsilon = 10^{20}$ (above maximum computer number), we obtain that:

$$\mathbf{a} = [-6.936 \cdot 10^{17}; 1.9816 \cdot 10^{18}; 3.27 \cdot 10^{18}]$$

which is nonsensical.

## CHAPTER 7

**2.** $\alpha = 0.5$ yields:

$$\mathbf{P}_2 = \begin{bmatrix} 1.8 \\ 1.35 \end{bmatrix}; \quad \mathbf{P}_3 = \begin{bmatrix} 1.74 \\ 1.23 \end{bmatrix}; \quad \mathbf{P}_4 = \begin{bmatrix} 1.90 \\ 1.145 \end{bmatrix}$$

$\alpha = 1.0$ yields:

$$\mathbf{P}_2 = \begin{bmatrix} 1.8 \\ 1.35 \end{bmatrix}; \quad \mathbf{P}_3 = \begin{bmatrix} 1.68 \\ 1.11 \end{bmatrix}; \quad \mathbf{P}_4 = \begin{bmatrix} 2.0 \\ 0.94 \end{bmatrix}$$

$\alpha = 1.5$ yields:

$$\mathbf{P}_2 = \begin{bmatrix} 1.8 \\ 1.35 \end{bmatrix} \quad \mathbf{p}_3 = \begin{bmatrix} 1.01 \\ 1.01 \end{bmatrix}; \quad \mathbf{P}_4 = \begin{bmatrix} 0.755 \\ 0.755 \end{bmatrix}$$

the true $\mathbf{P}$ being:

$$\mathbf{P} = \begin{bmatrix} 2 \\ 1 \end{bmatrix}$$

The solution above already indicates that for $\alpha \ll 1$, $\mathbf{P}$ converge slowly but surely, whereas $\alpha \geq 1$, $\mathbf{P}$ tend to oscillate.

**4.** $\mathbf{a}(t) = \begin{bmatrix} 2 \\ 2 \end{bmatrix}$ up to the tenth sampling interval and $\begin{bmatrix} 3 \\ 2 \end{bmatrix}$ thereafter.

## CHAPTER 8

**1.** Starting with the initial estimate $\hat{a}_1 = -0.12$ and noting the boundary (initial) condition $x(0) = 0$, we derive the first estimate $\hat{x}_1(t)\ \forall t > 0$, as follows:

$$\dot{x}_1(t) = -0.2x_1(t) + u(t)$$

yielding:

$$\hat{x}_1(t) = 1 - \exp(-0.2t) \qquad \forall t > 0$$

Defining the adjoined vector $\mathbf{z}$:

$$\mathbf{z} \triangleq [x_1, a]^T$$

we obtain, according to Equation (8.8):

$$\hat{\boldsymbol{\psi}}_\mu = \begin{bmatrix} \hat{a}\hat{x} + u \\ 0 \end{bmatrix}_\mu; \qquad \left.\frac{\partial \hat{\boldsymbol{\psi}}}{\partial \mathbf{z}}\right|_\mu = \begin{bmatrix} \hat{a} & \hat{x} \\ 0 & 0 \end{bmatrix}_\mu$$

and, noting Equation (8.7):

$$\hat{\mathbf{z}}_{\mu+1} = \begin{bmatrix} \hat{a}_\mu \hat{x}_\mu + u \\ 0 \end{bmatrix} + \begin{bmatrix} \hat{a}_\mu \hat{x}_{\mu+1} + \hat{a}_{\mu+1}\hat{x}_\mu - 2a_\mu x_\mu \\ 0 \end{bmatrix}$$

Subsequently:

$$\hat{\mathbf{z}}_{\mu+1}(t) = \hat{\boldsymbol{\Phi}}(t_1 t_0)\mathbf{z}_{\mu+1}(t_0) + \hat{\mathbf{q}}_{\mu+1}(t)$$

where, according to Equation (8.13):

$$\dot{\hat{\boldsymbol{\Phi}}}_{\mu+1}(t, t_0) = \begin{bmatrix} \hat{a}_\mu & \hat{x}_\mu \\ 0 & 0 \end{bmatrix} \hat{\boldsymbol{\Phi}}_{\mu+1}(t, t_0)$$

$$\hat{\boldsymbol{\Phi}}(t_0, t_0) = \mathbf{I}$$

such that:

$$\phi_{21,\mu}(t, t_0) = 0 \qquad \forall t, \mu$$
$$\phi_{22,\mu}(t, t_0) = 1 \qquad \forall t, \mu$$

Furthermore, Equation (8.15) yields:

$$\dot{\hat{\mathbf{q}}}_{\mu+1}(t) = \begin{bmatrix} \hat{a}_\mu \hat{x}_\mu(t) \\ 0 \end{bmatrix} - \begin{bmatrix} 2a_\mu x_\mu(t) \\ 0 \end{bmatrix} + \begin{bmatrix} a_\mu & \hat{x}_\mu \\ 0 & 0 \end{bmatrix} \cdot \hat{\mathbf{q}}_{\mu+1}(t)$$

with $\hat{\mathbf{q}}_{\mu+1}(t_0) = \mathbf{0}$, such that $q_{2,\mu}(t) = 0\ \forall \mu, t$ and:

$$\dot{\hat{q}}_{1,\mu+1}(t) = -\hat{a}_\mu \hat{x}_\mu(t) + \hat{a}_\mu \hat{q}_{1,\mu+1}(t)$$

Since $\hat{a}_1$; $\hat{x}_1(t)$ are now available $\forall t$, we now have $\hat{q}_{1,\mu+1}(t)$ at $\mu = 1$ for all $t$, as is required for computing $\mathbf{z}_2(t_0)$ from Equation (8.17), namely:

$$x(0) = \hat{\phi}_{11,2}(0, t_0)\hat{x}_2(t_0) + \hat{\phi}_{12,2}(0, t_0)\hat{a}_2 + \hat{q}_{1,2}(0)$$
$$x(1) = \hat{\phi}_{11,2}(1, t_0)\hat{x}_2(t_0) + \hat{\phi}_{12,2}(1, t_0)\hat{a}_2 + \hat{q}_{1,2}(1)$$
$$x(2) = \hat{\phi}_{11,2}(2, t_0)\hat{x}_2(t_0) + \cdots$$

Assuming that $t_0 = 0$, the expression for $x(1)$ above becomes:

$$x(1) = \hat{\phi}_{12,2}(1, 0)\hat{a}_2 + q_{1,2}(1)$$

and since $\hat{\boldsymbol{\Phi}}_2(1, 0)$; $\hat{q}_{1,2}(1)$ are already available, whereas $x(1)$ has been given in the data, the second estimate $\hat{a}_2$ of $a$ is now computable. Continuing in this manner, we finally converge to $\hat{a} = -0.1$.

**3.** For $\hat{a}_1 = -4$ or $-3$ the solution converges to approximately $-2$, whereas no convergence is obtained with $\hat{a}_1 = -10$.

## CHAPTER 9

**1.** We observe that $\dot{a} = \dot{b} = 0$ and define an adjoined state vector $\mathbf{y} = [x; a; b]^T$ and a cost functional $J$ given by:

$$J \triangleq \int_0^{t_f} (z - \hat{x})^2 \, dt$$

We subsequently consider the analysis of Example 9.1 of Chapter 9 to obtain, according to Equation (9.34):

$$\begin{bmatrix} \dot{\hat{y}}_1 \\ \dot{\hat{y}}_2 \\ \dot{\hat{y}}_3 \end{bmatrix} - \begin{bmatrix} \dot{Q}_{11} & \dot{Q}_{12} & \dot{Q}_{13} \\ \dot{Q}_{12} & \dot{Q}_{22} & \dot{Q}_{23} \\ \dot{Q}_{13} & \dot{Q}_{23} & \dot{Q}_{33} \end{bmatrix} \begin{bmatrix} C_1 \\ C_2 \\ C_3 \end{bmatrix}$$

$$- \begin{bmatrix} Q_{11} & Q_{12} & Q_{13} \\ Q_{12} & Q_{22} & Q_{23} \\ Q_{13} & Q_{23} & Q_{33} \end{bmatrix} \begin{bmatrix} 2(z - \hat{y}_1 + Q_{11}C_1 + Q_{12}C_2 + Q_{13}C_3) - C_1(\hat{y}_2 - Q_{12}C_1 - Q_{22}C_2 - Q_{23}C_3) \\ -C_1(\hat{y}_1 - Q_{11}C_1 - Q_{12}C_2 - Q_{13}C_3) \\ -C_1 u \end{bmatrix}$$

$$= \begin{bmatrix} (\hat{y}_1 - Q_{11}C_1 - Q_{12}C_2 - Q_{13}C_3)(\hat{y}_2 - Q_{12}C_1 - Q_{22}C_2 - Q_{23}C_3) + u(\hat{y}_3 - Q_{13}C_1 - Q_{23}C_2 - Q_{33}C_3) \\ 0 \\ 0 \end{bmatrix}$$

which yields, near $\mathbf{C} = \mathbf{0}$:

$$\begin{cases} \dot{\hat{y}}_1 - 2Q_{11}(z - \hat{y}_1) = \hat{y}_1\hat{y}_2 + u\hat{y}_3 \\ \dot{\hat{y}}_2 - 2Q_{12}(z - \hat{y}_1) = 0 \\ \dot{\hat{y}}_3 - 2Q_{13}(z - \hat{y}_1) = 0 \end{cases}$$

$$\begin{aligned} \dot{Q}_{11} &= -2(Q_{11}^2 - \hat{y}_2 Q_{11} - \hat{y}_1 Q_{12} - uQ_{13}) \\ \dot{Q}_{12} &= -2(Q_{11}Q_{12} + \hat{y}_2 Q_{12} + \hat{y}_1 Q_{22} + uQ_{23}) \\ \dot{Q}_{22} &= -2Q_{13}^2 \\ \dot{Q}_{13} &= -2Q_{11}Q_{13} + \hat{y}_2 Q_{13} + \hat{y}_1 Q_{23} + uQ_{33} \\ \dot{Q}_{23} &= -2Q_{12}Q_{13} \\ \dot{Q}_{33} &= -2Q_{21}^2 \end{aligned}$$

We note that sets of two equations for $\dot{Q}_{12}$, $\dot{Q}_{13}$, $\dot{Q}_{23}$ are derivable from Equation (9.34). However, the second equation for each, and any further equations for higher dimensional systems are equivalent to the first equation, such that no contradictions may occur.

The initial conditions to solve the latter sets of equations for $\dot{\mathbf{y}}$; $\dot{\mathbf{Q}}$ are chosen as follows:

$$\begin{aligned} \hat{y}_1(0) &= z(0) \\ -\hat{y}_2(0) &= y_3(0) = 1 \\ \mathbf{Q}(0) &= \mathbf{I} \end{aligned}$$

as dictated by the problem. The solution for $\hat{a}$, $\hat{b}$ thus becomes:

| | | | | | | | | | |
|---|---|---|---|---|---|---|---|---|---|
| $t =$ | 0 | 0.5 | 2.0 | 3.0 | 4.0 | 5.0 | 10 | 15 | 17.1 |
| $\hat{a} =$ | −1 | −1.003 | −1.067 | −1.022 | −.9712 | −.9702 | −.8887 | −.8138 | −.7766 |
| $\hat{b} =$ | 1 | .9825 | .8363 | .8445 | .8412 | .8328 | .7921 | .7607 | .7391 |

whereas the true values of $a$, $b$ are $a = -0.5$; $b = 0.5$.

**2.**

| | | | | | | | | | |
|---|---|---|---|---|---|---|---|---|---|
| $t =$ | 0 | 0.5 | 2.0 | 3.0 | 4.0 | 5.0 | 10 | 15 | 17.1 |
| $\hat{a} =$ | −1.5 | −1.508 | −1.636 | −1.579 | −1.536 | −1.543 | −1.452 | −1.314 | −1.261 |
| $\hat{b} =$ | 1.5 | 1.467 | 1.236 | 1.247 | 1.245 | 1.217 | 1.164 | 1.117 | 1.087 |

We note that convergence to the true $\hat{a}$, $\hat{b}$ is accomplished, although it is slower than with the better initial estimates of Problem 1. (Further runs with a longer measurements record and with the initial estimates of Problem 1 yielded convergence to $\hat{a} = -.569$ and $\hat{b} = .568$ at $t = 80$, whereas the present initial estimates yielded $a = -.677$ and $b = .668$ at $t = 80$, the true $\hat{a}$, $\hat{b}$ being $-0.5$ and $0.5$, respectively.)

**3.** For $Q(0) = 0.2 \cdot \mathbf{I}$:

| | | |
|---|---|---|
| $t =$ | 0 | 16.1 |
| $\hat{a} =$ | −1 | .9620 |
| $\hat{b} =$ | 1 | −.8924 |

For $\mathbf{Q}(0) = 5 \cdot \mathbf{I}$:

| | | | | | | | | | |
|---|---|---|---|---|---|---|---|---|---|
| $t =$ | 0 | 0.5 | 2.0 | 3.0 | 4.0 | 5.0 | 10 | 15 | 17.1 |
| $\hat{a} =$ | −1 | −1.009 | −1.07 | −.8928 | −.7514 | −.7441 | −.6269 | −.5909 | −.5699 |
| $\hat{b} =$ | 1 | .944 | .7564 | .7348 | .6859 | .6744 | .604 | .5825 | .5660 |

The convergence rate with $\mathbf{Q} = 5\mathbf{I}$ is thus faster than with $\mathbf{Q} = \mathbf{I}$ (compare with the solution for Problem 1).

For $\mathbf{Q}(0) = 10 \cdot \mathbf{I}$:

| | | | | |
|---|---|---|---|---|
| $t =$ | 0 | 0.2 | 0.3 | 0.4 |
| $\hat{a} =$ | −1 | −1.009 | −541.2 | $-5.496 \cdot 10^{37}$ |
| $\hat{b} =$ | 1 | .8833 | −4432 | $-4.453 \cdot 10^{38}$ |

The four different choices of $\mathbf{Q}(0)$, as in Problems 1 and 3, demonstrate the importance of an appropriate choice of $\mathbf{Q}(0)$. The best choice was shown to be near $\mathbf{Q}(0) = 5 \cdot \mathbf{I}$. A smaller $\mathbf{Q}(0)$ converged slowly whereas a too-large $\mathbf{Q}(0)$ resulted in divergence.

## CHAPTER 10

1. The response is almost identical to target trajectory, apart from a slight deviation from $t=0$ to $t=2$ and immediately after the 50% parameter disturbance at $t=9$, as follows:

| $t$ | 0 | 1 | 2 | 3 | 4 | 6 | 8 | 9 | 10 | 11 | 12 |
|---|---|---|---|---|---|---|---|---|---|---|---|
| $x_1$ | 0 | .2 | .79 | 1.07 | 1.13 | 1.01 | .97 | .99 | .97 | .93 | .97 |
| $x_d$ | 0 | .4 | .7 | 1.07 | 1.14 | 1.02 | .98 | .99 | 1.0 | 1.01 | 1.0 |

| $t$ | 13 | 14 | 16 | 18 | 20 |
|---|---|---|---|---|---|
| $x_1$ | .95 | .95 | .96 | .97 | .99 |
| $x_d$ | 1.0 | 1.0 | 1.0 | 1.0 | 1.0 |

(Very similar results are obtainable for zero weights on $x_3$, $x_4$, $x_5$).

3.

$$\sigma_x \cong \begin{bmatrix} 3.6 & 0.2 \\ -8.4 & -1.5 \end{bmatrix}$$

$$\sigma_y \cong \begin{bmatrix} 4 & 0 \\ 0 & -6 \end{bmatrix}$$

$$\sigma_{xd} \cong \begin{bmatrix} 8.2 & 0 \\ 0 & 18.2 \end{bmatrix}$$

## CHAPTER 11

1. $\mu = \dfrac{\log 0.02}{\log 0.9} = 35$

Namely, 35 cells must be checked by random.

3. $p(\mu) = \sum_{i=1}^{\mu} \binom{w}{i}\binom{r-w}{\mu-i} \Big/ \binom{r}{\mu}$ when $\binom{x}{y} = \dfrac{x!}{y!(x-y)!}$

4. $a \cong -3$; $b \cong 0.5$.

## CHAPTER 12

1. The predicted values for $y(t+\theta)$ are given below where $y^*(t+\theta)$ indicate results obtained from the procedure of Section 12.3 while $y'(t+\theta)$ are those obtained by a Taylor extrapolation of the curve fit.

| $(t+\theta)$ | 18 | 19 | 20 | 21 | 22 | 23 | 24 |
|---|---|---|---|---|---|---|---|
| $y^*(t+\theta)$ | .8521 | .6044 | .0677 | 1.03781 | 1.3812 | 1.0641 | .3524 |
| $y'(t+\theta)$ | .8065 | .2695 | −.0948 | 1.2317 | 1.8635 | .9957 | .2444 |

| $(t+\theta)$ | 25 | 26 | 27 | 28 | 29 | 30 | 31 |
|---|---|---|---|---|---|---|---|
| $y^*$ | .1251 | 1.406 | 1.7477 | .7274 | −.3289 | .7769 | 1.4873 |
| $y'$ | −.1621 | 1.1944 | 1.7210 | 1.6031 | −.2859 | −.1367 | 1.3024 |

| $(t+\theta)$ | 32 | 33 | 34 | 35 | 36 | 37 | 38 |
|---|---|---|---|---|---|---|---|
| $y^*$ | 1.7263 | 1.0718 | .0551 | .5234 | .9566 | 1.0268 | .0876 |
| $y'$ | 2.5384 | 1.4392 | −.208 | −.3229 | .9853 | 1.6925 | .4348 |

| $(t+\theta)$ | 39 | 40 | 41 | 42 | 43 | 44 | 45 |
|---|---|---|---|---|---|---|---|
| $y^*$ | .3266 | .8311 | .0145 | .5907 | .6178 | .9005 | .1256 |
| $y'$ | −.1654 | .5436 | .0987 | .8841 | .7354 | .6141 | .1586 |

| $(t+\theta)$ | 46 | 47 | 48 | 49 | 50 | 51 | 52 |
|---|---|---|---|---|---|---|---|
| $y^*$ | .3149 | −.8525 | −.1151 | −.5862 | .3561 | .5252 | .2366 |
| $y'$ | .3501 | −.7627 | −.4895 | −.4079 | .6273 | .4422 | .3414 |

| $(t+\theta)$ | 53 | 54 |
|---|---|---|
| $y^*$ | −.5345 | −1.4273 |
| $y'$ | −.6741 | −1.5363 |

We observe that $y^*$ was closer to the eventually-measured actual $y$ in 25 out of 37 cases. The RMS (root-mean-square) prediction error for $y^*$ was approximately 10% smaller than for $y'$, the true y being a pure sine wave.

**2.** After 17 iterations the following model was obtained:

$$y(k) = \phi_1 y(k-1) + \phi_2 y(k-2) + \theta_1 a(k) + \theta_2 a(k-1)$$

where $a(k)$ is a zero average uncorrelated sequence with $E[a^2(k)] = 1$, and $\hat{\phi}_1 = 0.9450$; $\hat{\phi}_2 = -0.4555$, $\hat{\theta}_1 = 1.006$, $\hat{\theta}_2 = 0.2996$; the true values being $\phi_1 = 0.955$, $\phi_2 = -0.456$, $\theta_1 = 1$, $\theta_2 = 0.3$.

## CHAPTER 13

**1.** When substituting the identified $\hat{\mathbf{A}}$, $\hat{\mathbf{B}}$ of the present problem into Equation (13.35), we obtain:

$$\begin{bmatrix} 0 & -1 \\ 1 & -1 \end{bmatrix}\begin{bmatrix} S_{11}^* & S_{12}^* \\ S_{12}^* & S_{22}^* \end{bmatrix} + \begin{bmatrix} S_{11}^* & S_{12}^* \\ S_{12}^* & S_{22}^* \end{bmatrix}\begin{bmatrix} 0 & 1 \\ -1 & -1 \end{bmatrix} + I - \begin{bmatrix} (S_{12}^*)^2 & S_{12}^* S_{22}^* \\ S_{12}^* S_{22}^* & (S_{22}^*)^2 \end{bmatrix} = \mathbf{0}$$

such that:

$$1 - (S_{12}^*)^2 + 2S_{12}^* = 0; \qquad S_{12}^* = -1 \pm \sqrt{2}$$

Since $S_{12}^* = -1 - \sqrt{2}$ yields an unstable closed-loop system, we derive $S_{12} = -1 + \sqrt{2} = 0.414$. Equation (13.35) further yields: $1 - 2S_{12}^* - 2S_{22}^* - (S_{22})^2 = 0$. Hence, for $S_{12} = 0.414$, we obtain $S_{22}^* = (-2 \pm 2.16)/0.172$. Again, to avoid closed-loop instability, we must choose $S_{22}^* = (-2 + 2.16)/0.172 = 0.9$. Similarly, the third expression derived from Equation (13.35), namely: $S_{11}^* - S_{12}^* - S_{22}^* - S_{12}^* S_{22}^* = 0$ yields $S_{11}^* = 1.69$, such that:

$$\mathbf{S}^* = \begin{bmatrix} 1.69 & 0.414 \\ 0.414 & 0.9 \end{bmatrix}$$

Subsequently, $\mathbf{F}^*$ becomes, according to eqn. (13.34):

$$\mathbf{F}^* = \mathbf{R}^{-1}\mathbf{B}^T\mathbf{S}^* = [0; 1] \cdot \begin{bmatrix} 1.69 & 0.414 \\ 0.414 & 0.9 \end{bmatrix} = [0.414; 0.9]$$

yielding:

$$\boldsymbol{\omega} = (\mathbf{A} - \mathbf{BF}^*) = \begin{bmatrix} 0 & 1 \\ -1 & -1 \end{bmatrix} - \begin{bmatrix} 0 & 0 \\ 0.414 & 0.9 \end{bmatrix} = \begin{bmatrix} 0 & 1 \\ -1.414 & -1.9 \end{bmatrix}$$

Finally, $\boldsymbol{\Gamma}$ is derived from Equation (13.28), as follows:

$$\begin{bmatrix} 0 & -1.414 \\ 1 & -1.9 \end{bmatrix}\begin{bmatrix} \Gamma_{11} & \Gamma_{12} \\ \Gamma_{12} & \Gamma_{22} \end{bmatrix} + \begin{bmatrix} \Gamma_{11} & \Gamma_{12} \\ \Gamma_{12} & \Gamma_{22} \end{bmatrix}\begin{bmatrix} 0 & 1 \\ -1.414 & -1.9 \end{bmatrix} + \begin{bmatrix} 3.38 & 0.828 \\ 0.828 & 1.8 \end{bmatrix} = \mathbf{0}$$

to yield three linear equations in the three unknowns $\Gamma_{11}, \Gamma_{12}, \Gamma_{22}$, namely:

$$-2.828\Gamma_{12} + 1 = 0$$
$$2\Gamma_{12} - 3.8\Gamma_{22} + 1 = 0$$
$$-1.414\Gamma_{22} + \Gamma_{11} - 1.9\Gamma_{12} = 0$$

such that: $\Gamma_{11} = .341$; $\Gamma_{22} = .445$; $\Gamma_{11} = 2.3$, and:

$$\frac{\partial J}{\partial \mathbf{A}} = \mathbf{S}\Gamma = \begin{bmatrix} 4.02 & .77 \\ 1.26 & .54 \end{bmatrix}$$

**3.** Repeating the derivation of Problem 1 for **S**, **F** at the optimum, we have:

$$\mathbf{S}^* = \begin{bmatrix} 1.69 & 0.414 \\ 0.414 & 0.9 \end{bmatrix}$$

$$\mathbf{F}^* = [0.414; 0.9]$$

and:

$$\boldsymbol{\omega} = \begin{bmatrix} 0 & 1 \\ -1.414 & -1.9 \end{bmatrix}$$

Consequently, we obtain, for $\Delta\mathbf{A} = \begin{bmatrix} 0 & 0 \\ .1 & .1 \end{bmatrix}$; $\Delta\mathbf{F} = [.029\ ; .063]$:

$$\boldsymbol{\omega}^T\boldsymbol{\lambda} + \boldsymbol{\lambda}\boldsymbol{\omega} + 2\mathbf{X}_0 - 4\mathbf{B}\Delta\mathbf{F}\boldsymbol{\Gamma} - 4\boldsymbol{\Gamma}\Delta\mathbf{F}^T\mathbf{B}^T = \mathbf{0}$$

to yield three linear equations for evaluating the three unknowns $\lambda_{11}$, $\lambda_{12}$, $\lambda_{22}$. Finally, by equation (13.50):

$$\frac{\partial J^*}{\partial \mathbf{A}} = \mathbf{S}^* \boldsymbol{\lambda}$$

# INDEX



* Bracketed numbers indicate pages with numerical reference only.